WORKBOOK

Student Notes and Problems

SNAP

PHYSICS 30
Alberta

CASTLE ROCK
RESEARCH CORP

Rao, Gautam, 1961 –
STUDENT NOTES AND PROBLEMS – Physics 30 Workbook
Alberta

1. Science – Juvenile Literature. I. Title

Published by
Castle Rock Research Corp.
2340 Manulife Place
10180 – 101 Street
Edmonton, AB T5J 3S4

9 10 11 FP 13 12 11

Publisher
Gautam Rao

Contributors
Wayne Ladner

Reviewers
Jessica Arzt
Chris Cookson

Dedicated to the memory of Dr. V. S. Rao

STUDENT NOTES AND PROBLEMS WORKBOOKS

Student Notes and Problems (SNAP) workbooks are a series of support resources in mathematics for students in grades 3 to 12 and in science for students in grades 9 to 12. SNAP workbooks are 100% aligned with curriculum. The resources are designed to support classroom instructions and provide students with additional examples, practice exercises, and tests. SNAP workbooks are ideal for use all year long at school and at home.

The following is a summary of the key features of all SNAP workbooks.

UNIT OPENER PAGE

- summarizes the curriculum outcomes addressed in the unit in age-appropriate language
- identifies the lessons by title
- lists the prerequisite knowledge and skills the student should know prior to beginning the unit

LESSONS

- provide essential teaching pieces and explanations of the concepts
- include example problems and questions with complete, detailed solutions that demonstrate the problem-solving process

NOTES BARS

- contain key definitions, formulas, reminders, and important steps or procedures
- provide space for students to add their own notes and helpful reminders

PRACTICE EXERCISES

- include questions that relate to each of the curriculum outcomes for the unit
- provide practice in applying the lesson concepts

REVIEW SUMMARY

- provides a succinct review of the key concepts in the unit

PRACTICE TEST

- assesses student learning of the unit concepts

ANSWERS AND SOLUTIONS

- demonstrate the step-by-step process or problem-solving method used to arrive at the correct answer

Answers and solutions for the odd-numbered questions are provided in each student workbook. A *SNAP Solutions Manual* that contains answers and complete solutions for all questions is also available.

CONTENTS

Atomic Physics: Atomic Structure

Atomic Physics: Atomic Nucleus and Elementary Particles

Answers and Solutions

Appendix

MOMENTUM AND IMPULSE

When you are finished this unit, you will be able to...
- Define momentum as a vector quantity equal to the product of the mass and the velocity of an object
- Explain, quantitatively, the concepts of impulse and change in momentum, using Newton's laws of motion
- Explain, qualitatively, that momentum is conserved in an isolated system
- Explain, quantitatively, that momentum is conserved in one- and two-dimensional interactions in an isolated system
- Define, compare, and contrast elastic and inelastic collisions, using quantitative examples, in terms of conservation of kinetic energy

PREREQUISITE SKILLS AND KNOWLEDGE

Prior to starting this unit, you should be able to...
- Understand the difference between a vector and a scalar
- Find and verify the solutions of rational equations
- Solve problems involving displacement, velocity, and acceleration
- Find the vector components of a vector in two-dimensions
- Find the motion of one object relative to another using displacement and velocity vectors
- Solve problems involving displacement, velocity, and acceleration in two-dimensions
- Understand the concepts of Newton's laws, applying them to the motion of one or more objects
- Understand the relationship between force, acceleration and mass
- Apply Newton's laws to solve algebraic problems of linear motion
- Understand the concepts of kinetic and potential energy, and how they relate to the mechanical energy of an isolated system
- Understand the law of conservation of energy
- Solve kinematics and dynamics problems that relate to the conservation of mechanical energy in an isolated system
- Understand how work and power relate to amount of energy transferred in an isolated system
- Solve work and power problems involving the rate of change of energy

Lesson 1 MOMENTUM AND IMPULSE

During the sixteenth and seventeenth centuries, many scientists believed that all objects possessed some quantity of motion that remained constant when they interacted, or collided. They discovered that this quantity of motion was the product of the object's mass and velocity. This quantity of motion is called momentum.

MOMENTUM

Symbol: $\vec{p}$

Definition: Momentum is the product of the mass and the velocity of an object.
$$\vec{p} = m\vec{v}$$

Units: kg · m/s or N · s

Momentum is a vector quantity.

When an object accelerates, its velocity changes. Therefore, its momentum also changes. The change in momentum is also called impulse.

impulse $= \Delta\vec{p}$
or
impulse $= m\Delta\vec{v}$

IMPULSE

Definition: Impulse is the product of the net force and the time the force acts on an object.
$$\text{impulse} = \vec{F}_{net}t = \vec{J}$$

Units: kg · m/s or N · s

When a net force acts on an object for a period of time, the object accelerates; that is, its momentum changes.
$$\vec{F}_{net}t = m\Delta\vec{v}$$

Impulse, like momentum, is a vector quantity. The direction of the impulse is the same as the direction of the force.

The equation $\vec{F}t = m\Delta\vec{v}$ shows that the longer a net force acts on an object, the greater the change in momentum. This is why athletes are told by their coaches to "follow through," or keep the bat (or club, etc.) in contact with the ball for a longer period of time.

Newton's second law

$$\vec{F}_{net} = m\vec{a}$$

$$\vec{F}_{net} = m\left(\frac{\Delta\vec{v}}{t}\right)$$

$$\vec{F}_{net}t = m\Delta\vec{v}$$

$\vec{F}_{net}$ is the symbol for net force.

Newton's first law of motion states that an object will remain at a constant velocity, including zero, unless acted on by an unbalanced force.
Newton's first law is known as the law of inertia. Inertia is the tendency of an object to remain at constant velocity, including zero. Inertia depends only on the mass of the object, whereas momentum depends on both the mass and the velocity.

Note that the equation $\vec{F}t = m\Delta\vec{v}$ is a form of Newton's second law, $\vec{F} = m\vec{a}$.

Derive $\vec{F}t = m\Delta\vec{v}$, starting from $\vec{F} = m\vec{a}$.

$$\vec{a} = \frac{\Delta\vec{v}}{t}$$
$$\therefore \vec{F} = m\vec{a}$$
becomes $\vec{F} = \dfrac{m\Delta\vec{v}}{t}$

or $\vec{F}t = m\Delta\vec{v}$ or $\vec{J} = m\Delta\vec{v}$

Example

Calculate the momentum of a 6.2 kg object travelling at a velocity of 5.0 m/s west.

Solution

$$\vec{p} = m\vec{v}$$
$$= (6.2 \text{ kg})(5.0 \text{ m/s})$$
$$= 31 \text{ kg} \cdot \text{m/s west}$$

Example

A net force of 12.0 N acts north on an object for 2.00×10^{-3} s.
Calculate the impulse of the object.

Solution

$$\vec{J} = \vec{F}_{net}t$$
$$= (12.0 \text{ N})(2.00 \times 10^{-3} \text{ s})$$
$$= 2.40 \times 10^{-2} \text{ N} \cdot \text{s north}$$

Example

A net force of 14.0 N south acts on a 6.00 kg object for 1.00×10^{-1} s.
What is the change in velocity of this object?

Solution

$$\vec{F}_{net}t = m\Delta\vec{v}$$
$$\Delta\vec{v} = \frac{\vec{F}_{net}t}{m}$$
$$= \frac{(14.0 \text{ N})(1.00 \times 10^{-1} \text{ s})}{6.00 \text{ kg}}$$
$$= 0.233 \text{ m/s south}$$

PRACTICE EXERCISE

Formulas: $\quad \bar{p} = m\bar{v}$ $\qquad\qquad \bar{F}t = \Delta\bar{p}$ $\qquad\qquad \bar{F}t = m\Delta\bar{v}$

Note: In order to complete this assignment, you may need to use the kinematic equations from Physics 20.

1. Calculate the momentum of a 4.0 kg object travelling at a velocity of 12.0 m/s east.

2. A 5.0 kg object has a momentum of 25.0 kg·m/s west. What is the object's velocity?

3. An object has a velocity of 8.0 m/s south and a momentum of 36.0 kg·m/s south. What is the mass of the object?

4. An object has a velocity of 2.0 m/s east and a momentum of 29 kg m/s east. What is the weight of the object?

5. A 6.6 N object travels with a velocity of 3.0 m/s north. What is the momentum of the object? (Express the answer in $kg \cdot m/s$.)

6. A 7.0 kg object travels 2.6 m west in 1.1 s. Assuming uniform velocity, what is the momentum of the object?

7. A 5.0 kg object drops from a height of 2.5 m above the floor. What is the object's momentum after 0.25 s?

8. An average net force of 17.0 N east acts on an object for 2.5×10^2 s. What is the impulse?

5

9. An average net force of 11.2 N west acts on an object, producing an impulse of 7.00 N·s west. How long does the force act on the object?

10. A 26.3 kg object travels with a velocity of 21.0 m/s north. What average net force is required to bring this object to a stop in 2.60 s?

11. An average net force of 31.6 N south accelerates a 15.0 kg object uniformly from rest to 10.0 m/s. How much time passes as the object accelerates?

12. An average net force of 25.0 N north acts on an object for 7.20×10^{-1} s. What is the change in the object's momentum?

13. A 5.00 kg object **uniformly accelerates** from rest to a velocity of 15.0 m/s east. What is the impulse on the object?

14. An average net force **causes** an 11.0 kg object to accelerate uniformly from rest. If this object travels 26.3 m west in 3.20 s, what is the change in the object's momentum?

15. A 3.0 kg object **drops from a height** of 6.5 m. How far has the object fallen when its momentum is 6.0 kg·m/s down?

16. A 1.0 kg ball hits **the floor with** a velocity of 2.0 m/s. If this ball bounces upward off the floor with a velocity of 1.6 m/s, **what is the ball's change in momentum?**

17. A 9.5×10^3 kg rocket is launched upward from rest by an average net force of 1.5×10^5 N up. After 15 s, the rocket runs out of fuel. What is the velocity of the rocket once it runs out of fuel?

18. Without finding the acceleration, calculate the average net force required to accelerate a 5.4 kg ball from rest to 3.0 m/s east in a time of 0.75 s.

19. Without finding the acceleration, calculate the time an average net force of 225 N must act on a 1.0×10^3 kg object to change its velocity from 2.0 m/s east to 5.0 m/s east.

20. Without finding the acceleration, calculate the change in velocity of a 15 kg object when an average net force of 95 N north acts on the object for 1.6 s.

Lesson 2   CONSERVATION OF MOMENTUM

COLLISIONS

Collisions can be classified as either elastic or inelastic.

An elastic collision occurs when both the momentum and kinetic energy are conserved.

An inelastic collision occurs when the momentum is conserved but the kinetic energy is not.

No collision at the macroscopic level is perfectly elastic. Perfectly elastic collisions occur only at the atomic and subatomic levels. This is because collisions at the macroscopic level involve some distortion, which creates thermal energy. More specifically, some of the kinetic energy converts into thermal energy. However, if the objects collide and do not stick together, there is some elastic component to the collision.

THE LAW OF CONSERVATION OF MOMENTUM

An isolated system is a system that involves two or more objects in which the only net forces acting on the objects are the forces that the objects exert on each other.

The following situations are examples of isolated systems:

• Two moving gliders collide on a level air track.
• One moving billiard ball collides with a stationary billiard ball on a level pool table.
• Two moving cars collide on a very icy level road.

Although gravity is acting on each of the objects in the given examples, the gravitational force in each situation is balanced by the normal force. Remember that the normal force is the force that the surface exerts on the object.

It is also true that whenever objects are in contact with a surface, there is friction acting on the objects. Therefore, the system is not truly an isolated system. However, in the given examples and in the problems in this unit, the friction is small and can be considered to be zero.

The law of conservation of momentum states that in an isolated system, the total momentum of the objects after an interaction (or collision) is equal to the total momentum before the interaction.

$\vec{P}_{after} = \vec{P}_{before}$

In order to investigate this law, you need a system in which you can cancel out all forces except those forces that the objects exert on each other.

NOTES

In **elastic collisions**, both momentum and kinetic energy are conserved.

In **inelastic collisions**, momentum is conserved but not kinetic energy.

An **isolated system** is a system that involves two or more objects in which the only net forces acting on these objects are the forces that the objects exert on each other.

You will use the law of conservation of momentum to complete a number of mathematical calculations. To help complete these calculations, the interactions are classified as linear interactions and two-dimensional interactions.

LINEAR INTERACTIONS

Linear interactions are collisions in which the objects collide but do not stick together. Linear interactions also include collisions in which the objects collide and stick together, as well as explosions. The motion of the objects will always be in one-dimension along a straight line.

TWO-DIMENSIONAL INTERACTIONS

Similar to linear interactions, two-dimensional interactions also include collisions that both do and do not stick together, as well as explosions. However, these interactions can occur at any angle on a flat, two-dimensional plane. Commonly, the interaction will be at 90°, but it can occur at angles other than 90° as well.

In the following collision problems, the process for solving the problem is the same regardless of what these colliding objects are. For example, these objects can be cars, billiard balls, curling stones, or any other objects.

The following steps can be taken to solve collision and explosion problems:
- Draw a before-after diagram.
- Write $m, \vec{v}, \vec{p}$ under each isolated object drawn.
- Using $m, \vec{v}, \vec{p}$, fill in as much data as possible.
- Calculate $\vec{p}$ where possible.
- Use law of conservation of momentum to find $\vec{p}_{after}$.
- Knowing $\vec{p}$ of object 1 and $\vec{p}_{after}$, you can calculate $\vec{p}$ of object 2.
- Knowing m of object 2 and $\vec{p}$ of object 2, use $\vec{p} = m\vec{v}$ to calculate $\vec{v}$ of object 2.

If the objects travelled in opposite directions, one of the directions must be indicated as negative.

COLLISIONS IN WHICH OBJECTS DO NOT STICK TOGETHER

When two objects collide and do not stick together, they are sometimes considered as perfectly elastic but are usually still treated as inelastic because some energy can be lost in the interaction. Momentum is always conserved and kinetic energy is conserved if the collision is elastic. When solving this type of momentum problem, you should always treat both objects separately before and after the collision.

Example

A 0.25 kg steel ball is travelling east at a velocity of 4.5 m/s when it collides head-on with a 0.30 kg steel ball travelling west at a velocity of 5.0 m/s. After the collision, the 0.25 kg ball is travelling west at a velocity of 2.0 m/s. What is the velocity of the 0.30 kg ball after the collision?

Solution
Before collision

$m = 0.25$ kg
$\vec{v} = 4.5$ m/s
$\vec{p} = 1.13$ kg·m/s

$m = 0.30$ kg
$\vec{v} = -5.0$ m/s
$\vec{p} = -1.5$ kg·m/s

$\vec{p}_{before} = 0.375$ kg·m/s west

After collision

$m = 0.25$ kg
$\vec{v} = -2.0$ m/s
$\vec{p} = -0.50$ kg·m/s

$m = 0.30$ kg
$\vec{v} = ?$
$\vec{p} = 0.125$ kg·m/s

$\vec{p}_{after} = 0.375$ kg·m/s west
$\vec{p} = m\vec{v}$
$\therefore \vec{v} = \dfrac{\vec{p}}{m}$
$= \dfrac{0.125 \text{ kg·m/s}}{0.30 \text{ kg}}$
$= 0.42$ m/s east

COLLISIONS WHEN OBJECTS STICK TOGETHER

When two objects collide and stick together, the collision is considered inelastic. Momentum is conserved, but kinetic energy is not.
When solving this type of momentum problem, you should treat the objects separately before the collision and as a single combined object after the collision.

Example

A 1.1×10^3 kg car travelling with a velocity of 25 km/h east collides head-on with a 1.3×10^3 kg car travelling with a velocity of 15 km/h west. During the collision, the two cars lock together. What is the velocity of the locked cars as they move together immediately after collision?

Solution
Before collision

$m_1 = 1.1 \times 10^3$ kg

$\vec{v}_1 = 25$ km/h east

$\vec{p}_1 = 2.75 \times 10^4$ kg·km/h east

$m_2 = 1.3 \times 10^3$ kg

$\vec{v}_2 = 15$ km/h west

$\vec{p}_2 = 1.95 \times 10^4$ kg·km/h west

$$\begin{aligned}\vec{p}_{\text{before}} &= \vec{p}_1 + \vec{p}_2 \\ &= 2.75 \times 10^4 \text{ kg·km/h east} + 1.95 \times 10^4 \text{ kg·km/h west} \\ &= 2.75 \times 10^4 \text{ kg·km/h} - 1.95 \times 10^4 \text{ kg·km/h} \\ &= 8.0 \times 10^3 \text{ kg·km/h east}\end{aligned}$$

It is not necessary to convert km/h to m/s since the units will cancel in conservation of momentum problems.

Because the cars stick together after the collision, treat the combined cars as a single object.

After collision

$m_{1+2} = 2.4 \times 10^3$ kg

$\vec{v}_{1+2} = ?$

$\vec{p}_{\text{after}} = 8.0 \times 10^3$ kg·km/h east

$$\begin{aligned}\vec{v}_{1+2} &= \frac{\vec{p}_{\text{after}}}{m} \\ &= \frac{8.0 \times 10^3 \text{ kg·km/h}}{2.4 \times 10^3 \text{ kg}} \\ &= 3.3 \text{ km/h east}\end{aligned}$$

EXPLOSIONS

When two objects explode apart, the interaction is considered inelastic. Momentum is conserved, but kinetic energy is not. When solving this type of momentum problem, you should treat the objects as a single combined object before the explosion and as two separate objects after the explosion.

Example

A 0.050 kg bullet is fired from a 2.0 kg gun. If the velocity of the bullet is 275 m/s, what is the recoil velocity of the gun?

Solution

Before explosion

$m = 2.05 \text{ kg}$
$\vec{v} = 0$
$\vec{p} = 0$

After explosion

The mass before explosion is the mass of the gun and bullet.

$m_{\text{gun}} = 2.0 \text{ kg}$ $m_{\text{bullet}} = 0.050 \text{ kg}$
$\vec{v}_{\text{gun}} = ?$ $\vec{v}_{\text{bullet}} = 275 \text{ m/s}$
$\vec{P}_{\text{gun}} = -13.75 \text{ kg} \cdot \text{m/s}$ $\vec{P}_{\text{bullet}} = 13.75 \text{ kg} \cdot \text{m/s}$

$\vec{P}_{\text{after}} = 0$

$$\vec{v}_{\text{gun}} = \frac{\vec{P}_{\text{gun}}}{m_{\text{gun}}}$$

$$= \frac{-13.75 \text{ kg} \cdot \text{m/s}}{2.0 \text{ kg}}$$

$$= -6.9 \text{ m/s}$$

The negative sign indicates that the gun moves in the opposite direction to the bullet.

ACTIVITY #1

Purpose:

To study the conservation of momentum in a one-dimensional elastic collision.

Apparatus:

- An air track (a dynamics track with carts may be used)
- Two gliders with spring (elastic) bumpers and equal masses
- Two photogates with timing devices (a photogate timer)
- Two index cards
- A ruler
- A balance

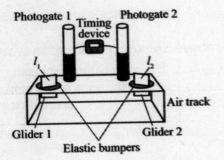

Procedure:

1. Set up the apparatus as shown in the given diagram.
2. Level the air track.
3. Place an index card vertically on top of each glider.
4. Adjust the heights of both photogates so that the cards will cut through the signals.
5. Turn on and adjust the timing device you are using.
6. Measure the lengths of cards l_1 and l_2.
7. Place Glider 2 between Photogate 1 and Photogate 2 so it remains stationary.
8. Place Glider 1 on the left end of the air track and give it a gentle push so it moves toward the right and collides with Glider 2. During this process, Photogate 1 will measure the time it takes for Card 1 to pass through Photogate 1, and Photogate 2 will measure the time it takes for Card 2 to pass through Photogate 2.

Note: If the two gliders are of equal mass, Glider 1 will stop when it collides with Glider 2.

9. Repeat this procedure three times.
10. Complete the following data tables.

Mass of Glider (kg)		Time Recorded by Timing Device (s)		Length of Card (m)	
Glider 1	Glider 2	Glider 1 Before	Glider 2 After	Card 1	Card 2
1.					
2.					
3.					

	Velocity of Glider 1 (m/s)		Velocity of Glider 2 (m/s)	
	Before	After	Before	After
1.		0	0	
2.		0	0	
3.		0	0	

Note: The velocities of the gliders can be calculated using the following formula:

$$\vec{v} = \frac{\vec{d}}{t}$$ ← length of card
← length of time that card is passing through the photogate

	Momentum of Glider 1 (kg · m/s)		Momentum of Glider 2 (kg · m/s)		Total Momentum of Gliders (kg · m/s)		
	Before	After	Before	After	Before	After	% Difference
1.							
2.							
3.							

Note: % difference = $\dfrac{\text{difference in momentum before and after}}{\text{momentum before}} \times 100$

Questions:

1. Was the momentum conserved in this collision?

2. Was the kinetic energy conserved in this collision? (Remember: $E_k = \dfrac{1}{2}mv^2$)

   (Complete the following table.)

	Total Kinetic Energy of Gliders (J)		
	Before	After	% Difference
1.			
2.			
3.			

3. Would you call this collision an elastic collision?

If you were not able to do this activity, use the following data.

Mass of Glider (kg)		Time Recorded by Timing Device (s)		Length of Card (m)	
1	**2**	**Glider 1 Before**	**Glider 2 After**	**Card 1**	**Card 2**
1. 0.125	0.125	0.461	0.477	5.00×10^{-2}	5.00×10^{-2}
2. 0.125	0.125	0.316	0.333	5.00×10^{-2}	5.00×10^{-2}
3. 0.125	0.125	0.640	0.659	5.00×10^{-2}	5.00×10^{-2}

Velocity of Glider 1 (m/s)		Velocity of Glider 2 (m/s)	
Before	**After**	**Before**	**After**
1.	0	0	
2.	0	0	
3.	0	0	

ACTIVITY #2:

Purpose:
To study the conservation of momentum in a one-dimensional inelastic collision.

Apparatus:
- An air track (a dynamics track with carts may be used)
- Two gliders with Velcro strips placed at the ends so they will stick together after the collision (they do not need to have equal masses)
- Two photogates with timing devices (a photogate timer)
- One index card
- A ruler
- A balance

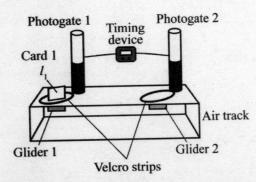

16

Procedure:

1. Set up the apparatus as shown in the given diagram.
2. Place the index card vertically on top of Glider 1 only.
3. Adjust the height of both photogates so that the cards will cut through the signals.
4. Turn on and adjust the timing device.
5. Measure the length of the card, l_1.
6. Place Glider 2 between Photogate 1 and Photogate 2 so it remains stationary.
7. Place Glider 1 on the left end of the air track and give it a gentle push so it moves to the right, colliding with and sticking to Glider 2.
8. Repeat this procedure three times.
9. Complete the following data tables.

	Mass of Gliders (kg)		Time Recorded by Timing Device (s)		Length of Card (m)
	1	2	Glider 1 Before	Gliders 1 and 2 After	
1.					
2.					
3.					

	Velocity of Glider 1 (m/s)		
	Glider 1 Before	Glider 2 Before	Gliders 1 and 2 After
1.		0	
2.		0	
3.		0	

Note: The velocities of the gliders can be calculated using the following formula:

$$\vec{v} = \frac{d}{t} \quad \begin{array}{l}\leftarrow \text{length of card} \\ \leftarrow \text{length of time that card is passing through the photogate}\end{array}$$

	Momentum of Gliders Before (kg · m/s)		Momentum of Gliders Combined After (kg · m/s)	Total Momentum of Gliders (kg · m/s)		
	1	2		Before	After	% Difference
1.						
2.						
3.						

Note: % difference $= \dfrac{\text{difference in momentum before and after}}{\text{momentum before}} \times 100$

Questions:

1. Was the momentum conserved in this collision?

2. Was the kinetic energy conserved in this collision?
   (Complete the following table.)

Total Kinetic Energy of Gliders (J)		
Before	After	% Difference
1.		
2.		
3.		

If you were not able to do this activity, use the following data:

Mass of Gliders (kg)		Time Recorded by Timing Device (s)		Length of Card (m)
1	2	Glider 1 Before	Gliders 1 and 2 After	
1.	0.250	0.225	0.312	0.625	5.00×10^{-2}
2.	0.250	0.225	0.262	0.534	5.00×10^{-2}
3.	0.250	0.225	0.425	0.833	5.00×10^{-2}

ACTIVITY #3

Design an experiment to determine if momentum is conserved in an explosion interaction using an air track or a dynamics track.

Collect data from your experiment, and do the necessary calculation to determine if momentum is conserved in this type of interaction and if kinetic energy is conserved in this type of interaction.

PRACTICE EXERCISE

Formula: $\vec{p} = m\vec{v}$

1. A 30.0 kg object moving to the right at 1.00 m/s collides with a 20.0 kg object moving to the left at 5.00 m/s. If the 20.0 kg object has a velocity of 1.25 m/s to the left after the collision, what is the velocity of the 30.0 kg object after the collision?

2. A 4.50×10^3 kg railway car travelling with a velocity of 5.0 m/s east on a level, frictionless track collides with a stationary 6.50×10^3 kg railway car. If the two cars lock together upon collision, what is the velocity of the combined cars following the collision?

3. A 925 kg car moving at a velocity of 18.0 m/s right collides with a stationary truck with an unknown mass. If the two vehicles lock together upon collision and move away with a velocity of 6.50 m/s, what is the mass of the truck?

4. A 50.0 g bullet strikes a 7.00 kg stationary wooden block. If the bullet becomes embedded in the block, and the block with the embedded bullet moves away with a velocity of 5.00 m/s to the right after the impact, what was the velocity of the bullet immediately before striking the block?

5. A 40.0 g object moving with a velocity of 9.00 m/s to the right collides with a 55.0 g object moving with a velocity of 6.00 m/s to the left. If the two objects stick together after colliding, what is their velocity after the collision?

6. A 76 kg student, standing at rest on a frictionless horizontal surface, throws a 0.20 kg object horizontally with a velocity of 22 m/s left. What is the velocity of the student immediately after releasing the object?

7. A 1.1×10^3 kg launcher fires a 25 kg projectile horizontally. If the projectile has a horizontal velocity of 325 m/s east, what is the recoil velocity of the launcher?

8. A rail vehicle with a rocket engine is tested on a smooth horizontal track. Starting from rest, the engine fires for a short period of time, releasing 4.5×10^2 kg of gases. The estimated average velocity of the gases is 1.4×10^3 m/s to the right, while the maximum velocity of the vehicle is 45 m/s to the left. What is the mass of the rail vehicle?

9. A 7.0 kg object at rest explodes into two parts. If the first part has a mass of 2.0 kg and a velocity of 10.0 m/s right, what is the velocity of the second part?

10. A 1.0×10^5 N truck moving at a velocity of 15 m/s north collides head-on with a 1.0×10^4 N car moving at a velocity of 25 m/s south. If the vehicles stick together upon impact, what is the velocity of the combined masses immediately after colliding?

11. A 225 g ball moves with a velocity of 30.0 cm/s to the right. This ball collides with a 125 g ball moving with a velocity of 10.0 cm/s in the same direction. After the collision, the velocity of the 125 g ball is 24.0 cm/s to the right.

a) What is the velocity of the 225 g ball after the collision?

b) Is this an elastic or inelastic collision? Provide mathematical evidence for your answer. (**Hint:** Calculate the kinetic energy of the objects before and after the collision. If these energies are not the same, the collision is classified as inelastic.)

c) What happened to the lost kinetic energy?

12. A 10.0 g object moving with a velocity of 20.0 cm/s to the right collides with a stationary 30.0 g object. After the collision, the 10.0 g object moves with a velocity of 6.00 cm/s to the left.

a) What is the velocity of the 30.0 g object after the collision?

b) Is this an elastic or inelastic collision? Provide mathematical evidence for your answer.

c) What happened to the kinetic energy that was lost?

Lesson 3 *TWO-DIMENSIONAL INTERACTIONS*

In the collisions to this point, all of the motion has occurred along a straight line. However, most collisions are not linear. Consider some non-linear collisions.

COLLISIONS AT 90°

Collisions that occur at 90° are the simplest type of two-dimensional collisions. Since the directions of each object are perpendicular to each other, there is no need to break the motion into horizontal and vertical components. The resultant momentum can be calculated using the Pythagorean theorem.

Example

A 4.0 kg object travelling with a velocity of 2.8 m/s south collides with a 6.0 kg object travelling with a velocity of 3.0 m/s east. If these two objects stick together upon colliding, what is the velocity of the combined objects after the collision?

Solution
Before collision

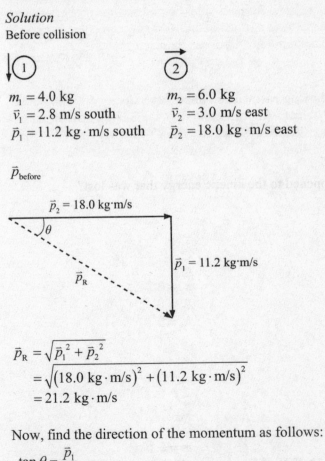

$m_1 = 4.0$ kg $m_2 = 6.0$ kg
$\vec{v}_1 = 2.8$ m/s south $\vec{v}_2 = 3.0$ m/s east
$\vec{p}_1 = 11.2$ kg·m/s south $\vec{p}_2 = 18.0$ kg·m/s east

$\vec{P}_{before}$

$\vec{p}_2 = 18.0$ kg·m/s

θ

$\vec{p}_1 = 11.2$ kg·m/s

$\vec{p}_R$

$$\vec{p}_R = \sqrt{\vec{p}_1^{\,2} + \vec{p}_2^{\,2}}$$
$$= \sqrt{(18.0 \text{ kg} \cdot \text{m/s})^2 + (11.2 \text{ kg} \cdot \text{m/s})^2}$$
$$= 21.2 \text{ kg} \cdot \text{m/s}$$

Now, find the direction of the momentum as follows:

$$\tan\theta = \frac{\vec{p}_1}{\vec{p}_2}$$
$$= \frac{11.2 \text{ kg} \cdot \text{m/s}}{18.0 \text{ kg} \cdot \text{m/s}}$$
$$\theta = 31.9° \text{ S of E}$$
$$\vec{P}_{before} = 21.2 \text{ kg} \cdot \text{m/s } 31.9° \text{ S of E, or } 58.1° \text{ E of S}$$

24

After collision

$\widehat{(1+2)}$

$m_{1+2} = 10.0 \text{ kg}$
$\vec{v}_{1+2} = ?$
$\vec{p}_{1+2} = 21.2 \text{ kg} \cdot \text{m/s } 31.9° \text{ S of E}$

$$\vec{v} = \frac{\vec{p}}{m}$$
$$= \frac{(21.2 \text{ kg} \cdot \text{m/s})}{(10.0 \text{ kg})} \; 31.9° \text{ S of E}$$
$$= 2.1 \text{ m/s } 32° \text{ S of E}$$

COLLISIONS AT ANGLES OTHER THAN 90°

Collisions that occur at angles other than 90° in two-dimensions are slightly more complicated to calculate. The momentum of each object must be broken down into horizontal and vertical components and treated separately. Once the total horizontal and vertical momentums are calculated, the resultant momentum can be calculated.

Example

A 4.0 kg object moving east with an unknown velocity collides with a 6.1 kg stationary object. After the collision, the 4.0 kg object travels with a velocity of 2.8 m/s 32.4°N of E, and the 6.1 kg object travels with a velocity of 1.5 m/s 41.0°S of E. What was the velocity of the 4.0 kg object before the collision?

Solution
Before collision

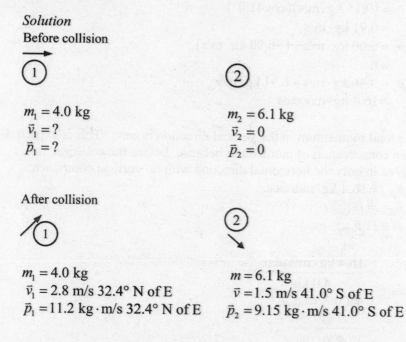

$m_1 = 4.0 \text{ kg}$ $m_2 = 6.1 \text{ kg}$
$\vec{v}_1 = ?$ $\vec{v}_2 = 0$
$\vec{p}_1 = ?$ $\vec{p}_2 = 0$

After collision

$m_1 = 4.0 \text{ kg}$ $m = 6.1 \text{ kg}$
$\vec{v}_1 = 2.8 \text{ m/s } 32.4° \text{ N of E}$ $\vec{v} = 1.5 \text{ m/s } 41.0° \text{ S of E}$
$\vec{p}_1 = 11.2 \text{ kg} \cdot \text{m/s } 32.4° \text{ N of E}$ $\vec{p}_2 = 9.15 \text{ kg} \cdot \text{m/s } 41.0° \text{ S of E}$

Find the magnitudes of the horizontal and vertical components of $11.2 \text{ kg} \cdot \text{m/s } 32.4°\text{N of E.}$

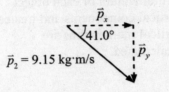

$\vec{p}_1 = 11.2 \text{ kg·m/s}$

$32.4°$

$\vec{p}_y$

$\vec{p}_x$

$p_{1y} = p_1 \sin \theta$
$= (11.2 \text{ kg} \cdot \text{m/s})(\sin 32.4°)$
$= 6.00 \text{ kg} \cdot \text{m/s}$

$p_{1x} = p_1 \cos \theta$
$= (11.2 \text{ kg} \cdot \text{m/s})(\cos 32.4°)$
$= 9.46 \text{ kg} \cdot \text{m/s}$

Find the magnitudes of the horizontal and vertical components of $9.15 \text{ km} \cdot \text{m/s S of E.}$

$\vec{p}_x$

$41.0°$

$\vec{p}_2 = 9.15 \text{ kg·m/s}$

$\vec{p}_y$

$p_{2y} = p_2 \sin \theta$
$= (9.15 \text{ kg} \cdot \text{m/s})(\sin 41.0°)$
$= -6.00 \text{ kg} \cdot \text{m/s}$

$p_{2x} = p_2 \cos \theta$
$= (9.15 \text{ kg} \cdot \text{m/s})(\cos 41.0°)$
$= 6.91 \text{ kg} \cdot \text{m/s}$

$\sum \vec{p}_y = 6.00 \text{ kg} \cdot \text{m/s} + (-6.00 \text{ kg} \cdot \text{m/s})$
$= 0$

$\sum \vec{p}_x = 9.46 \text{ kg} \cdot \text{m/s} + 6.91 \text{ kg} \cdot \text{m/s}$
$= 16.4 \text{ kg} \cdot \text{m/s east}$

The total momentum in the vertical direction is zero. This is expected from conservation of momentum because, before the collision, m_1 moved in only the horizontal direction with no vertical component.

$\therefore \vec{p}_{after} = 16.4 \text{ kg} \cdot \text{m/s east}$

$\vec{p}_{after} = \vec{p}_{before}$

$\vec{v}_1 = \dfrac{\vec{p}_{before}}{m_1}$

$= \dfrac{16.4 \text{ kg} \cdot \text{m/s east}}{4.0 \text{ kg}}$

$= 4.1 \text{ m/s east}$

ACTIVITY #4

Purpose: To study the conservation of momentum in a two-dimensional collision.

Apparatus:
- An air table apparatus with a spark timer and steel pucks
- A ruler
- A balance

Procedure:
1. Set up the air table apparatus.
2. Level the table.
3. Set the spark timer to spark 10 times per second.
4. Turn on the spark timer.
5. Turn on the air supply.
6. Place puck 2 near the centre of the air table. This puck will need to be held in place to keep it stationary and released carefully once puck 1 is pushed (some practice may be necessary to do this).
7. Place puck 1 near the edge of the air table and give it a gentle push so it will glance off the stationary puck (puck 2), as shown in the given diagram. Some practice may be necessary.

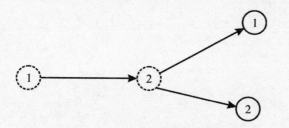

8. Press the foot switch immediately after you release pucks 1 and 2. Be careful not to touch the table surface or the steel puck once you or your partner presses the foot switch. There will be an electric current flowing through them.
9. No matter what direction puck 1 travels before the collision, use that direction as the *x*-axis.
10. Analyze the spark tracks on the paper to determine the velocity of both pucks before and after the collision.

Complete the following calculations to fill in the table:
- Velocity of puck 1 before collision:

- Velocity of puck 1 after collision:

- Velocity of puck 2 after collision:

- Momentum of puck 1 before collision:

- Momentum of puck 1 after collision:

- Momentum of puck 2 after collision:

- Components of momentum after collision:

- Total momentum before collision:
  (sum of $\vec{p}_{x \text{ before}}$ and $\vec{p}_{y \text{ before}}$)

- Total momentum after collision:
  (sum of $\vec{p}_{x \text{ after}}$ and $\vec{p}_{y \text{ after}}$)

28

Mass of Puck (kg)		Velocity of Puck Before (m/s)		Direction of Puck After (measured from x-axis)		Velocity of Puck After (m/s)	
1	2	1	2	1	2	1	2
			0				

Momentum of Puck Before (kg · m/s)		Momentum of Puck After (kg · m/s)		Components of Momentum Before (kg · m/s)		Components of Momentum After (kg · m/s)	
1	2	1	2	$\sum p_x$	$\sum p_y$	$\sum p_x$	$\sum p_y$

Questions:

1. Was momentum conserved in this collision?

2. What are the sources of error?

3. Is kinetic energy conserved in this collision?

If you are not able to do this activity, use the following spark tracks obtained from an air table apparatus to complete **Activity #4**.

Frequency of spark timer = 10 Hz

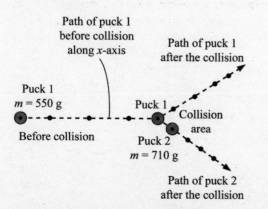

PRACTICE EXERCISE

Formula: $\vec{p} = m\vec{v}$

1. A 1.4×10^3 kg car driving with a velocity of 37.0 km/h west collides with a 2.0×10^3 kg truck driving with a velocity of 35.0 km/h north. If these two vehicles lock together when they collide, what is the initial velocity of the vehicles after the collision?

2. Object A has a mass of 6.2 kg and a velocity of 3.0 m/s north when it collides with object B, which has a mass of 8.0 kg and a velocity of 3.5 m/s west. If these two masses stick together upon colliding, what is their velocity after the collision?

3. A 4.0×10^4 N truck travelling with a velocity of 8.0 m/s west collides with a 3.0×10^4 N truck travelling with a velocity of 5.0 m/s south. If these two vehicles lock together upon colliding, what is the initial velocity of the vehicles after the collision?

4. A 50.0 kg object moving east at an unknown velocity collides with a 60.0 kg stationary object. After the collision, the 50.0 kg object travelled away with a velocity of 6.0 m/s 50.0° N of E (or 50.0°), and the 60.0 kg object travelled away with a velocity of 6.3 m/s 38° S of E (or 322°).

   a) What was the velocity of the 50.0 kg object before the collision?

   b) Was this an elastic or inelastic collision? Provide mathematical evidence for your answer.

   c) What happened to the lost kinetic energy?

5. A 15.0 kg object travelling with a velocity of 7.0 m/s east collides with a 10.0 kg stationary object. After the collision, the 15.0 kg object travels with a velocity of 4.2 m/s 20.0° S of E (or 340°).

   a) What is the velocity of the 10.0 kg object after the collision?

   b) Is this an elastic or inelastic collision? Provide mathematical evidence for your answer.

   c) What happened to the lost kinetic energy?

6. An object explodes into three equal masses. One mass travels with a velocity of 15.0 m/s east. If a second mass travels with a velocity of 10.0 m/s 45.0° S of E, what is the velocity of the third mass?

PRACTICE QUIZ

1. What is the weight of an object that has a velocity of 10.0 m/s and a momentum of 2.0×10^2 kg·m/s?

2. A 1.20×10^3 kg car accelerates uniformly from rest to 25.0 m/s in 10.3 s. What is the net force acting on the car?

Use the following information to answer the next question.

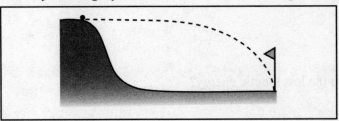

3. A golfer hits a 5.0×10^{-2} kg ball from a ledge, as shown in the given diagram. If the ball leaves the face of the golf club with a horizontal velocity of 30.0 m/s, what is the impulse due to the club?

4. A 1.1×10^3 kg car travelling at a velocity of 10.0 m/s collides head-on with a brick wall. If the car comes to a complete rest in 0.25 s, what was the average force exerted on the car during the collision?

5. If a 0.15 kg object has 9.0 J of kinetic energy, what is the magnitude of its momentum?

6. If Annemarie drops a 0.85 kg object from a height of 2.2 m above the floor, what will be the object's momentum immediately before the ball hits the floor?

7. A 50.0 g bullet travelling at a velocity of 375 m/s becomes embedded 25.0 cm deep in a massive wooden block. Calculate the average force exerted on the bullet by the wood.

8. If a 0.50 kg object launches vertically and reaches a maximum height of 15 m, what is the maximum momentum of the object?

Use the following information to answer the next question.

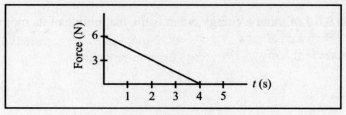

9. A force-time graph for a 0.75 kg object that accelerated from rest is shown. Calculate the velocity of the object at 4.0 s. (**Note:** The area under the graph represents the impulse.)

Use the following information to answer the next question.

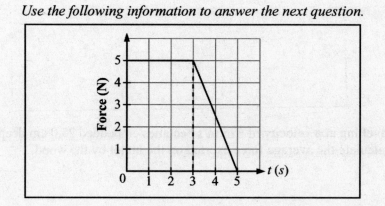

10. A force-time graph for a 0.50 kg object that accelerated from rest is shown. Calculate the velocity of the object at 5.0 s.

11. If a 2.0 kg object accelerates horizontally from rest at a uniform rate of 3.5 m/s^2, what is the momentum of the object after 2.5 s?

12. If Travis throws a 0.15 kg ball at a velocity of 12 m/s vertically upward, what is the momentum of the ball when it has travelled halfway toward its maximum height?

Use the following information to answer the next question.

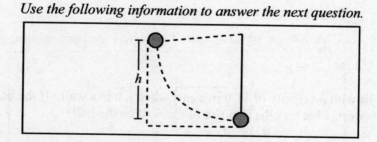

13. A 0.020 kg pendulum bob is dropped from a height of h. If the bob has momentum of 0.070 kg · m/s at its equilibrium position, what is the value of h?

Use the following information to answer the next question.

A 0.010 kg pendulum bob is dropped from a height of h above its equilibrium position, as shown in the given diagram. When the bob reaches its equilibrium position, the string breaks, and the bob then acts as a projectile. After the string breaks, the bob falls 1.5 m while moving 2.0 m horizontally.

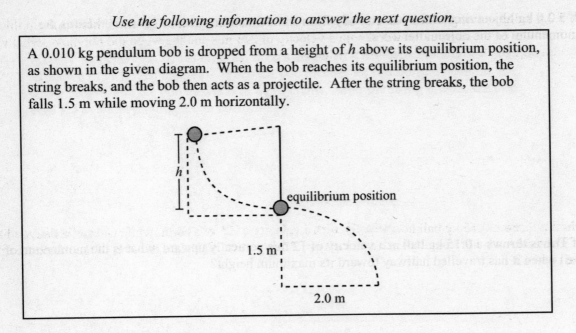

14. Calculate the height (h) from which the bob was released.

15. A 0.45 kg ball travels with a velocity of 11.0 m/s east when it hits a wall. If the ball rebounds with a velocity of 10.0 m/s west, what was the impulse of the wall on the ball?

16. A 5.0 g bullet moving with a velocity of 375 m/s hits a stationary block of wood that is 6.0 cm thick. If the bullet emerges from the wood with a velocity of 225 m/s and the wood did not move, what was the average force exerted on the bullet by the wood?

17. Munira threw a 0.15 kg ball horizontally with a velocity of 25 m/s north, while Gabriella threw a ball of identical mass horizontally with a velocity of 22 m/s west. Calculate the sum of the momenta of the two balls.

Use the following information to answer the next question.

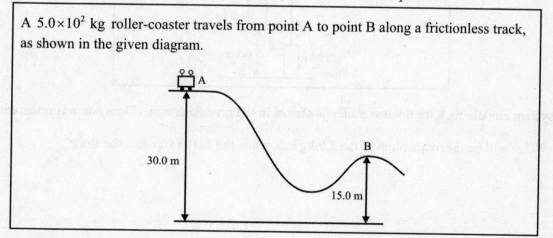

A 5.0×10^2 kg roller-coaster travels from point A to point B along a frictionless track, as shown in the given diagram.

18. If the momentum of the roller-coaster is zero at point A, what is its momentum at point B?

Use the following information to answer the next question.

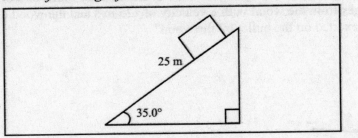

19. A 98.0 N box slides 25.0 m along a 35.0° incline, as shown in the given diagram. If the force of friction along the incline is 32.0 N and the box starts from rest at the top, what is the momentum of the box at the bottom?

Use the following information to answer the next question.

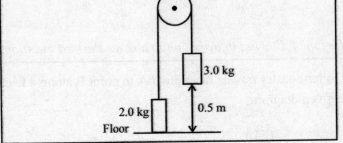

20. A system containing a frictionless pulley is shown in the given diagram. The system is released.

a) What will be the momentum of the 2.0 kg box when the 3.0 kg box hits the floor?

b) What will be the momentum of the 3.0 kg box when it hits the floor?

21. Ilya, a 45 kg student, threw a 0.25 kg object at a velocity of 9.0 m/s east while standing on a frictionless surface. Calculate Ilya's velocity after he released the object.

22. A car moving with a velocity of 10.0 m/s east collides with a stationary truck with exactly twice the mass of the car. If the two vehicles lock together, calculate the velocity of their combined mass immediately after collision.

23. A 6.0 g ball moving with a velocity of 3.0 m/s north collides head-on with an identical ball moving at a velocity of 2.0 m/s south, resulting in an elastic collision. Immediately after the collision, the first ball moves with a velocity of 1.0 m/s south. What is the velocity of the second ball after the collision?

24. A 5.0 g ball collides with and sticks to a second ball that is at rest. If the combined mass moves with a velocity that is $\frac{1}{4}$ the magnitude of the original velocity of the 5.0 g ball, what is the mass of the second ball?

25. A gun with an unloaded weight of 25 N, fires a 6.0×10^{-2} kg bullet at a velocity of 325 m/s west. What is the recoil velocity of the gun?

26. A 40.0 kg object moving with a velocity of 2.00 m/s east collides with a 30.0 kg object moving with a velocity of 2.00 m/s north. If the objects stick together upon collision, what is the velocity of the combined mass immediately after the collision?

27. A 2.0 kg object moving with a velocity of 5.0 m/s west collides with a stationary 3.0 kg object. After the collision, the 2.0 kg object moves with a velocity of 1.5 m/s west.

   a) Calculate the velocity of the 3.0 kg object after the collision.

   b) Is this an elastic or inelastic collision? Provide mathematical evidence for your answer. What happened to the kinetic energy lost?

28. A 7.0 kg object moving north with an unknown velocity collides with a 5.0 kg stationary object. After the collision, the 7.0 kg object moves with a velocity of 3.0 m/s 30.0° E of N, and the 5.0 kg object moves with a velocity of 5.0 m/s 25.0° W of N.

    a) Calculate the velocity of the 7.0 kg object before the collision.

    b) Is this an elastic or inelastic collision? Provide mathematical evidence for your answer. What happened to the kinetic energy lost?

29. Two cars collided at an intersection. The first car had a mass of 775 kg and was travelling west. The second car had a mass of 1 125 kg and was travelling north. Immediately after impact, the first car had a velocity of 65.0 km/h 33.0° W of N, while the second car had a velocity of 42.0 km/h 46.0° W of N. What were the velocities of these two cars immediately before the collision?

Use the following information to answer the next question.

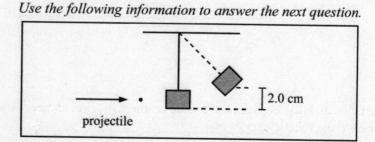

projectile   2.0 cm

30. A 4.0 g projectile is fired at a 2.0 kg wooden pendulum, as shown in the given diagram. If the pendulum swings to a height of 2.0 cm after the projectile becomes embedded in it, how fast was the projectile travelling when it hit the pendulum? Explain using conservation laws.

REVIEW SUMMARY

- Momentum and impulse

  $\vec{p} = m\vec{v}$

  $\vec{F}t = m\Delta\vec{v}$

- One-dimensional collisions and explosions using the law of conservation of momentum

  $\vec{P}_{\text{before}} = \vec{P}_{\text{after}}$

- Two-dimensional collisions using the law of conservation of momentum

  $\vec{P}_{\text{before}} = \vec{P}_{\text{after}}$

- The following formulas were used in this unit:

  $\vec{p} = m\vec{v}$

  $\overline{\text{impulse}} = \vec{F}t = m\Delta\vec{v}$

- The following equations from Physics 20 were also used:

  $\vec{v} = \dfrac{d}{t}$

  $\vec{a} = \dfrac{\vec{v}_{\text{f}} - \vec{v}_{\text{i}}}{t}$

  $d = \vec{v}_{\text{i}}t + \dfrac{1}{2}\vec{a}t^2$

  $d = \left(\dfrac{\vec{v}_{\text{f}}^{\,2} + \vec{v}_{\text{i}}^{\,2}}{2}\right)t$

  $v_{\text{f}}^{\,2} = v_{\text{i}}^{\,2} + 2ad$

  $\vec{F} = m\vec{a}$ (Newton's second law)

  $E_{\text{k}} = \dfrac{1}{2}mv^2$ (kinetic energy)

  $E_{\text{p}} = mgh$ (gravitational potential energy)

PRACTICE TEST

1. Which of the following properties increases when an object is lifted vertically at a constant velocity?

   A. Potential energy

   B. Kinetic energy

   C. Momentum

   D. Mass

2. Momentum is conserved in

   A. elastic collisions only

   B. inelastic collisions only

   C. all collisions except explosions

   D. all collisions, including explosions

3. Which of the following properties may an object at rest have?

   A. Velocity

   B. Momentum

   C. Kinetic energy

   D. Potential energy

4. Which of the following units is used to express impulse?

   A. $\text{kg} \cdot \text{m}^2/\text{s}^2$

   B. $\text{kg} \cdot \text{m/s}^2$

   C. $\text{N} \cdot \text{s}$

   D. N/s

5. If an object has constant momentum and is infinitely distant from any source of gravitation, it will also have

   A. weight

   B. impulse

   C. kinetic energy

   D. potential energy

6. In an elastic collision, which of the following properties are conserved?

   A. Momentum and potential energy

   B. Momentum and kinetic energy

   C. Impulse and potential energy

   D. Impulse and kinetic energy

7. If an object has a mass of m and a kinetic energy of E_k, its momentum is

   A. $\sqrt{\dfrac{2E_k}{m}}$

   B. $\sqrt{2E_k m}$

   C. $\dfrac{4E_k^{\,2}}{m}$

   D. $\sqrt{2E_k}$

8. When the velocity of an object is tripled, which of the following quantities is also tripled?

   A. Inertia

   B. Momentum

   C. Kinetic energy

   D. Potential energy

Use the following information to answer the next question.

An object has the following quantities:
i) Momentum
ii) Potential energy
iii) Kinetic energy

9. When an object slides along a horizontal, frictionless surface, which of the given quantities remains constant?

   A. i) and ii) only

   B. i) and iii) only

   C. ii) and iii) only

   D. i), ii), and iii)

10. The impulse experienced by an object is equivalent to its change in

    A. velocity

    B. momentum

    C. kinetic energy

    D. potential energy

Use the following information to answer the next question.

Ellen, an astronaut with a mass of 1.30×10^2 kg, including her equipment, connects a safety line (length = 22 m) to herself and to her spacecraft (mass = 2.80×10^3 kg). (This is the initial state of the astronaut and the spacecraft, with velocities relative to each other of 0 m/s.) Ellen then pushes against the craft and moves away at a constant velocity of 9.00 m/s relative to her previous null velocity.

11. How long will it take for Ellen's safety line to become tight?

    A. 0.418 s

    B. 0.900 s

    C. 2.34 s

    D. 2.44 s

12. An uncharged subatomic particle, which has a speed of v and a mass of m, strikes the nucleus of a large atom. Assuming that the collision is perfectly elastic and that the particle rebounds back along the incident path, the change in the momentum of the subatomic particle is closest to

    A. 0

    B. $\dfrac{mv}{2}$

    C. mv

    D. $2mv$

13. A perfectly elastic collision conserves

    A. momentum but not kinetic energy

    B. kinetic energy but not momentum

    C. both momentum and kinetic energy

    D. neither momentum nor kinetic energy

14. A 0.25 kg ball hits a wall with a velocity of 3.0 m/s perpendicular to the wall. If the ball bounces off the wall with a velocity of 2.5 m/s, also perpendicular to the wall, what was the impulse on the ball during its contact with the wall?

   A. 0.031 N·s

   B. 0.13 N·s

   C. 1.4 N·s

   D. 3.8 N·s

15. A 1.1×10^3 kg car travelling with a velocity of 25 km/h east collides head-on with a 2.3×10^3 kg car travelling with a velocity of 15 km/h west. During the collision, the two cars lock together. What is the velocity of the locked cars as they move off together immediately after collision?

   A. 1.2 km/h east

   B. 2.1 km/h west

   C. 1.8×10^1 km/h west

   D. 4.0×10^1 km/h east

ELECTRIC FORCES AND FIELDS

When you are finished this section of the unit, you should be able to …

- Explain electrical interactions in terms of the law of conservation of charge
- Explain electrical interactions in terms of the repulsion and attraction of charges
- Compare the methods of transferring charge (conduction and induction)
- Explain, qualitatively, the distribution of charge on the surfaces of conductors and insulators
- Explain, qualitatively, the principles pertinent to Coulomb's torsion balance experiment
- Apply Coulomb's law, quantitatively, to analyze the interaction of two point charges
- Determine, quantitatively, the magnitude and direction of the electric force on a point charge due to two or more other point charges in a plane
- Compare, qualitatively and quantitatively, the inverse square relationship as it is expressed by Coulomb's law and by Newton's universal law of gravitation
- Define vector fields
- Compare forces and fields
- Compare, qualitatively, gravitational potential energy and electric potential energy
- Define electric potential difference as a change in electric potential energy per unit of charge
- Explain, quantitatively, electric fields in terms of intensity (strength) and direction, relative to the source of the field and to the effect on an electric charge
- Describe, quantitatively, the motion of an electric charge in a uniform electric field
- Explain, quantitatively, electrical interactions using the law of conservation of energy

PREREQUISITE SKILLS AND KNOWLEDGE

Prior to starting this unit, you should be able to…

• Solve kinematics and dynamics problems in one- and two-dimensions

• Understand Newton's laws of motion and Newton's law of universal gravitation

• Solve problems in kinematics and dynamics using concepts of mechanical energy and conservation of energy

• Understand the concept of vector and scalar fields and how fields can be applied to gravity and Newton's universal law of gravitation

• Understand the concepts of simple harmonic motion, circular motion, and the difference between them

• Describe uniform circular motion in terms of frequency, period, and radius

• Understand the concept of centripetal force and how it is related to the net force on an object

• Know the relationship between period and frequency of an object in simple harmonic motion and circular motion

• Solve circular motion problems involving centripetal force, centripetal acceleration, velocity, mass, and radius

Lesson 1 ELECTRIC FORCES

The study of electricity began in 700 BC when it was discovered that when amber was rubbed with fur, it would attract small pieces of dried leaves or straw. However, it was not until 1800, when Volta produced the first battery, that any practical use of electricity was developed. Today's world would be very different without electricity and the many technological devices that use it.

STATIC ELECTRICITY

Amber is a form of fossilized tree sap. The ancient Greeks knew that when it was rubbed with fur, it would attract small objects. Similarly, if you were to rub a plastic comb through dry hair, the comb would be able to attract small bits of paper. This is referred to as the amber effect. Because of this property of amber, some people believed amber had mystical properties. The word "electricity" is derived from the Greek word for amber. When other substances, such as glass, rubber, and plastic, are rubbed, they can produce the same effect as amber.

Scientists have discovered that materials can be classified as conductors and insulators. Conductors are materials that allow electric charges (electrons) to move about within it. Insulators are materials that do not allow electric charges (electrons) to move about. Metals are good examples of conductors. Amber, glass, rubber, fur, silk, and plastic are good examples of insulators. Insulators, when rubbed, produce the amber effect.

In the eighteenth century, Benjamin Franklin attempted to explain the amber effect by suggesting a model of matter in which an "electric fluid" transferred from one object to another. Thus, static electricity was "electric fluid" at rest. When a piece of amber (or another substance, such as glass, rubber, or plastic) was rubbed by a cloth, either "electric fluid" was removed from the material or the material gained "electric fluid" from the cloth. Other scientists developed a two-fluid model of matter, which included the flow of positive and negative fluids. Although the "electric fluid" models could explain the amber effect, they were replaced as knowledge about the structure of matter increased.

Today, the amber effect is explained in terms of electron transfer. Scientists now know that matter contains both electrons (or negative particles) and protons (or positive particles). The protons are not free to move, so they do not transfer by rubbing. Therefore, an object can have a negative charge only if it has an excess number of electrons, and it can have a positive charge only if it has a shortage of electrons. An object is neutral when it has an equal number of positive and negative charges (that is, an equal number of electrons and protons).

NOTES

Static electricity is electricity at rest.

Conductors are materials that allow electrons to move about with ease.

Insulators are materials that do not allow electrons to move about with ease.

The amber effect is now explained in terms of electron transfer.

A negative charge is caused by an excess of electrons.

A positive charge is caused by a shortage of electrons.

Grounding an object neutralizes the charge.

After an object becomes charged, it can become neutral by grounding it. Grounding means to provide a path for electrons to enter or leave an object. For example, electrical panels in the basement of most homes are grounded to the water main, which is buried in the ground. This maintains electrical neutrality within the home.

CHARGING BY FRICTION

If you rub a rubber rod with fur or wool, the rod will become negative; that is, the rod gains electrons. The wool will become positive because it loses electrons.

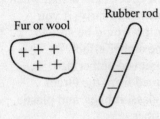

Fur or wool

Rubber rod

If you rub a glass rod with a silk cloth, the rod will become positive because electrons transfer from the rod to the silk. The silk will become negatively charged.

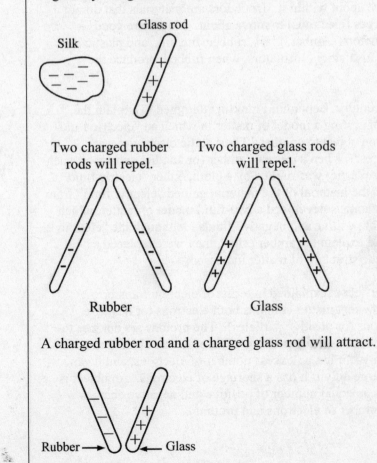

Glass rod

Silk

Two charged rubber rods will repel.

Two charged glass rods will repel.

Rubber

Glass

A charged rubber rod and a charged glass rod will attract.

Rubber →   ← Glass

The process of charging materials by rubbing them together is called charging by friction. It is one method used to transfer charges between materials.

While scientists have identified two types of charges (positive and negative), they have also found that like charges repel one another and unlike charges attract one another. This is called the law of charges.

This explains how an insulator becomes charged. However, it still cannot explain how the amber effect works. Why does an insulator attract small neutral objects, such as small bits of paper, when it is rubbed?

CHARGING BY INDUCTION

If a positively charged rod is brought near, but does not touch, a conductor, the electrons in the neutral conductor will be attracted to the charged rod. This will cause the electrons to move to the side closest to the charged rod. The neutral conductor has not gained or lost electrons, but it has rearranged the position of the electrons within it. This is called charging by induction.

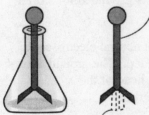

Positively
charged rod

Neutral object
(conductor)

An electroscope is an instrument with a known charge that is used to detect the presence and nature (positive or negative) of another charge.

This part is a conductor

Neutral position of leaves

NOTES

Laws of electric charges:
• There are only two kinds of charges: positive and negative.
• Like charges repel.
• Unlike charges attract.

An electroscope is an instrument used to detect the presence and nature of a charge.

NOTES

When a positively charged rod is brought near the head on an electroscope, electrons are attracted to the head.

An electroscope may be charged by induction. When a charged rod is brought near a neutral electroscope (that is, it has an equal number of electrons and protons), the following events will occur:

• A positively charged rod will attract electrons from the leaves to the head of the electroscope, causing the leaves to be positively charged.

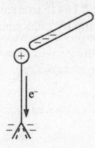

• A negatively charged rod will repel electrons from the head of the electroscope into the leaves, causing the leaves to be negatively charged.

When a negatively charged rod is brought near the head on an electroscope, electrons are repelled to the leaves.

In both cases, the electroscope is neutral, but the electrons are induced to change their relative positions without physically touching or transferring electrons to the electroscope. The leaves have the same charge as the rod doing the charging.

Consider different cases in which the electroscope is grounded for a brief period of time.

Case 1: A positively charged rod is brought near a neutral electroscope. While the rod is in place, the electroscope is grounded. The ground allows the electrons from the ground to be attracted to the head of the electroscope. Now, the electroscope has extra electrons.

If the ground is then removed before the charged rod is removed, the extra electrons cannot escape to the ground when the rod is removed. They are trapped on the electroscope. When the rod is removed, the electroscope will have a permanent negative charge. This charge is opposite to the charge on the rod.

A positively charged rod is used to induce a negative charge on an electroscope.

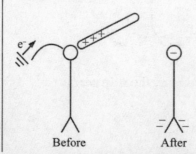

Before   After

Case 2: Similar to case 1, a positive charge is placed on the electroscope by using a negatively charged rod and following the same steps. In this case, the electrons are induced to leave the electroscope.

A negatively charged rod is used to induce a positive charge on an electroscope.

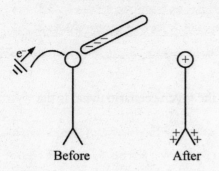

Before   After

This is called charging by induction.

How do you determine the charge on a strip of plastic if it is rubbed by a piece of cotton? You cannot tell by looking at it, but you can use an electroscope to test for the charge. Begin by inducing a known charge on the electroscope. For example, if you rub a rubber rod with fur, you know the rod will have a negative charge. Then, use this rod to put a positive charge on an electroscope, as in case 2.

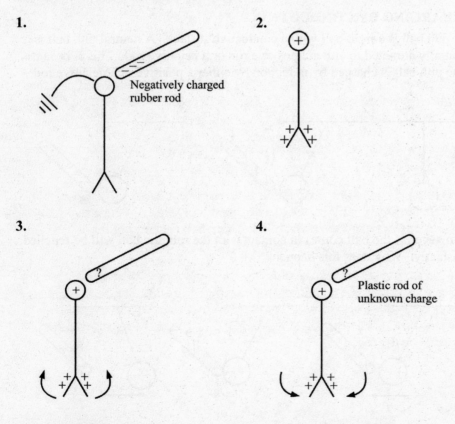

1.
Negatively charged
rubber rod

2.

3.

4.
Plastic rod of
unknown charge

Now, rub the plastic strip with the cotton, and bring the strip near the electroscope.

NOTES

Example

If the leaves diverge (move apart) in the given scenario, what is the charge on the plastic?

   Solution
   Positive

Example

If the leaves converge (come together) in the given scenario, what is the charge on the plastic?

   Solution
   Negative

This explains why small, neutral objects, such as tiny bits of paper, can be attracted to your plastic comb when you pull it through your hair. Your comb has an electrostatic charge (positive or negative). When you bring the charged comb near a tiny piece of paper, the paper is charged by induction. This is the explanation of the amber effect: amber does not have mystical properties, but it obtains an electrostatic charge when rubbed.

CHARGING BY CONDUCTION

A pith ball is a light ball with a conductive surface. A neutral pith ball is initially attracted to either a positive rod or a negative rod. This is because the pith ball is charged by induction by either a positive or a negative rod.

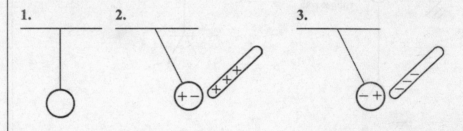

However, if the ball comes in contact with the rod, the ball will be repelled instantly. Why does this happen?

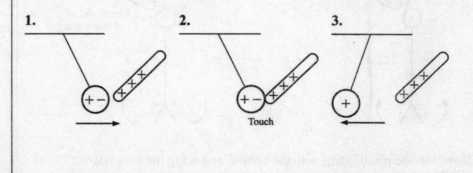

When the ball comes in contact with the positive rod, the ball gives up enough electrons to the rod to balance the charge between the ball and the rod. The rod remains positive. However, the ball is no longer neutral; it is also positive. Thus, the ball and the rod repel each other when they are no longer in contact. This is an example of charging by conduction.

An object can obtain an electrostatic charge in three ways:
• Friction
• Induction
• Conduction

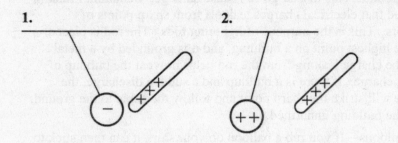

You have now seen three methods for charging an object (giving the object an electrostatic charge):

• Friction: When you rub an insulator, you place a charge on the rod by friction.

• Induction: When you bring a charged object near a neutral conductor, the electrons are pushed or pulled to one side or the other.

• Conduction: A neutral object touches a charged object, and electrons are transferred between the objects.

The following situations are examples of electrostatic charging:

• Static shock—When you walk across a carpeted floor and then touch a conductor (such as a light switch, tap, or door handle), you may receive a slight shock. This is because you built up an electrostatic charge on yourself by friction, and when you touched the conductor, the charge on your body was transferred by conduction. The electrons discharging from (leaving) your body produce the shock that you feel.

• Static cling in your clothes dryer—Here, different materials rub against one another as they tumble in the dryer. In the dry atmosphere of the dryer, electrons can transfer from one material to another by friction. The clothes will then cling together because of their opposite charges.

NOTES

• Thunderstorms—Clouds may become charged due to friction between the particles in the clouds. Most lightning is the discharge of electrons between oppositely charged parts of clouds. However, a charged cloud can also induce an opposite charge on the ground below, and a buildup of this induced charge may cause a sudden discharge between the cloud and the ground. This discharge can cause damage. Benjamin Franklin discovered that electrical charges leak off from sharp points of conductors. This is the purpose of lightning rods. The rod is placed above the highest point on a building, and it is grounded by a metal cable. The charge leaking from the rod helps prevent the buildup of electrical charge. If there is a buildup and a sudden discharge, the discharge will strike the sharp point and follow the cable to the ground, leaving the building unharmed.

• Sticky balloons—If you rub a balloon on your shirt, it can then stick to the wall. This is because you have charged the balloon by friction. The balloon then induces an opposite charge on the wall, and the two will attract.

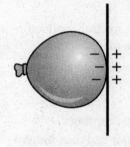

It should be noted that if an object is charged by friction, induction, or conduction, electric charges are neither created nor destroyed; they only move from one place to another. This is the law of conservation of charges.

ELECTRIC CHARGE DISTRIBUTION

If electrons transfer to an insulator, the electrons will remain at the point at which they were added. This is because insulators do not allow electrons to move about.

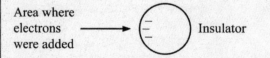

When electrons are added to a conductor, the electrons will repel one another and will move as far away from one another as possible. This means they will end up on the surface of the conductor. If this conductor is spherical, the charge distribution will be uniform over the entire conductor surface.

On a spherical conductor, the charge will be distributed uniformly over the entire surface.

56

However, if the conductor is not spherical, the distribution of charges will not be uniform. Instead, the concentration of charges depends on the curvature of the conductor: the greater the curvature, the greater the concentration of charge.

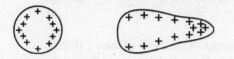

Higher concentration of excess charge

> On a non-spherical conductor, the charge concentration is greatest where the curvature is greatest.

If the electrons are removed from a conductor, there will be excess positive charges. These excess positive charges are distributed on the surface of the conductor in the same way as the excess electrons.

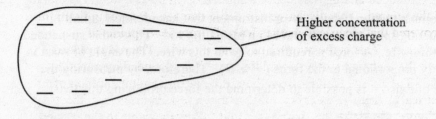

ELECTRIC FORCE LAW (COULOMB'S LAW)

The attraction and repulsion between charged objects are the result of electric forces between the charges. For example, say there is an electric force between two negatively charged pith balls. How strong is this force? What variables does this force depend on? Is there any relationship that expresses what the magnitude (size) of the force depends on?

Joseph Priestley suggested in 1767 that charged objects exert these electric forces on one another and that the mathematical relationship describing these forces is parallel to Newton's law of universal gravitation. Priestley came to this conclusion when he discovered that a charged pith ball placed inside a hollow, charged sphere has no electrical force acting on it.

> No electrical force exists inside a charged, hollow sphere.

Priestley remembered that in Newton's development of the law of universal gravitation, Newton showed mathematically that if a mass were placed inside a hollow mass, there would be no gravitational force on the mass. This is because there are forces acting in all directions and the forces cancel one another out. The net force is zero. Priestley hypothesized that this is the same reason that the charged pith ball placed inside the charged sphere seemed to have no electrical force acting on it. The net electric force on the pith ball was zero.

In the case of a charged pith ball within a hollow charged conductor, the net force is also zero.

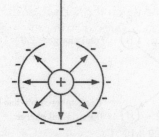
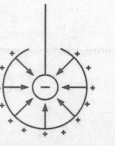

NOTES

In 1785, a French scientist named Charles Augustin de Coulomb used a torsion balance to study the electric force law. Coulomb was inspired by Priestley's suggestion, and he set out to show this to be true. The electric force law is today called Coulomb's law.

Coulomb's torsion balance is an instrument that has identical, small conducting spheres at each end of an insulating rod. This rod is suspended by a thin wire. A force is required to twist this wire. The angle of twist is directly proportional to the force ($F \propto \theta$). Therefore, by measuring the angle of twist, it is possible to determine the force producing this twist.

The angle of twist is directly proportional to the force.

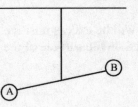

The given diagram shows Coulomb's setup. Coulomb placed a third sphere, C, near sphere A. By varying the distance between spheres A and C, he was able to determine that $F \propto \dfrac{1}{r^2}$. Measuring the impact of the sizes of the charges by doubling, tripling, or halving the charges on spheres A and C was more difficult.

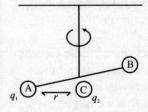

To this point, all the units you have used are derived from the basic units of time (the second), distance (the metre), and mass (the kilogram). The unit for charge is the coulomb (C). One coulomb is the charge of 6.25×10^{18} electrons.

Coulomb used a torsion balance to determine the relationship between the electric force and distance between charges.

Example

Suppose you have two identical spheres and you put a charge of 2.0×10^{-6} C on one sphere and nothing on the other. If you allow these spheres to touch and then separate again, what will be the charge on each sphere?

Solution

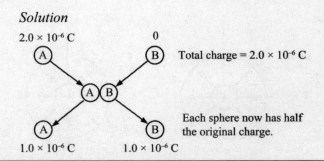

The coulomb is the unit of electric charge.

Coulomb used this method to give spheres A and B equal charges. He would charge one sphere, and then he would touch the second sphere to the first sphere.

Coulomb showed the following relationships:
- The electric force between two charges varies directly with the product of their charges.

$$F_e \propto q_1 q_2$$

- The electric force between two charges varies inversely with the square of the distance between the two charges.

$$F_e \propto \frac{1}{r^2}$$

- The magnitude of the electrical force between two point charges is directly proportional to the product of the charges and is inversely proportional to the square of the distance between them.

$$F_e \propto \frac{q_1 q_2}{r^2} \quad \text{or} \quad F_e = \frac{k q_1 q_2}{r^2}$$

- In this equation, k is Coulomb's constant, $8.99 \times 10^9 \ \frac{\text{N} \cdot \text{m}^2}{\text{C}^2}$.

- Recall that Newton's law of universal gravitation states the following relationships:
- The gravitational force between two masses varies directly with the product of their masses.

$$F_g \propto m_1 m_2$$

- The gravitational force between two masses varies inversely with the square of the distance between the centres of their masses.

$$F_g \propto \frac{1}{r^2}$$

- Therefore, the force of gravity between two masses is directly proportional to the product of the masses and is inversely proportional to the square of the distance between them.

By placing Coulomb's law and Newton's law of universal gravitation together, you can see that they are similar.

$$F_g = \frac{G m_1 m_2}{r^2} \text{ (only attractive)} \quad F_e = \frac{k q_1 q_2}{r^2} \text{ (attractive or repulsive)}$$

Recall that $G = 6.67 \times 10^{-11} \ \frac{\text{N} \cdot \text{m}^2}{\text{kg}^2}$ (a very small value), which indicates that gravity is a weak force that requires very large masses to be effective. In contrast, electrical forces have a proportionality constant of

$k = 8.99 \times 10^9 \ \frac{\text{N} \cdot \text{m}^2}{\text{C}^2}$ (a very large value), which indicates that electric

forces are very large compared to gravitational forces, and they are still very effective with small charges.

Coulomb's law:

$$F_e \propto q_1 q_2 \text{ and } F_e \propto \frac{1}{r^2}$$

A proportional sign can be replaced by an equal sign and a constant.

Coulomb's law is parallel to Newton's law of universal gravitation. Both are cases of forces acting at a distance.

To solve mathematical problems involving Coulomb's law, always solve for the absolute value and ignore the sign on the charge. The sign on the charge is used only to determine the direction of the electric force.

Example

Calculate the electric force between charges of 1.00×10^{-6} C and 1.50×10^{-6} C when they are 5.00×10^{-1} m apart.

Solution

$$F_e = \frac{kq_1q_2}{r^2}$$

$$= \frac{\left(8.99 \times 10^9 \ \frac{N \cdot m^2}{C^2}\right)\left(1.00 \times 10^{-6} \ C\right)\left(1.50 \times 10^{-6} \ C\right)}{\left(5.00 \times 10^{-1} \ m\right)^2}$$

$$= 5.39 \times 10^{-2} \ N$$

Example

Calculate the gravitational force between two objects when they are 7.50×10^{-1} m apart. Each object has a mass of 5.00×10^1 kg.

Solution

$$F_g = \frac{Gm_1m_2}{r^2}$$

$$= \frac{\left(6.67 \times 10^{-11} \ \frac{N \cdot m^2}{kg^2}\right)\left(5.00 \times 10^1 \ kg\right)\left(5.00 \times 10^1 \ kg\right)}{\left(7.50 \times 10^{-1} \ m\right)^2}$$

$$= 2.96 \times 10^{-7} \ N$$

Example

Two point charges of 1.8×10^{-6} C and 2.4×10^{-6} C produce a force of 2.2×10^{-3} N on each other. How far apart are these two charges?

Solution

$$F_e = \frac{kq_1q_2}{r^2}$$

$$r = \sqrt{\frac{kq_1q_2}{F_e}}$$

$$= \sqrt{\frac{\left(8.99 \times 10^9 \ \frac{N \cdot m^2}{C^2}\right)\left(1.8 \times 10^{-6} \ C\right)\left(2.4 \times 10^{-6} \ C\right)}{2.2 \times 10^{-3} \ N}}$$

$$= 4.2 \ m$$

Example

A charge of 1.7×10^{-6} C is placed 2.0×10^{-2} m from a charge of 2.5×10^{-6} C and 3.5×10^{-2} m from a charge of -2.0×10^{-6} C, as shown in the given diagram.

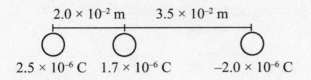

2.0×10^{-2} m 3.5×10^{-2} m

2.5×10^{-6} C 1.7×10^{-6} C -2.0×10^{-6} C

Calculate the magnitude of the net electric force on the 1.7×10^{-6} C charge.

Solution

There are two forces acting on the charge of 1.7×10^{-6} C. Identify the size and direction of each. Use Coulomb's law to determine the force between the two positive charges.

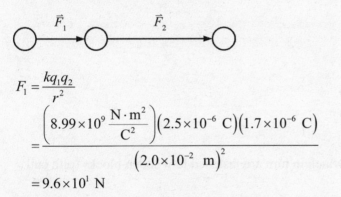

$\vec{F}_1$ $\vec{F}_2$

$$F_1 = \frac{kq_1q_2}{r^2}$$

$$= \frac{\left(8.99 \times 10^9 \; \frac{\text{N} \cdot \text{m}^2}{\text{C}^2}\right)\left(2.5 \times 10^{-6} \; \text{C}\right)\left(1.7 \times 10^{-6} \; \text{C}\right)}{\left(2.0 \times 10^{-2} \; \text{m}\right)^2}$$

$$= 9.6 \times 10^1 \; \text{N}$$

Although the third charge $\left(-2.0 \times 10^{-6} \; \text{C}\right)$ is negative, do not use the negative sign in the equation; use the absolute value of the charge. Whenever you use Coulomb's law, always use the absolute value of the charge. The negative sign on the charge is used only to determine whether the force is an attraction or repulsion force with respect to the other charges that may be present.

$$F_2 = \frac{\left(8.99 \times 10^9 \; \frac{\text{N} \cdot \text{m}^2}{\text{C}^2}\right)\left(2.0 \times 10^{-6} \; \text{C}\right)\left(1.7 \times 10^{-6} \; \text{C}\right)}{\left(3.5 \times 10^{-2} \; \text{m}\right)^2}$$

$$= 2.5 \times 10^1 \; \text{N}$$

Add the magnitudes F_1 to F_2, because the forces act in the same direction. If the forces acted in opposite directions, they would be subtracted.

$$\vec{F}_{\text{net}} = \vec{F}_1 + \vec{F}_2$$

$$= 9.6 \times 10^1 \; \text{N} + 2.5 \times 10^1 \; \text{N}$$

$$= 1.2 \times 10^2 \; \text{N to the right}$$

ACTIVITY #5

Coulomb's law states in part that the magnitude of the electric force between two charges varies directly with the product of those charges.

Purpose: To verify that the magnitude of the electric force between two charges varies directly with the product of those charges.

Apparatus:
- Three identical pith balls
- Cat or rabbit fur
- Ebonite rod

Apparatus Assembly:

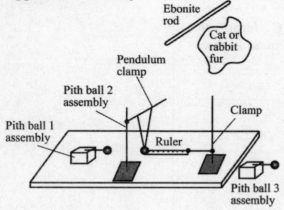

1. Place two pith balls on insulating handles, which in turn are fastened to wooden blocks (pith ball assembly 1 and 3).

2. The third pith ball should have a cotton or nylon thread (≈ 60 cm) running through its centre, which is suspended by a pendulum clamp and ring stand (pith ball assembly 2).

3. Place a ruler close to pith ball 2 but in a position to avoid interfering with the movement of pith ball 2. The ruler is supported horizontally to the lab table by a ring stand and clamp. You may want to clamp this ruler at both ends to make it more stable.

4. The ruler assembly is placed parallel to the line of movement of pith ball 2 when pith ball 2 is allowed to swing freely. When pith ball 2 is at its equilibrium position, its centre should be at the zero mark of the ruler.

Procedure:

Before starting the procedure, keep the following considerations in mind:
- Static charge will leak off the pith balls, so collect the data as quickly as possible.
- Placing static charges on the pith balls will be difficult if the humidity is high.
- Pith ball 2 needs two supports (as shown in the given diagram) so it will deflect along a straight line.

1. Set up the apparatus as described and shown in the given diagram.
2. Pith ball 1 should move toward pith ball 2 so that they touch and are at the same vertical height.
3. Rub the ebonite rod with the fur.
4. Touch the tip of the ebonite rod briefly to either pith ball 1 or 2. They should now repel each other.
5. Record the position of the centre of pith ball 2.
6. Ground pith ball 3 briefly, and bring it in contact with pith ball 2.
7. Record the new position of pith ball 2.
8. Ground pith ball 3 briefly, and bring it into contact with pith ball 1. Record the position of pith ball 2.
9. Ground pith ball 3 briefly again, and bring it into contact with pith ball 2. Record the position of pith ball 2.
10. Ground pith ball 3 briefly again, and bring it into contact with pith ball 1. Record the position of pith ball 2.
11. Complete the following table.

	Position of Pith Ball 2 (d) (m)	Charge of Pith Ball 1 (C)	Charge of Pith Ball 2 (C)	Product of Charges (C^2)
1.		q	q	q^2
2.				
3.				
4.				
5.				

Notes:

• Record the charges of the pith balls (1 and 2) as a fraction of q.

• You have not calculated the electric force between pith balls 1 and 2.

If you want to do this, you will have to measure the mass of pith ball 2 and the vertical distance that the centre of pith ball 2 is below the pendulum clamp (it is not the length of the thread). However, you do not have to do this. Instead, you can use the position of pith ball 2 (d) as the electric force (F_e).

The variable d can be used in place of F_e for the following reason:

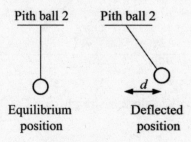

Pith ball 2   Pith ball 2

d

Equilibrium   Deflected
position   position

Triangle 1:

$$\sin\theta = \frac{\text{opp}}{\text{hyp}} = \frac{d}{l}$$

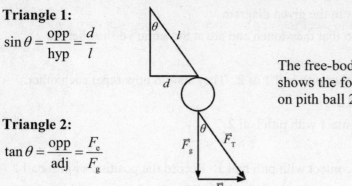

The free-body diagram
shows the forces acting
on pith ball 2

Triangle 2:

$$\tan\theta = \frac{\text{opp}}{\text{adj}} = \frac{F_e}{F_g}$$

d = position of pith ball 2 measured from the equilibrium position (d is the magnitude of the deflection).
l = the vertical distance that the centre of pith ball 2 is below the pendulum clamp

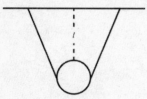

θ = angle of deflection

It is true that $\sin\theta \approx \tan\theta$ when the angle of deflection is very small. In this activity, assume that
$\sin\theta = \tan\theta$.

$\sin\theta\,(\text{triangle 1}) = \tan\theta\,(\text{triangle 2})$

$$\frac{d}{l} = \frac{F_e}{F_g} \quad \text{or} \quad F_e = \frac{F_g d}{l} \quad \text{or} \quad F_e = \frac{mgd}{l}$$

Because m, g, and l are constants in this activity, it can be said that $F_e \propto d$.

Draw a graph showing the magnitude of the deflection (d) as a function of the product of the charges.

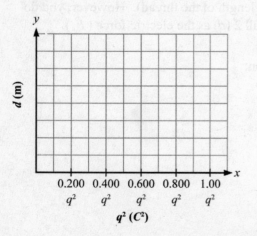

Question:

1. Did you verify that the deflection (*d*) and the electric force between the two charges vary directly with the product of the charges?

If you were not able to do this activity, use the following data:

- Mass of pith ball $2 = 0.0500$ kg (m)

- Vertical distance that the centre of pith ball 2 is below the pendulum clamp $= 0.250$ m (l)

Position of Pith Ball 2 (*d*) (m)	Charge of Pith Ball 1 (C)	Charge of Pith Ball 2 (C)	Product of Charges (C^2)	Electric Force Using $F_e = \dfrac{mgd}{l}$ (N)
0.008 0	q	q	q^2	
0.004 1	$0.500\,q$	q	$0.50\,q^2$	
0.001 9	$0.500\,q$	$0.50\,q$	$0.25\,q^2$	
0.001 0	$0.25\,q$	$0.50\,q$	$0.13\,q^2$	
0.000 55	$0.25\,q$	$0.25\,q$	$0.063\,q^2$	

Complete column 5 only if you wish to plot the electric force versus the product of the charges instead of the deflection (*d*) versus the product of the charges.

ACTIVITY #6

Coulomb's law states in part that the magnitude of the electric force between two charges varies inversely with the square of the distance between the centres of these charges.

Purpose: To verify that the magnitude of the electric force between two charges varies inversely with the square of the distance between the centres of these charges.

Apparatus:
- Two pith balls
- Cat or rabbit fur
- Ebonite rod

Apparatus Assembly:

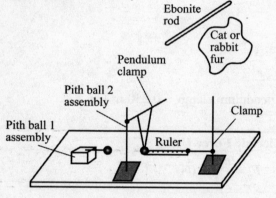

1. Place one pith ball on an insulating handle, which is fastened to a wooden block (pith ball assembly 1).

2. Run a cotton or nylon thread ($\approx$ 60 cm) through the centre of the second pith ball, and suspend the pith ball by a ring stand and pendulum clamp (pith ball assembly 2).

3. Place a ruler close to pith ball 2, in a position that does not interfere with the movement of pith ball 2. The ruler is supported horizontally to the lab table by a ring stand and clamp. You may want to clamp this ruler at both ends to make it more stable.

4. The ruler assembly is placed parallel to the line of movement of pith ball 2 when pith ball 2 is allowed to swing freely. When pith ball 2 is at its equilibrium position, its centre should be at the zero mark of the ruler.

Procedure:

Before starting the procedure, keep the following considerations in mind:

- Static charge will slowly leak off the pith balls, so collect the data as quickly as possible.
- Placing static charges on the pith balls will be difficult if the humidity is high.
- Pith ball 2 needs two supports (as shown in the given diagram) so it will deflect along a straight line.

1. Set up the apparatus as described and shown in the given diagram.

2. Rub the ebonite rod with the fur.

3. Touch the tip of the ebonite rod briefly to pith ball 1.

4. Rub the ebonite rod again with the fur, and briefly touch the tip of this rod to pith ball 2.

5. Carefully slide pith ball 1 assembly toward pith ball 2 until pith ball 1 is at the zero mark of the ruler (do not let pith ball 1 touch the ruler).

6. Record the positions of pith balls 1 and 2.

7. Slide pith ball 1 toward pith ball 2 so that pith ball 1 is at 0.50 cm mark of the ruler.
   Note: The measurement of 0.50 cm is only a suggestion. You may wish to use a different value.

8. Record the positions of pith balls 1 and 2.

9. Repeat this process eight more times, as shown in the given diagram.

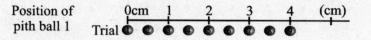

10. Complete the following table.

Trial	Position of Pith Ball 1 (m)	Position of Pith Ball 2 (d) (m)	Distance between Balls 1 and 2 (r) (m)	$\sqrt{r}$	$\dfrac{1}{r^2}$
1	0				
2					
3					
4					
5					
6					
7					
8					
9					

d = deflection of pith ball 2 (column 2)
r = distance between the centres of the two charges (column 3)

Note: As in Activity #5, d will be used instead of F_e.

11. Draw a graph showing d as a function of r.

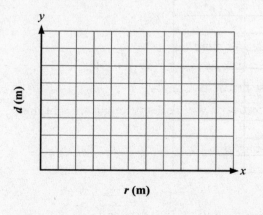

Complete the necessary column in the data table so that you can draw a straight line graph when you plot *d* versus the column you completed. Draw this graph.

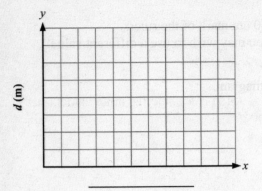

Question:
1. Did you verify that the magnitude of the deflection (*d*) and the magnitude of the electric force between two charges vary inversely with the square of the distance between the charges? Explain.

If you were not able to do this activity, use the following data:
• Mass of pith ball 2 = 0.0500 kg (*m*)
• Vertical distance that the centre of pith ball 2 is below the pendulum clamp = 0.250 m (*l*)

Complete the remaining columns in the following chart only if you need to in order to complete this activity.

Trial	Position of Pith Ball 2 (*d*) (m)	Distance between Balls 1 and 2 (*r*) (m)	Electric Force Using $F_e = \dfrac{mgd}{l}$ (N)	$\sqrt{r}$	$\dfrac{1}{r^2}$
1.	0.0060	0.030			
2.	0.0090	0.025			
3.	0.012	0.021			
4.	0.015	0.019			
5.	0.019	0.017			
6.	0.024	0.015			
7.	0.027	0.014			
8.	0.033	0.013			
9.	0.040	0.012			

d = deflection of pith ball 2 (electric force)
r = distance between the centres of the two charges

PRACTICE EXERCISES

Formulas: $\qquad F_e = \dfrac{kq_1q_2}{r^2} \qquad\qquad F_g = \dfrac{Gm_1m_2}{r^2}$

Note: Problems on gravitational forces are included for comparison.

1. Two students are sitting 1.50 m apart. One student has a mass of 70.0 kg, and the other student has a mass of 52.0 kg. What is the gravitational force between them?

$$F_g = \frac{9.81 \cdot 70 \cdot 52}{1.5^2} = \frac{35708.4}{2.25} = 15870.4 \ldots$$

$$\&$$

2. What gravitational force does the moon $\left(\text{mass} = 7.34 \times 10^{22} \text{ kg}\right)$ produce on Earth $\left(\text{mass} = 5.98 \times 10^{24} \text{ kg}\right)$ if the centres of Earth and the moon are 3.88×10^8 m apart?

$$F_g = \frac{9.81 \cdot 7.34 \cdot 10^{22} \cdot 5.98 \cdot 10^{24}}{3.88 \cdot 10^8}$$

3. Calculate the electric force between two point charges of 4.00 μC and 3.00 μC when they are 2.00 cm apart (μC = microcoulomb, $1 \text{ μC} = 1 \times 10^{-6}$ C).

$$F_e = \frac{8.99 \cdot 10^9 \cdot 4 \cdot 10^{-6} \cdot 3 \cdot 10^{-6}}{(0.02\text{m})^2}$$

4. Two points of equal charge produce an electric force on each other of 3.40×10^{-2} N when placed 1.00×10^{-1} m apart. What is the charge on each point?

$$3.4 \cdot 10^{-2} \, F_g = \frac{8.99 \cdot 10^9 \cdot x^2}{(1 \cdot (0^{-1})^2}$$

5. How far apart are two point charges of 2.0×10^{-6} C and 4.0×10^{-6} C if they produce an electric force on each other of 5.6×10^{-1} N?

$$5.6 \cdot 10^{-1} = \frac{8.99 \cdot 10^9 \cdot 2 \cdot 10^{-6} \cdot 4 \cdot 10^{-6}}{r^2}$$

6. Two point charges produce an electric force on each other of 6.20×10^{-2} N. What is the electric force if the distance between the points increases three times?

7. Two point charges produce an electric force on each other of 4.5×10^{-3} N. What is the electric force if the charges on both objects triple and the distance between them doubles?

Use the following information to answer the next question.

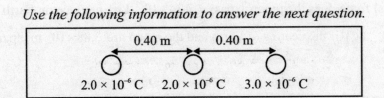

8. Three point charges are placed in a line, as shown in the given diagram. Calculate the magnitude of the net electric force on the centre charge due to the other two charges.

9. The electric force between two charged objects is 5.2×10^{-4} N when the objects are 3.11×10^{-1} m apart. What is the electric force between the same objects if the distance is changed to 4.04×10^{-1} m?

Use the following information to answer the next question.

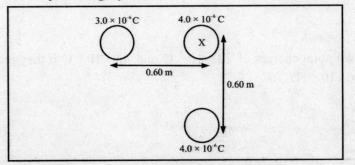

10. Three point charges are placed at the corners of a right triangle, as shown in the given diagram. Calculate the magnitude of the net electric force on charge X due to the other two charges.

11. Two small spheres have the same mass and volume. One sphere has a charge of 4.00 μC, and the other sphere has a charge of −1.00 μC. If these two spheres are brought into brief contact with each other and then separated to a distance of 2.00×10^{-1} m, what is the electric force between them at this distance?

12. Two small spheres, each with a mass of 2.00×10^{-5} kg, are placed 3.50×10^{-1} m apart. One sphere has a charge of −2.00 μC and is fixed in position. The other sphere has a charge of −3.00 μC and is free to move without friction. What is the initial acceleration due to the electric force on the sphere that is free to move?

Use the following information to answer the next question.

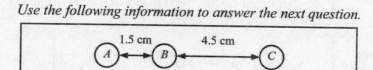

13. Spheres A, B, and C are equally charged spheres lying along one line, as shown in the given diagram. If the distance between spheres A and B is 1.5 cm, and the distance between spheres B and C is 4.5 cm, how does the force that sphere C exerts on sphere B compare with the force that sphere A exerts on sphere B?

Lesson 2 ELECTRIC FIELDS

NOTES

Fields are defined as spheres of influence.

Scalar fields include the following:
• Heat fields
• Sound fields

Vector fields include the following:
• Gravitational fields
• Electric fields
• Magnetic fields

Electric fields are defined as force per unit charge.

The direction of an electric field is the direction of the force on a positive test object.

Electric fields are drawn away from positive charges.

Electric fields are drawn toward negative charges.

The gravitational field around Earth is similar to the electric field around a charge.

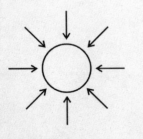

FIELD EXPLANATION

To explain the forces between objects that are not in contact, scientists developed the concept of fields. Just as masses like Earth and the moon are surrounded by gravitational fields, an electrical charge is surrounded by an electric field. Fields are defined as spheres of influence, and they can be either scalar or vector.

Examples of scalar fields are sound fields and heat fields. If you are standing near a campfire, you are in the sphere of influence of the heat from the fire. You can measure the intensity of the heat at different points (that is, you can measure the temperature). Temperature is a scalar quantity, and the field is described by the collection of these points. Therefore, the heat field is a scalar field.

Vector fields, like vector quantities, have direction as well as magnitude (size). Electric fields and gravitational fields are examples of vector fields.

ELECTRIC FIELDS

Symbol: $\vec{E}$

Units: N/C

Definition: Force per unit charge $\vec{E} = \dfrac{\vec{F_e}}{q}$

Other formula: $E = \dfrac{kq}{r^2}$

The direction of an electric field is defined as the direction that a positive test charge will move when placed within the field. A positive test charge will move away from a positive object and toward a negative object. Therefore, an electric field is directed away from a positive charge and toward a negative charge.

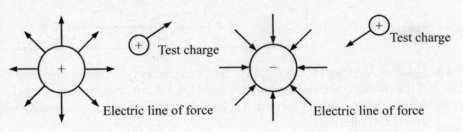

Remember that the strength of a vector field is represented by the density of the arrows (lines of force). The more dense the lines of force are, the stronger the field. The direction of the field is represented by the direction of the arrows.

Consider the following two formulas:

1. $\vec{E} = \dfrac{\vec{F}_e}{q}$

2. $E = \dfrac{kq}{r^2}$

The first formula is the definition of an electric field. The field strength, or intensity, at any point around a charged object can be found by placing a test charge in the field and finding the electric force that acts on it. Dividing this electric force by the charge of the test object determines the field strength at the location of the test charge.

$$\vec{E} = \dfrac{\vec{F}_e}{q}$$

Force on test object

Charge on test object

The second formula uses the charge (q) of the object that produces the field to determine the magnitude of the electric field at a distance (r), which is measured from the object producing the field to the location of the test charge within the electric field.

$$E = \dfrac{kq}{r^2}$$

Charge on object producing field

Distance from object producing field

Gravitational field formulas:

$$\vec{g} = \dfrac{\vec{F}_g}{m} \begin{pmatrix} \text{test object} \\ \text{equation} \end{pmatrix}$$

$$g = \dfrac{Gm}{r^2} \begin{pmatrix} \text{producing} \\ \text{object equation} \end{pmatrix}$$

Summary:

Test charge: $\vec{E} = \dfrac{\vec{F}_e}{q}$

Producing charge: $E = \dfrac{kq}{r^2}$

The equations that describe electric fields are very similar to the gravitational field equations. To solve electric field problems, use the absolute values and ignore the sign on the charge, which is what you did to solve problems involving electric force. The sign on the charge is used only to determine the direction of the field.

NOTES

Lines of force are drawn toward a negative charge, and the electric field points toward the negative charge.

Lines of force are drawn away from a positive charge, and the electric field points away from the positive charge.

Electric fields are described in terms of field lines (or lines of force).

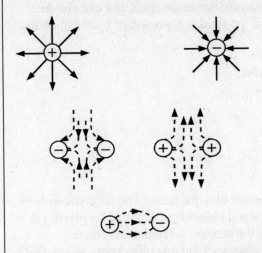

Note: The lines of force are always drawn away from the positive charge and toward the negative charge. This is the path a positive test charge would take in the electric field. These lines of force also indicate like-charge repulsion and unlike-charge attraction. Also, the lines of force do not cross.

In order to solve some problems, it is necessary to be familiar with the masses and charges of alpha particles, electrons, and protons.

	Mass	Charge
Alpha particle	6.65×10^{-27} kg	3.20×10^{-19} C
Electron	9.11×10^{-31} kg	-1.60×10^{-19} C
Proton	1.67×10^{-27} kg	1.60×10^{-19} C

Example

Find the electric field strength 4.50×10^{-1} m from a 5.00 μC charged object.

Solution

$$E = \frac{kq}{r^2}$$
$$= \frac{\left(8.99 \times 10^9 \, \frac{N \cdot m^2}{C^2}\right)\left(5.00 \times 10^{-6} \, C\right)}{\left(4.50 \times 10^{-1} \, m\right)^2}$$
$$= 2.22 \times 10^5 \, N/C$$

Example

What is the electric field strength at a point where a $-2.00\ \mu C$ test charge experiences an electric force of $5.30 \times 10^{-2}\ N$?

Solution

$$\vec{E} = \frac{\vec{F}_e}{q}$$
$$= \frac{5.30 \times 10^{-2}\ N}{2.00 \times 10^{-6}\ C}$$
$$= 2.65 \times 10^4\ N/C$$

Example

Calculate the gravitational field strength on the surface of Earth.

Solution

$$g = \frac{Gm}{r^2}$$
$$= \frac{\left(6.67 \times 10^{-11}\ \frac{N \cdot m^2}{kg^2}\right)\left(5.98 \times 10^{24}\ kg\right)}{\left(6.37 \times 10^6\ m\right)^2}$$
$$= 9.83\ N/kg$$

The values found here for the strength of the gravitational field differ slightly because the constants for the mass and radius of Earth have been rounded.

Example

On the surface of Earth, an object has a weight (force due to gravity) of 76.3 N and a mass of 7.78 kg. Using this information, what is the gravitational field strength on the surface of Earth?

Solution

$$\vec{F}_g = m\vec{g}$$
$$\vec{g} = \frac{\vec{F}_g}{m}$$
$$= \frac{76.3\ N}{7.78\ kg}$$
$$= 9.81\ N/kg$$

Example

What is the electric field strength at the midpoint between charged objects of $-3.50 \ \mu C$ and $3.00 \ \mu C$ that are placed 4.40×10^{-1} m apart?

Solution

Draw a diagram, and show the direction of the electric fields using arrows. Remember, the direction of the field is the same as the direction a positive test charge would move.

$-3.50 \ \mu C$ $\vec{E}_1$ $\vec{E}_2$ $3.00 \ \mu C$

4.40×10^{-1} m

$$\vec{E}_1 = \frac{kq}{r^2}$$

$$= \frac{\left(8.99 \times 10^9 \ \dfrac{N \cdot m^2}{C^2}\right)\left(3.50 \times 10^{-6} \ C\right)}{\left(2.20 \times 10^{-1} \ m\right)^2}$$

$$= 6.50 \times 10^5 \ N/C$$

$$\vec{E}_2 = \frac{\left(8.99 \times 10^9 \ \dfrac{N \cdot m^2}{C^2}\right)\left(3.00 \times 10^{-6} \ C\right)}{\left(2.20 \times 10^{-1} \ m\right)^2}$$

$$= 5.57 \times 10^5 \ N/C$$

$$\vec{E}_{net} = \vec{E}_1 + \vec{E}_2$$
$$= 6.50 \times 10^5 \ N/C + 5.57 \times 10^5 \ N/C$$
$$= 1.21 \times 10^6 \ N/C$$

PRACTICE EXERCISES

Formulas: $\qquad E = \dfrac{kq}{r^2}$ $\qquad\qquad \vec{E} = \dfrac{\vec{F}_e}{q}$ $\qquad\qquad g = \dfrac{Gm}{r^2}$ $\qquad \bar{g} = \dfrac{\vec{F}_g}{m}$

1. What is the electric field strength 7.50×10^{-1} m from a 8.00 µC charged object?

2. Calculate the gravitational field strength on the surface of Mars. Mars has a radius of 3.43×10^6 m and a mass of 6.37×10^{23} kg.

3. At a point a short distance from a 4.60×10^{-6} C charged object, the electric field strength is 2.75×10^5 N/C. What is the distance to the charged object producing this field?

4. On the surface of planet X, an object has a weight of 63.5 N and a mass of 22.5 kg. What is the gravitational field strength on the surface of planet X?

5. If an alpha particle experiences an electric force of 0.250 N at a point in space, what electric force would a proton experience at the same point?

6. What is the electric field strength at a point in space where a 5.20×10^{-6} C charged object experiences an electric force of 7.11×10^{-3} N?

7. What is the initial acceleration on an alpha particle when it is placed at a point in space where the electric field strength is 7.60×10^{4} N/C?

8. Calculate the electric field strength at the midpoint between a 4.50 µC charged object and a −4.50 µC charged object if the two charged objects are 5.00×10^{-1} m apart.

9. Calculate the electric field strength at the midpoint between a 3.0 µC charged object and a 6.0 µC charged object if the objects are 8.0×10^{-1} m apart.

10. Calculate the electric field strength at the midpoint between two $3.0\ \mu C$ charged objects if they are $9.0 \times 10^{-1}\ m$ apart.

11. What is the electric field strength at a point in space where an electron experiences an initial acceleration of $7.50 \times 10^{12}\ m/s^2$?

12. The electric field strength at a distance of $3.00 \times 10^{-1}\ m$ from a charged object is $3.60 \times 10^5\ N/C$. What is the electric field strength at a distance of $4.50 \times 10^{-1}\ m$ from the same object?

13. At a distance of $7.50 \times 10^{-1}\ m$ from a small, charged object, the electric field strength is $2.10 \times 10^4\ N/C$. At what distance from this same object would the electric field strength be $4.20 \times 10^4\ N/C$?

Lesson 3 ELECTRIC POTENTIAL IN A UNIFORM ELECTRIC FIELD

NOTES

Look at the given electric field between parallel charged plates:

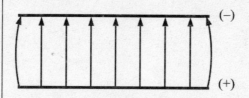

(−)

(+)

The electric field between parallel charged plates is uniform.

The density of the lines of force is uniform between the plates; therefore, the electric field between parallel charged plates is uniform. If this field is uniform, it cannot be described by the formula $E = \dfrac{kq}{r^2}$.

Therefore, a new formula is needed to describe this uniform electric field. In order to describe this field, you will need to understand the concept of potential difference. The concept of potential difference was developed from concepts developed in mechanics (the study of motion and the forces that change it).

The electric field around a point charge decreases as the distance increases; it is not constant.

Remember that an object's velocity changes when an unbalanced force acts on it. This is Newton's first law of motion. When a mass falls within a gravitational field, the mass will accelerate from a position of high gravitational potential energy to a position of lower gravitational potential energy because of the force of gravity acting on it.

In order to move a mass from a position of low gravitational potential energy to a position of higher gravitational potential energy, work is done on the mass against gravity. Work done against gravity can be defined in mathematical terms by the following equations:

$W = F_{g}d$ or $W = mgh$

Mechanics:
the study of motion and the forces that change it.

These formulas use the following variables:
W = work
F = force
d = displacement
m = mass
g = gravitational field strength
h = height

The change in gravitational potential energy can also be defined by the following equation:
$E_{p} = mgh$

Therefore, the gravitational potential energy depends on the following factors:

- The mass of the object $\left(E_p \propto m\right)$

- The gravitational field strength $\left(E_p \propto g\right)$

- The height the object is moved $\left(E_p \propto h\right)$

From the law of conservation of energy, the loss in gravitational potential energy of an object becomes kinetic energy.

ELECTRIC POTENTIAL ENERGY

$$E_k = \frac{1}{2}mv^2$$

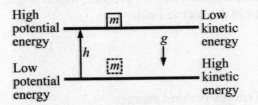

When a charged object moves in an electric field, the charge will accelerate from a position of high electrical potential energy to a position of lower electrical potential energy because of the electric force acting on it. In order to move a charged object (for example, a positive particle) in that field (for example, toward a positive plate), work is done (against the electric field in the given example) on the object. The work done on the object can be determined mathematically using the definition of work. Since $W = Fd$ and $F_e = qE$, it follows that $W = qEd$.

Therefore, the electrical potential energy depends on the following factors:

- The charge of the object $\left(E_p \propto q\right)$

- The electric field strength $\left(E_p \propto E\right)$

- The distance moved parallel to the force $\left(E_p \propto d\right)$

According to the law of conservation of energy, the loss in electrical potential energy of a charged object becomes kinetic energy:

$$E_k = \frac{1}{2}mv^2$$

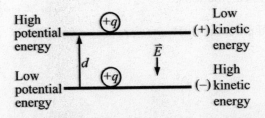

Potential difference depends on the following factors:
- Charge of object
- Electric field
- Distance

Law of conservation of energy:
$$\Delta E_k + \Delta E_p + \Delta E_T = 0$$

If there is no friction,
$$\Delta E_T = 0$$
$$\therefore \Delta E_k = -\Delta E_p$$

Note:
E_T = thermal energy

NOTES

Therefore, work can be calculated using the following formulas:

$$W = \Delta E_p = Fd\cos\theta$$

or $W = mgh$ (gravitational)

or $W = qEd$ (electrical)

This is the work done by an external force to move a charge against the electric field. However, often the work being done is not by an external force but by the electric field itself. The work done by an electric field when a change is moved against it is given by the following equation:

$$W = \Delta E_p = -qEd$$

This work done is negative as expected since the electric field is in the opposite direction of the displacement of the charge.

The electric potential energy is related to the electric potential, which is the energy per unit charge at any point in an electric field.

ELECTRIC POTENTIAL

• Symbol: V

• Definition: Electric potential energy per unit charge

When an electric charge moves within an electric field, its electric potential may change. This change in the electric potential is the potential difference (also called voltage).

POTENTIAL DIFFERENCE (VOLTAGE)

• Symbol: ΔV

• Definition: The change in the electric potential, or the change in the electric potential energy per unit charge

$$\Delta V = \frac{\Delta E_p}{q}$$

Potential difference is the meaningful quantity when you are dealing with uniform electric fields because all problems deal with the change in electric potential (potential difference) between two arbitrary points in an electric field, with one point usually being assigned a value of zero electric potential for convenience (similar to assigning the ground or a table top a gravitational potential energy of zero). Because of this, potential difference, or voltage, is often written simply as V for convenience since the electric potential is not used in calculations.

Note: Both electric potential and potential difference are scalar quantities.

If $\Delta V = \dfrac{\Delta E_p}{q}$,

$\Delta E_p = q\Delta V$, and then the law of conservation of energy as it applies here becomes $\Delta E_k = -\Delta E_p$ or

$\dfrac{1}{2}m\left(v_f^{\,2} - v_i^{\,2}\right) = -q\Delta V$.

A negative sign indicates that if kinetic energy is gained, electric potential is lost.

82

A battery is a source of potential difference. Just as a water pump can increase the gravitational potential energy of water, a battery will increase the electrical potential energy of a charge.

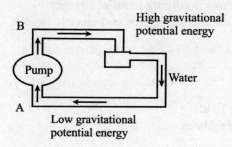

An increase in gravitational potential energy potential takes place between points A and B.

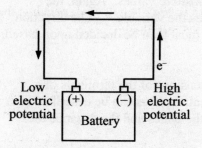

An increase in electric potential takes place within the battery.

The first battery was produced by Alessandro Volta in 1800. The first battery (cell) was a salt solution sandwiched between two different metals. A battery changes chemical energy into electrical energy.

It is now possible to define potential difference in terms of the electric field. Recall that the work done by an electric field on a charge moving against the field resulting in an increase in electric potential energy is given by the following formula:

$$W = \Delta E_p = -qEd$$

Substituting this into the potential difference results in the following:

$$\Delta V = \frac{\Delta E_p}{q}$$
$$= \frac{-qEd}{q}$$
$$\Delta V = -Ed$$

NOTES

The negative sign indicates that electric potential increases in the opposite direction of the electric field.

To simplify matters, in many applications involving parallel charged plates, the relationship between the potential difference and electric field is expressed as

$$E = \frac{V}{d}$$

where E = magnitude of the electrical field
       V = potential difference between plates
       d = distance between plates

When using this equation, always give the potential difference, the charge, and the magnitude of the electric field as positive values. Again, the potential difference is simply represented as the variable V. The direction of motion of the particle and electric field must then be decided upon based on the configuration of the system.

Consider the parallel charged plates as extensions of the terminals of a battery. The electric field between the parallel plates can be described in terms of the potential difference between the plates and the distance the plates are apart $\left(E \propto V \text{ and } E \propto \frac{1}{d} \right)$.

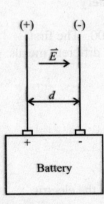

Example

Calculate the electric field strength between two parallel plates that are 6.00×10^{-2} m apart. The potential difference between the plates is 12.0 V.

Solution

$$E = \frac{V}{d}$$
$$= \frac{12.0 \text{ V}}{6.00 \times 10^{-2} \text{ m}}$$
$$= 2.00 \times 10^{2} \text{ V/m}$$

Example

An electron is accelerated from rest through a potential difference of 3.00×10^4 V. What is the kinetic energy gained by the electron?

Solution

$$\Delta E_k = \Delta E_p = qV$$

$$V = \frac{\Delta E}{q}$$

or $\Delta E = qV$

$$= \left(1.60 \times 10^{-19} \text{ C}\right)\left(3.00 \times 10^4 \text{ V}\right)$$

$$= 4.80 \times 10^{-15} \text{ J}$$

Calculate in terms of electron volts:

$$\frac{1 \text{ eV}}{1.60 \times 10^{-19} \text{ J}} = \frac{x}{4.80 \times 10^{-15} \text{ J}}$$

$$x = 3.00 \times 10^4 \text{ eV}$$

Energy may be expressed in terms of electron volts (eV)
$1.00 \text{ eV} = 1.60 \times 10^{-19}$ J

PRACTICE EXERCISES

Formulas: $E = \dfrac{V}{d}$ $V = \dfrac{\Delta E}{q}$

1. Two parallel plates are connected to a 12.0 V battery. If the plates are 9.00×10^{-2} m apart, what is the electric field strength between them?

2. The electric field between two parallel plates is 5.0×10^3 V/m. If the potential difference between the plates is 2.0×10^2 V, how far apart are the plates?

3. Two parallel plates are 7.3 cm apart. If the electric field strength between the plates is 2.0×10^3 V/m, what is the potential difference between the plates?

4. An alpha particle gained 1.50×10^{-15} J of kinetic energy when it passed through a potential difference. What was the magnitude of the potential difference that accelerated the particle?

5. A potential difference of 7.20×10^2 V accelerated a proton. What was the change in the proton's kinetic energy?

6. What will be the maximum speed of an alpha particle if it travels from rest through a potential difference of 7.50×10^3 V?

Use the following information to answer the next question.

A proton is placed in an electric field between two parallel plates. The plates are 6.0 cm apart and have a potential difference between them of 7.5×10^1 V.

7. a) How much work is done against the electric field when the proton is moved 3.0 cm parallel to the plates?

b) How much work would be done against the electric field if the proton were moved 3.0 cm perpendicularly to the plates?

8. A potential difference of 4.20×10^2 V accelerated a charged particle from rest. If this particle's kinetic energy increased to 3.00×10^{-17} J, what potential difference would be needed to increase the kinetic energy of the same particle to 9.00×10^{-17} J from rest?

Use the following information to answer the next two questions.

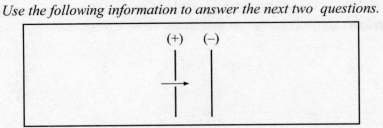

9. An alpha particle with an initial speed of 7.15×10^4 m/s enters into an electric field between two parallel plates through a hole in the positive plate. If the distance between the plates is 9.00×10^{-2} m and the electric field is 1.70×10^2 V/m, what will be the alpha particle's speed when it reaches the negative plate?

10. An electron with a speed of 5.0×10^5 m/s enters into an electric field between two parallel plates through a hole in the positive plate and collides with the negative plate at a speed of 1.0×10^5 m/s. What is the potential difference between the plates?

11. The electric field strength between two parallel plates is 9.3×10^2 V/m when the plates are 7.0 cm apart. What would the electric field strength be if the plates were 5.0 cm apart?

12. What is the electric field strength 1.00 cm from the positively charged plate if the parallel plates are 5.00 cm apart and the potential difference between the plates is 3.00×10^2 V?

13. What potential difference must an electron accelerate through from rest in order to achieve a speed of 6.00×10^6 m/s?

14. If a uniform electric field accelerates an alpha particle from rest through a distance of 4.00 cm in 2.50×10^{-5} s, what is the strength of the electric field?

15. What is the potential difference between two parallel charged plates that are 7.50 cm apart if a force of 5.30×10^{-14} N is needed to move an alpha particle from the negative plate to the positive plate?

16. An electric field of 2.40×10^2 N/C is produced by two horizontal, parallel plates set 4.00 cm apart. If a charged particle of 2.00 μC moves 3.00 cm perpendicularly to the electric field, what is the work done against the electric field?

Use the following information to answer the next question.

A proton accelerates from rest from plate X to plate Y at the same time as an electron accelerates from rest from plate Y to plate X. The potential difference between the two plates is 60.0 V.

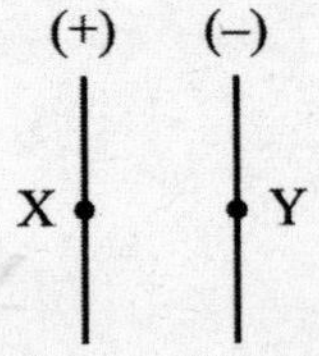

(+)   (−)

X •   • Y

17. a) What is the speed of the proton when it reaches plate Y?

   b) What is the speed of the electron when it reaches plate X?

18. A potential difference of 2.50×10^5 V accelerated a charged particle from rest. If the particle reached a maximum speed of 2.90×10^4 m/s, what potential difference would be required to accelerate this particle from rest to a velocity of 7.25×10^4 m/s?

19. A potential difference of 5.00×10^3 V accelerates an electron from rest. What is the resulting speed of this electron?

Use the following information to answer the next question.

An electron travelling horizontally at a velocity of 8.70×10^6 m/s to the right enters into an electric field of 1.32×10^3 N/C between two horizontal, parallel plates, as shown in the given diagram.

20. Calculate the vertical displacement of the electron as it travels between the plates.

PRACTICE QUIZ

1. How far from Earth's surface $\left(m_E = 5.98 \times 10^{24} \, \text{kg}, \, r_E = 6.38 \times 10^6 \, \text{m} \right)$ is the gravitational field strength 6.13×10^{-1} N/kg?

2. Calculate the gravitational field strength at a point in space where the weight of a 1.10×10^2 kg object is 7.22×10^2 N.

3. What is the weight of a 15.0 kg object on the surface of a planet that has a mass of 3.40×10^{27} kg and a radius of 5.74×10^7 m?

4. Calculate the electric force between two point charges of 2.00 μC and 2.70 μC that are 1.00×10^{-1} m apart.

5. Two small, charged objects of the same mass and volume are brought into brief contact with each other. If the initial charges on the two objects are −3.00 μC and −1.50 μC, what is the electric force between the objects when they are separated to a distance of 5.00×10^{-1} m after contact?

Use the following information to answer the next question.

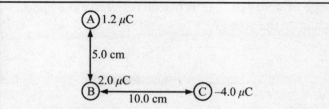

6. Three point charges are at the corners of a right triangle, as shown in the given diagram. What is the magnitude of the electric force acting on charge B that is caused by the other two charges?

7. If the electric field strength at a point 1.50 m from a charged point source is 2.70×10^{4} N/C, what is the electric field strength at a point 7.50×10^{-1} m from the same source?

8. Calculate the electric field strength at the midpoint between two point charges of 3.00 μC and 4.20 μC that are 4.60×10^{-1} m apart.

9. If a lithium nucleus $\left(\text{Li}^{3+}\right)$ experiences an electric force of 2.44×10^{-14} N at a point in space, what is the electric field intensity at this point?

10. The potential difference between two parallel plates that are 3.00 cm apart is 7.10×10^3 V. If an object with a charge of 4.80×10^{-15} C is placed between these plates, what is the magnitude of the electric force acting on the object?

11. What is the potential difference between two parallel plates 5.00 cm apart that produce an electric force of 3.50×10^{-13} N on an object containing a charge of 2.00×10^{-16} C when it is placed between the plates?

12. A 3.00 μC charge moves 1.65 cm at a constant speed from point A to point B. If the potential difference between these two points is 12.0 V, how much work was done on the charge against the electric field?

Use the following information to answer the next question.

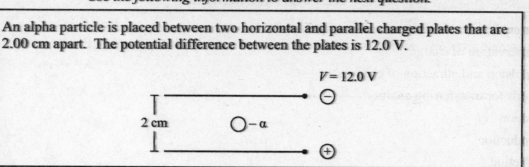

An alpha particle is placed between two horizontal and parallel charged plates that are 2.00 cm apart. The potential difference between the plates is 12.0 V.

$V = 12.0$ V

2 cm $\bigcirc - \alpha$

13. a) What is the electric force acting on the alpha particle?

b) What is the gravitational force acting on the alpha particle, assuming the experiment is conducted at sea level?

c) Assuming the electric force and the gravitational force are acting in opposite directions, what is the net force acting on the alpha particle?

d) What is the acceleration of the alpha particle?

e) What potential difference would be required between the plates in order for the alpha particle to become suspended?

REVIEW SUMMARY

- Electrical interactions in terms of:
  - Conservation of charge
  - Repulsion and attraction of charges
- Methods for transferring charges:
  - Friction
  - Conduction
  - Induction
- Coulomb's law
- Newton's law of universal gravitation
- Electric fields
  - Comparing gravitational potential energy and electric potential energy
- The physics of a charged particle in a uniform electric field
- The following formulas were used in this section:

  $$- \quad F_g = \frac{Gm_1 m_2}{r^2}$$

  $$- \quad F_e = \frac{kq_1 q_2}{r^2}$$

  $$- \quad g = \frac{Gm}{r^2}$$

  $$- \quad E = \frac{kq}{r^2}$$

  $$- \quad \vec{E} = \frac{\vec{F}_e}{q}$$

  $$- \quad V = \frac{\Delta E_p}{q}$$

  $$- \quad E = \frac{V}{d}$$

PRACTICE TEST

1. If an object has a weight of 2.0 N at the surface of Earth, what is its weight at a distance of one Earth radius above Earth's surface?

    A. 0.50 N

    B. 1.0 N

    C. 2.0 N

    D. 4.0 N

2. Which of the following graphs **best** represents the relationship between the magnitude of the gravitational field strength (g) due to Earth and the distance (r) from the centre of Earth?

Use the following information to answer the next question.

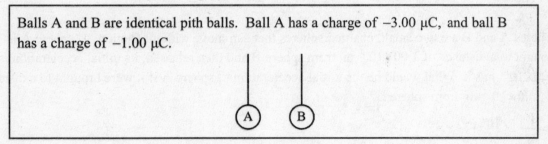

Balls A and B are identical pith balls. Ball A has a charge of -3.00 μC, and ball B has a charge of -1.00 μC.

3. If these two balls are brought into brief contact with each other and are then separated to a distance of 2.00×10^{-2} m, what is the electric force between them?

    A. 1.35 N

    B. 1.80 N

    C. 67.4 N

    D. 90.0 N

4. Two point charges are initially 6.0 cm apart. They are then moved until they are 2.0 cm apart. If the initial force between these two point charges was F, what is the new force?

   A. $0.11F$

   B. $0.33F$

   C. $3.0F$

   D. $9.0F$

Use the following information to answer the next question.

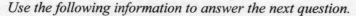

Spheres A, B, and C are three small, charged spheres that are positioned in a right triangle, as shown in the given diagram.

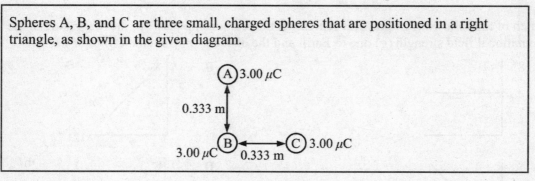

5. What is the magnitude of the net electric force on sphere B caused by the other two charged spheres?

   A. 0.344 N

   B. 0.486 N

   C. 1.03 N

   D. 1.46 N

6. Spheres A and B are two small, charged spheres that can move without friction. If sphere A is brought to a distance of 1.00×10^{-2} m from sphere B and then released, its initial acceleration is 1.00×10^{10} m/s^2. What would be the initial acceleration of sphere A if it were brought to a distance of 3.00×10^{-2} m from sphere B?

   A. 1.11×10^9 m/s^2

   B. 3.33×10^9 m/s^2

   C. 3.00×10^9 m/s^2

   D. 9.00×10^9 m/s^2

Use the following information to answer the next question.

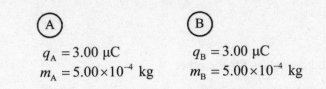

Spheres A and B are two small, charged spheres that can move without friction.

$q_A = 3.00\ \mu C$ $q_B = 3.00\ \mu C$
$m_A = 5.00\times10^{-4}$ kg $m_B = 5.00\times10^{-4}$ kg

7. If sphere A is brought to a distance of 2.00×10^{-2} m from sphere B and then released, what will its initial acceleration be?

   A. 2.02×10^{2} m/s^2

   B. 8.09×10^{2} m/s^2

   C. 4.05×10^{5} m/s^2

   D. 1.35×10^{11} m/s^2

8. If a potential difference of 2.00×10^{3} V accelerates an alpha particle from rest, what is the particle's maximum speed?

   A. 3.10×10^{5} m/s

   B. 4.39×10^{5} m/s

   C. 2.65×10^{7} m/s

   D. 2.53×10^{8} m/s

9. An electron is placed into a strong, uniform electric field between two charged plates. The direction of the acceleration of the electron will be

   A. perpendicular to the electric field

   B. in the direction of the electric field

   C. in the opposite direction of the electric field

   D. unknown because the gravitational field will be in the opposite direction to the electric field

10. Electric potential can be defined as

   A. electric potential energy × charge

   B. electric potential energy ÷ charge

   C. electric potential energy × distance

   D. electric potential energy ÷ distance

11. When a positive point charge moves toward another positive point charge, the electric potential energy of the point charges

    A. increases

    B. decreases

    C. remains the same

    D. increases for one and decreases for the other

12. The direction of an electric field is defined in terms of the direction of the electric

    A. force on a positive test object

    B. force on a negative test object

    C. potential of a positive test object

    D. potential of a negative test object

Use the following information to answer the next question.

> Two charged parallel plates are shown in the given diagram.
>
> ———————————— +
>
> ———————————— −

13. Which of the following diagrams shows the correct direction of the electric field between these two plates?

    A. ↑

    B. ↓

    C. →

    D. ←

14. If you rub a balloon with your cotton shirt, you are placing a static charge on it by

    A. friction

    B. induction

    C. insulation

    D. conduction

Use the following information to answer the next question.

> You can use the following steps to determine the nature of a static electric charge on a plastic rod:
> **i)** Bring a plastic rod near to the head of an electroscope.
> **ii)** Bring a rubber rod with a known negative charge near to the head of an electroscope.
> **iii)** Briefly touch the head of the electroscope with your finger.

15. In what order would you perform the given steps to determine the nature of the charge on the plastic rod?

    A. i), ii), iii)

    B. ii), iii), i)

    C. iii), ii), i)

    D. i), iii), ii)

16. You have a positively charged electroscope and an unknown static charge on an insulating rod. When you bring the insulating rod near to the head of the electroscope, the leaves converge somewhat. What is the nature of the unknown charge on the insulating rod?

    A. Neutral

    B. Positive

    C. Negative

    D. Can be either positive or negative

17. You have an electroscope that contains an unknown electric charge. When you bring a negative rubber rod near to the head of the electroscope, the leaves converge somewhat. What is the nature of the unknown charge on the electroscope?

    A. Positive

    B. Negative

    C. It is neutral.

    D. It can be either positive or negative.

18. If you bring a charged rubber rod near the head of an uncharged electroscope while you briefly touch the head of the electroscope with your finger, you are placing a static electric charge on the electroscope by

    A. friction

    B. induction

    C. insulation

    D. conduction

Use the following information to answer the next two questions.

The given diagram represents a solid metal object that contains a net negative charge. Positions 1, 2, and 4 represent positions on the metal's surface, while position 3 is somewhere near the metal's centre.

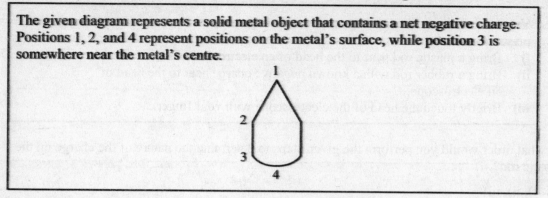

19. At which of the positions is the electron concentration the **greatest**?

  A. 1

  B. 2

  C. 3

  D. 4

20. At which of the positions is the electron concentration the **least**?

  A. 1

  B. 2

  C. 3

  D. 4

MAGNETIC FORCES AND FIELDS

When you are finished this section of the unit, you will be able to...

- Describe magnetic interactions in terms of forces and fields
- Compare gravitational, electric, and magnetic fields (caused by permanent magnets and moving charges) in terms of their sources and directions
- Describe how the discoveries of Oersted and Faraday form the foundation of the theory relating electricity to magnetism
- Describe, qualitatively, a moving charge as a source of a magnetic field, and predict the orientation of the magnetic field from the direction of the motion
- Explain, qualitatively and quantitatively, how a uniform magnetic field affects a moving electric charge, using the relationships among charge, motion, and field direction
- Explain, quantitatively, how uniform magnetic and electric fields affect a moving electric charge, using the relationships among charge, motion, and field direction
- Describe and explain, qualitatively and quantitatively, the interaction between a magnetic field and a moving charge and between a magnetic field and a current-carrying conductor
- Describe, qualitatively, the effects of moving a conductor in an external magnetic field, in terms of moving charges in a magnetic field

PREREQUISITE SKILLS AND KNOWLEDGE

Prior to starting this unit, you should be able to...

- Describe the interaction of charge particles using the law of conservation of energy
- Understand that like charges repel and unlike charges attract
- Predict the distribution and transfer of charge through conduction and induction on conductors and insulators
- Describe the similarities and differences between electric and gravitational fields
- Understand, qualitatively and quantitatively, the inverse square relationships expressed by Newton's law of universal gravitation and Coulomb's law
- Determine the magnitude and direction of electric forces between two or more point charges
- Compare gravitational potential energy to electric potential energy
- Understand the concept of electric potential and potential differences as a property of the field, independent of a charged particle placed in the field
- Describe electric fields in terms of magnitude and direction relative to the source producing the field
- Solve algebraic problems involving the motion of an electric charge, and electric and gravitational forces between particles in uniform electric and gravitational fields

Lesson 1 MAGNETIC FORCES AND FIELDS

Lodestone is a type of metallic rock (iron ore) found by the early Greeks in a place called Magnesia. By the twelfth century, needle-shaped lodestone was used in the navigation of ships. When the needle-shaped lodestone was placed on a cork floating freely in a container of water, the needle would rotate so that it pointed north and south. These needlelike lodestones were the first compasses.

William Gilbert studied magnetism in the seventeenth century.

Gilbert was the first to understand that Earth is essentially a giant magnet.

Gilbert wanted to find the reason that the needle-shaped lodestones always pointed north and south. He hypothesized that Earth acted like, or was made up of, lodestone. He set out to test his hypothesis by constructing a model of Earth from lodestone. He found that lodestone needles placed around the model would always point in the same direction. He concluded that Earth was a large lodestone. Although Earth is not actually a large lodestone, it does have magnetic properties like lodestone does.

A compass needle is actually a small magnet. If you suspend a bar magnet by a thread, the magnet will align so that one end points north and the other end points south. This is where the terms north pole and south pole come from. However, the north and south poles of a magnet are actually called the north-seeking and south-seeking poles, respectively.

Magnetic poles occur in pairs called dipoles.

The north and south poles in a magnet cannot be separated. This means that if you break a magnet in two, each part will have a north pole and a south pole.

MAGNETIC POLES

Magnetic poles act similarly to electric charges. They produce a magnetic field similarly to how an electric charge produces an electric field. However, magnetic poles must occur in pairs called dipoles. For material to have magnetic properties and produce a magnetic field, it must have north and south poles. Like positive and negative charges, like poles repel, and unlike poles attract.

Why does a compass align itself north and south?

Remember, Gilbert discovered that Earth is a magnet. That is, Earth has a north magnetic pole and a south magnetic pole. Earth's north magnetic pole attracts the south pole of a magnet, and Earth's south magnetic pole attracts the north pole of a magnet.

If the end of the magnet (compass) pointing north is the north-seeking pole, then Earth's geographic North Pole must be a magnetic south pole.

Magnetic fields are vector fields.

Magnetic fields, like gravitational and electric fields, are vector fields. These magnetic fields can be represented by the following diagrams:

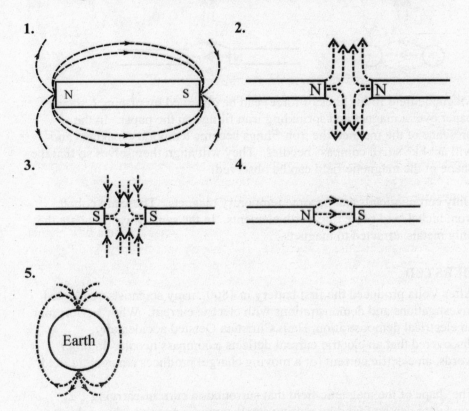

The lines drawn to represent magnetic fields can be called lines of force. The direction of the magnetic field (lines of force) is defined as the direction in which the north-seeking pole of a compass needle will point or move. A compass's north-seeking pole will point to the South Pole. In all these drawings, the arrows on the field lines point toward the south and away from the north.

The direction of a magnetic field is defined as the direction in which the north-seeking pole of a compass needle will point.

NOTES

There are similarities between magnetic fields and electric fields.

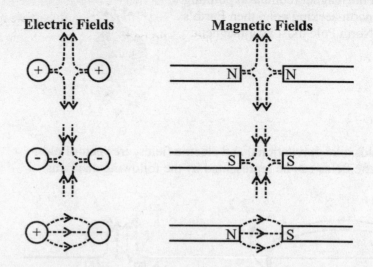

Magnetic field lines (lines of force) can be observed by placing a sheet of paper over a magnet and sprinkling iron filings on the paper. In the presence of the magnet, the iron filings become temporary magnets and will act like small compass needles. They will align themselves so that the shape of the magnetic field can be observed.

Only certain metals can become temporary magnets. These are cobalt, iron, nickel, and some rare-earth elements. In the same way, these are the only metals attracted to magnets.

OERSTED

After Volta produced the first battery in 1800, many scientists conducted investigations and demonstrations with electric current. While performing an electrical demonstration, Hans Christian Oersted accidentally discovered that an electric current deflects a compass needle. In other words, an electric current (or a moving charge) produces a magnetic field.

The shape of the magnetic field that surrounds a current-carrying conductor can be found by putting small compass needles around the conductor. It has been found that this magnetic field circles the conductor.

In diagrams, the symbol ⊙ is used to represent current flowing out of the page through a conductor, and the symbol ⊗ is used to represent current flowing into the page through a conductor.

⊙ Out   ⊗ In

Oersted discovered that a current through a conductor will produce a magnetic field.

Magnetic fields circle a conductor.

Current flowing out of page
⊙

Current flowing into page
⊗

Magnetic Fields around a Conductor

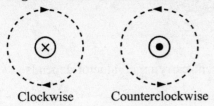

Clockwise   Counterclockwise

The direction of the magnetic field around a conductor is not simply directed toward the S-pole and away from the N-pole, because there is no S-pole or N-pole in this scenario. Instead, the left-hand rule is used to obtain the direction of the field.

FIRST LEFT-HAND RULE

Using your left hand, point your thumb in the direction of the current (electron flow). Let your fingers circle the wire. The fingers will be circling the wire in the same direction that the magnetic field circles the current-carrying conductor.

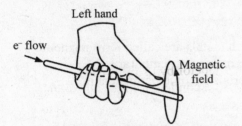

Left hand

e⁻ flow

Magnetic field

In many physics books, electric current is not represented as electron flow, but as positive flow. Positive flow is called the conventional current, which flows in the opposite direction of electric current. When conventional current is used, the right hand is used to determine the direction of the magnetic field around a current-carrying conductor; this is the right-hand rule. Using your right hand, point your thumb in the direction of the conventional current. Let your fingers circle the wire. The fingers will be circling the wire in the same direction as the magnetic field.

If a compass is placed below a current-carrying conductor, which way will the needle point if the current (electron flow) is flowing into the page?

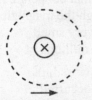

Compass points east.

The compass needle will align itself as the tangent to the circular lines of force (magnetic field), in the same direction as the magnetic field at that point.

Left-hand rule:
The thumb represents the direction of electron flow, and the fingers represent the direction of the magnetic field. Use the left-hand rule when the current is electron flow.

Right-hand rule:
The thumb represents the direction of conventional current (positive flow). Use the right-hand rule when the current is conventional flow.

NOTES

The tesla was named after the renowned physicist and inventor Nikola Tesla, who also experimented with electricity and magnetism.

Formula for calculating the magnetic field strength around a straight current-carrying conductor:

$$B = \frac{\mu_0 I}{2\pi r}$$

Some typical magnetic field values:

Interstellar space 10^{-14} T

Earth's magnetic field 5×10^{-5} T

Small bar magnet 0.01 T

Big electromagnet 1.5 T

Neutron star 10^7 T

High mass star 10^{10} T

MAGNETIC FIELDS

Symbol: $\bar{B}$

Unit: tesla (T)

The magnetic field around a straight current-carrying conductor depends on the following two factors:

- The current through the conductor (I)

- The distance from the conductor (r)

To find the magnitude of the magnetic field around a current-carrying conductor, use the following formula:

$$B = \frac{\mu_0 I}{2\pi r}$$

where μ_0 = permeability of free space—an indication of the extent that a magnetic field can extend into a vacuum

$$\mu_0 = 4\pi \times 10^{-7} \frac{T \cdot m}{A}$$

MAGNETIC DOMAINS

Iron, cobalt, nickel, and some rare-earth metals are called ferromagnetic materials because they can become permanent or temporary magnets. How do ferromagnetic materials become permanent or temporary magnets?

Since electric currents (moving electrons) can produce magnetic fields, you might conclude that the movement of electrons within the atoms in these materials is responsible for the material's magnetic properties. However, if this were the case, all materials would have magnetic properties. This is true only to a small extent (other materials are called diamagnetic materials and paramagnetic materials). Only ferromagnetic materials can become permanent or temporary magnets. Therefore, ferromagnetic materials must have something special about the electron movement within their atoms.

The special property of these materials has to do with the spin nature of unpaired electrons in these atoms. In a ferromagnetic substance, the unpaired electron in each atom has a spin that produces a "cooperative effect" with 10^{15} to 10^{20} other atoms. This group of atoms that cooperate is called the magnetic domain. It should be noted that although the magnetic domain contains many atoms, the size of these domains is very small (about 10^{-6} m). This means that within a magnet, there are millions of these magnetic domains.

In a demagnetized piece of material containing one of these ferromagnetic materials, the domains are randomly aligned.

If this same material is placed into an external magnetic field, these domains will rotate so that they point in the same direction.

In a permanent magnet, these domains will continue to point in the same direction so that the magnetic field of each domain is in the same direction.

In a temporary magnet, these domains will return to a random alignment when the external magnetic field is removed.

SOLENOIDS AND ELECTROMAGNETS

When a conductor (wire) is wound into a coil that has many loops, it is called a solenoid or electromagnet.

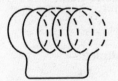

The magnitude of the magnetic field inside the coil is nearly uniform and depends on the following factors:

- Current through the coil (I)
- Number of turns of coil per metre of coil (n)
- Permeability of free space (μ_0)

$$\mu_0 = 4\pi \times 10^{-7} \frac{\text{N} \cdot \text{m}}{\text{A}}$$

$$B = \mu_0 n I$$

A magnetic field for a solenoid can be represented by the following diagram:

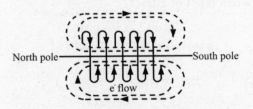

Note that the magnetic field around the outside of a solenoid has the same shape as the magnetic field around a bar magnet.

Formula for calculating the magnetic field strength inside a current-carrying solenoid:
$$B = \mu_0 n I$$

When a solenoid contains a soft iron core, the magnetic field strength within the solenoid core greatly increases. The soft iron core increases the magnetic field strength within the solenoid because the relative permeability of soft iron is much greater than that of free space (air). Soft iron is almost pure iron that becomes a temporary magnet when placed in any magnetic field. When a solenoid contains a soft iron core and electricity flows through the solenoid, it is called an electromagnet.

Soft iron also loses its magnetism instantly when removed from an external magnetic field. This means that when the electric current stops flowing through the electromagnet, the soft iron will no longer act as a magnet. This is an advantage of using a solenoid or electromagnet to produce a magnetic field. Because of this property, electromagnets have a wide variety of applications.

SECOND LEFT-HAND RULE

The direction of the magnetic field inside an electromagnet is the direction your thumb points when the fingers of your left hand curl in the direction of the electron flow.

The second left-hand rule is used to determine the direction of the magnetic field produced within a solenoid. Curl the fingers of your left hand in the direction the current flows (electron flow) in the coil. Keep your thumb straight. Your thumb will point in the same direction as the north pole of a compass—in the direction of the magnetic field.

INTERACTIONS BETWEEN MAGNETIC FIELDS

Recall that like poles of magnets repel and unlike poles attract.

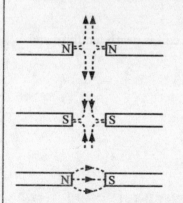

What happens in the case of a current-carrying conductor? If the current in two parallel current-carrying conductors flows in the same direction, do the magnetic fields produced by these wires repel or attract?

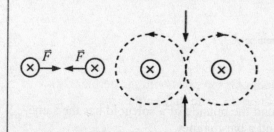

In this diagram, the current is electron flow. The arrows indicate the direction of the magnetic fields.

The magnetic fields between the two conductors are in opposite directions. As a result, the magnetic fields apply a force on each other that causes the two conductors to attract. The size of this force depends on the size of the current flowing through both conductors.

In this diagram, the current is electron flow. The arrows indicate the direction of the magnetic fields.

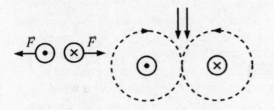

Current flowing in opposite directions through parallel conductors will create a force that repels the conductors. This is because the magnetic fields between the conductors point in the same direction. Therefore, the magnetic lines of force repel each other. The magnetic fields apply a force on each other that causes the conductors to repel.

Since current-carrying conductors can produce magnetic forces, the unit for current is defined in terms of these effects. One ampere is the amount of current in each of two long, straight, parallel conductors, set one metre apart, that causes a force of 2×10^{-7} N to act on each metre of wire.

To calculate the magnitude of these attractive and repulsive forces between conductors, use the following formula:

$$\frac{F}{l} = \frac{\mu_0 I_1 I_2}{2\pi r}$$

where $\dfrac{F}{l}$ = magnitude of the force per unit length

I_1 = current in conductor one
I_2 = current in conductor two
r = distance between the two conductors

MAGNETIC FORCES ON CURRENT-CARRYING CONDUCTORS

A current-carrying conductor will experience a force when placed in a magnetic field.

The magnetic field around the conductor interacts with the permanent magnetic field. In the following diagram, note that both of the magnetic fields above the conductor are in the same direction. Therefore, the magnetic lines of force produced by the permanent magnet repel the magnetic lines of force produced by the current-carrying conductor.

An ampere is defined in terms of forces between current-carrying conductors.

Formula for calculating the magnitude of the force between two parallel current carrying conductors:

$$\frac{F}{l} = \frac{\mu_0 I_1 I_2}{2\pi r}$$

Below the conductor, the magnetic fields are in the opposite direction. Therefore, the magnetic lines of force between the conductor and the permanent magnet attract. Therefore, the magnetic lines of force produced by the permanent magnet attract the magnetic lines of force produced by the current-carrying conductor. As a result, the conductor is forced downward because the interaction of the fields above the conductor push it down, while the interaction of the fields below the conductor pull it downward.

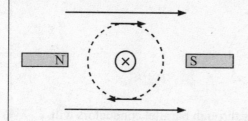

The current in this diagram is electron flow.

THIRD LEFT-HAND RULE

To obtain the direction of the force on a conductor in a magnetic field, use your left hand. With this rule, keep the fingers straight and the thumb perpendicular to the fingers.

Left-hand rule for magnetic force:

Fingers: magnetic field
Thumb: current (electron flow)
Palm: force

The left-hand rule is used for electron flow.

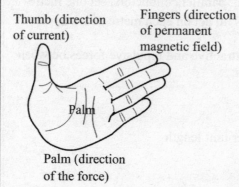

Thumb (direction of current)

Fingers (direction of permanent magnetic field)

Palm

Palm (direction of the force)

Point your thumb in the direction of the current (electron flow) and your fingers in the direction of the magnetic field. The direction of your palm is the direction of the force.

Right-hand rule for magnetic force:

Finger: magnetic field

Thumb: current (positive flow)

Palm: force

The right-hand rule is used with conventional current.

MOTOR EFFECT

The left-hand rule can be used to explain the principles of the electric motor.

In a simple DC motor, a loop of wire passes through a magnetic field. The ends of the loop are attached to a split-ring commutator, which turns with the loop. Both halves of the split ring make contact with fixed brushes, which in turn are connected to a voltage source (battery).

Conventional current is positive flow.

In the given diagram, the loop on the right side is always forced down. In the same way, the loop on the left side is always forced up.

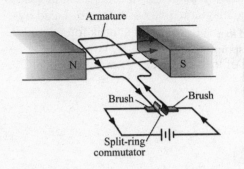

The current in this diagram is electron flow.

The magnitude of the magnetic force on a current-carrying conductor can be calculated using the following formula:

$$F_m = BIl \sin \theta$$

where B = magnetic field strength

I = current through the conductor

l = length of conductor

θ = angle at which the conductor passes through the magnetic field

The equation can be simplified to $F_m = B_\perp Il$ because sin 90° is 1.

If the conductor is parallel to the direction of the magnetic field, there is no magnetic force. This is because both sin 0° and sin 180° equal 0.

The symbol $B_\perp$ means that the current flows through the conductor perpendicularly to the magnetic field.

AC motors do not require a split-ring commutator, because AC current reverses itself. Most electric motors are AC motors because industrial and household electric energy is transmitted as alternating current. An example of a DC motor is the starter motor in a car.

GALVANOMETERS (ELECTRIC METERS)

Galvanometers are instruments used to detect an electric current. A galvanometer can be calibrated to measure current, in which case it is called an ammeter. It can also be calibrated to measure potential difference, in which case it is called a voltmeter. These instruments also make use of the motor principle.

Electric motors apply the interactions between magnetic fields.

In an actual DC motor, there are many loops of wire—these loops are called the armature.

If the conductor is perpendicular to the magnetic field, this formula can be reduced to $F_m = B_\perp Il$.

NOTES

In simple terms, galvanometers form the basis of all electric meters.

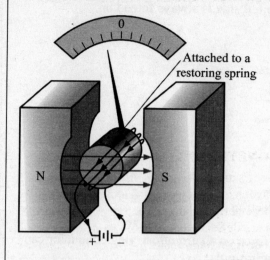

Attached to a restoring spring

Current flows through a coil in a galvanometer as shown in the given diagram. The resulting interaction between the two magnetic fields creates a force that rotates the movable coil against a spring, turning a needle to create a scale reading. It should be noted that a galvanometer will produce a full scale reading with very low current through the coil.

A galvanometer can convert into an ammeter by placing a shunt (a wire) of low resistance parallel to the coil. This provides a parallel path for the electrons so that only a small fraction of the electrons flow through the movable coil.

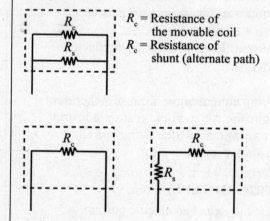

R_c = Resistance of the movable coil
R_c = Resistance of shunt (alternate path)

Since $V = IR \Rightarrow I = \dfrac{V}{R}$, the current can be controlled by the ammeter by making the resistance appropriately large.

A galvanometer can convert into a voltmeter by placing a shunt (a wire) of high resistance in series with the coil. This reduces the current that flows through the electric meter.

Ammeters are placed in series in an electric circuit, and voltmeters are placed in parallel.

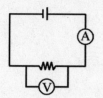

MOVING CHARGES IN MAGNETIC FIELDS

Not only current-carrying conductors are deflected by magnetic fields. All moving charges (electrons, protons, and alpha particles) can be deflected by magnetic fields. These particles are deflected similarly to how current-carrying conductors are deflected. However, to determine the direction of the deflection, use your right hand instead of your left hand for positive particles (protons and alpha particles). Use your left hand for electrons, as you did for electric current (electric current is the flow of electrons).

The right-hand rule is used with conventional current.

Conventional current is positive flow.

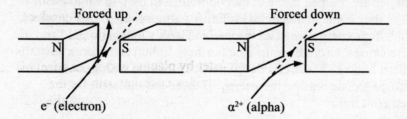

The magnitude of the deflecting magnetic forces on moving, charged particles (electrons, protons, and alpha particles) can be calculated using the following formula:

$$F_m = qvB\sin\theta$$

When the charged particles move perpendicularly to the magnetic field, this formula can be simplified as follows:

$$F_m = qvB_\perp$$

Also, like magnetic forces on conductors, the magnetic force on the charged particle moving parallel to the magnetic field is zero.

Like the magnetic force on conductors, the formula for calculating the magnitude of deflecting magnetic forces can be reduced to $F_m = qvB_\perp$.

NOTES

In strong, broad magnetic fields within a vacuum, charged particles can be continually deflected so that they travel in a circle within the field.

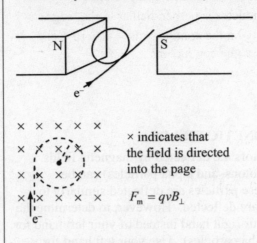

× indicates that the field is directed into the page

$F_m = qvB_\perp$

VAN ALLEN RADIATION BELTS

Earth's magnetic field deflects charged particles from space. Some of these particles are trapped in the magnetic field, and they spiral to Earth's poles where they come in contact with Earth's atmosphere. This contact between the high-energy particles trapped in Earth's magnetic field and the atmosphere causes aurora borealis (the northern lights) and aurora australis (the southern lights). The high-energy particles collide with gas molecules in the atmosphere, increasing the energy of these gas molecules, which then emit light.

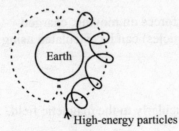

High-energy particles

The regions where these high energy particles are trapped in the magnetic field are called Van Allen belts.

Example 1

Calculate the magnitude of the magnetic force on an electron travelling at a speed of 3.60×10^4 m/s perpendicularly through a magnetic field of 4.20 T.

Solution

$$F_m = qvB_\perp$$
$$= \left(1.60 \times 10^{-19} \text{ C}\right)\left(3.60 \times 10^4 \text{ m/s}\right)\left(4.20 \text{ T}\right)$$
$$= 2.42 \times 10^{-14} \text{ N}$$

Example 2

A 3.20×10^{-1} m long conductor is placed in a magnetic field of 2.10×10^{-1} T. Assuming the conductor is perpendicular to the magnetic field and the magnetic force acting on the conductor is 4.00×10^{-2} N, what is the current flowing through the conductor?

Solution

$$F_{\mathrm{m}} = B_{\perp} Il$$

$$I = \frac{F_{\mathrm{m}}}{B_{\perp} l}$$

$$= \frac{\left(4.00 \times 10^{-2}\ \mathrm{N}\right)}{\left(2.10 \times 10^{-1}\ \mathrm{T}\right)\left(3.20 \times 10^{-1}\ \mathrm{m}\right)}$$

$$= 5.95 \times 10^{-1}\ \mathrm{A}$$

Example 3

Calculate the upward acceleration on an electron travelling with a velocity of 8.30×10^4 m/s east through a magnetic field of 3.10×10^{-1} T south.

Solution

Find the magnetic force first.

$$F_{\mathrm{m}} = qvB_{\perp}$$

$$= \left(1.60 \times 10^{-19}\ \mathrm{C}\right)\left(8.30 \times 10^4\ \mathrm{m/s}\right)\left(3.10 \times 10^{-1}\ \mathrm{T}\right)$$

$$= 4.12 \times 10^{-15}\ \mathrm{N}$$

$$\vec{F} = m\vec{a}$$

$$\vec{a} = \frac{\vec{F}}{m}$$

$$= \frac{4.12 \times 10^{-15}\ \mathrm{N}}{9.11 \times 10^{-31}\ \mathrm{kg}}$$

$$= 4.52 \times 10^{15}\ \mathrm{m/s}^2\ \mathrm{up}$$

PRACTICE EXERCISES

Formulas: $F_m = B_\perp Il$ $\qquad\qquad\qquad\qquad\qquad$ $F_m = qvB_\perp$

1. A proton travelling vertically at a speed of 2.10×10^5 m/s through a horizontal magnetic field experiences a magnetic force of 9.50×10^{-14} N. What is the magnitude of the magnetic field?

2. A copper wire ($l = 0.222$ m) carries a conventional current of 0.960 A north through a magnetic field $\left(B = 7.50 \times 10^{-4} \text{ T} \right)$ directed vertically upward. What is the magnitude and direction of the magnetic force acting on the wire?

3. Calculate the magnitude and direction of the magnetic force on an electron travelling with a velocity of 3.52×10^5 m/s north through a magnetic field of 2.80×10^{-1} T vertically upward.

4. Calculate the magnitude and direction of the magnetic force on an alpha particle travelling with a velocity of 7.40×10^4 m/s south through a vertically upward magnetic field of 5.50 T.

5. Calculate the magnitude and direction of the magnetic field that produces a magnetic force of 1.70×10^{-14} N east on a proton travelling 1.90×10^{4} m/s north through the magnetic field.

6. An electron experiences an upward force of 7.1×10^{-14} N as it travels with a velocity of 2.7×10^{5} m/s south through a magnetic field. What is the magnitude and direction of the magnetic field?

7. Calculate the magnitude and direction of the magnetic force on an alpha particle travelling upward at a speed of 2.11×10^{5} m/s through a magnetic field directed downward.

8. A 2.50×10^{-1} m long wire in the armature of an electric motor is perpendicular to a magnetic field of 5.00×10^{-1} T. Calculate the magnetic force on the wire when it carries a current of 3.60 A.

9. A potential difference of 1.70×10^3 V accelerates an electron from rest. The electron then enters perpendicularly into a magnetic field of 2.50×10^{-1} T. What is the magnitude of the magnetic force acting on the electron?

10. A potential difference accelerates an electron from rest, which then travels perpendicularly through a magnetic field of 7.20×10^{-1} T where it experiences a magnetic force of 4.1×10^{-13} N. What is the potential difference through which the electron is accelerated?

11. Calculate the downward acceleration on an electron that travels horizontally at a speed of 6.20×10^5 m/s perpendicular to a horizontal magnetic field of 2.30×10^{-1} T.

Use the following information to answer the next the question.

A solenoid lies on a horizontal plane with a current balance, WXYZ, balanced horizontally in the solenoid's core at points Z and W, as shown in the given diagram.

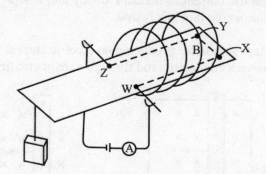

A current balance is a device used to determine the magnetic field strength inside a solenoid. It is a flat, insulating material that has a conductor (WXYZ) around the perimeter. This device is inserted inside the solenoid and acts like a teeter-totter.

Before any current flows through the solenoid or the conductor (WXYZ), the current balance is horizontal. However, when a current flows through both the solenoid and the conductor, a magnetic force acts on the current balance, causing the current balance to tip so that end A moves upward. To rebalance the device, masses are attached to end A. The sides WX and ZY of the current balance conductor are 7.10 cm long, side YX is 1.90 cm long, and a current of 6.00 A flows through the conductor on the current balance.

12. If a mass of 1.76×10^{-2} kg is necessary to balance the current balance, what is the magnetic field strength in the solenoid?

Lesson 2 ELECTROMAGNETIC INDUCTION

NOTES

After Oersted discovered that an electric current produces a magnetic field, many scientists investigated whether a magnetic field could produce an electric current. Michael Faraday and Joseph Henry independently discovered that this is true.

One method for producing an electric current through a conductor is to move a conducting rod through a magnetic field, as shown in Diagram 2.

Magnetic field into the page

```
×   ×   ×   ×

×   ×   ×   ×

×   ×   ×   ×

×   ×   ×   ×
```

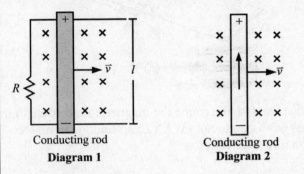

Conducting rod	Conducting rod
Diagram 1	**Diagram 2**

Magnetic field out of the page

```
•   •   •   •

•   •   •   •

•   •   •   •

•   •   •   •
```

In this method, the electrons move to one end of the rod, leaving one end positive and the other end negative. In other words, a voltage is induced within the rod. If the rod is part of an electric circuit, as shown in Diagram 1, the rod will act like a voltage source, forcing electrons to move within the circuit.

The process of inducing a voltage in a conductor using a magnetic field is called electromagnetic induction.

The process of inducing a voltage in a conductor by using a magnetic field is called electromagnetic induction. When a conductor in which a voltage is induced is part of a circuit, the induced voltage will cause electrons to flow through the conductor. This flow of electrons is called an induced current.

An electric current can be produced using a magnetic field by a number of methods. Faraday produced an electric current by using an induction coil as shown in the following diagram:

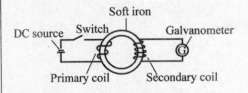

Soft iron loses its magnetic properties the instant the electric current stops flowing (the instant the switch is opened).

Faraday discovered that when the switch of his induction coil was closed or opened, the galvanometer deflected, indicating that a brief current passed through the secondary coil. It should be noted that when the switch remained closed or opened, no deflection occurred (that is, there was no current in the secondary coil). As well, when the switch was closed, the galvanometer deflected in one direction, while the deflection occurred in the opposite direction when the switch was opened.

In a similar demonstration, you can connect a galvanometer to a solenoid and move a magnet in and out of the solenoid.

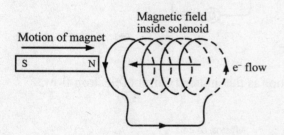

Bar magnet is moved in and out of the coil.

An electric current is produced (induced) in the solenoid when it is moving relative to the magnetic field. When the magnet moves into the solenoid, the galvanometer will deflect in one direction, and it will deflect in the opposite direction when the magnet is pulled out of the solenoid. However, it does not matter if the magnet or solenoid is moving, as long as they are moving relative to each other. The direction of the induced current can be found using Lenz's law.

Lenz's law states that the induced current flows in the direction that produces a magnetic force that opposes the direction of the applied force (the relative motion of the magnet).

Lenz's law is an application of the law of conservation of energy. Electrical energy cannot come from nothing. It must come from somewhere.

For example, when a magnet is pushed into the coil, a current is induced in the coil. Lenz's law indicates that the current will flow so that the magnetic field inside the coil opposes the magnetic field of the magnet.

Motion of magnet

Magnetic field inside solenoid

S   N

e⁻ flow

For the setup in the given diagram, use your left hand to indicate the direction of the magnetic field inside the coil. Your thumb will point in the direction of the north-seeking pole (or pole that is equivalent to the north-seeking pole).

Note: This field opposes the magnetic field of the magnet. If this were not the case, the electrical energy would appear from nowhere.

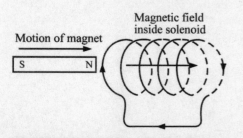

Motion of magnet

Magnetic field inside solenoid

S   N

Lenz's law:
The induced current flows in the direction to produce a magnetic force that opposes the direction of the applied force.

Lenz's law is a form of the law of conservation of energy.

The left-hand rule indicates the magnetic field inside the coil by opposing the magnetic field of the permanent magnet.

Energy must be put into the system in order for energy to get out.

The induced magnetic field cannot occur in the direction as indicated in this diagram.

NOTES

If the current (electron flow) in the conductor occurs as indicated in the given diagram, the magnetic field would attract the magnet. As a result, no work or energy would be required to slide the magnet into the coil, so electrical energy could not be produced in the coil.

The magnetic field produced by the induced current must oppose the magnetic field of the magnet producing the current. This is Lenz's law.

Question 1: In what direction is the induced current (electron flow) through point G?

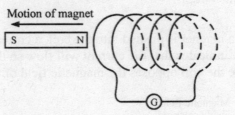

Answer: Left

Question 2: In what direction is the induced current (electron flow) through point G?

Answer: Left

Question 3: In what direction is the induced current (electron flow) through G?

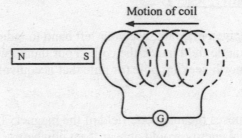

Answer: Left

In the same way, if a conducting rod moves through a magnetic field, the magnetic field of the induced current opposes the magnetic field that produced the induced current. This also follows Lenz's law.

Conducting rod

To find the direction of current:

- Left palm faces opposite of v.
- Fingers point into page.
- Thumb points down in the direction of electron flow.

Lenz's law indicates that the magnetic force on the conducting rod must be in the opposite direction to its motion (opposite to v). Using your left hand (opened), point your palm in the opposite direction to v and your fingers in the direction of the magnetic field. Your thumb will point in the direction of the induced current (electron flow). In the given diagram, the current flows clockwise through the circuit.

Question 4: In what direction is the induced current (electron flow) in this circuit?

Conducting rod

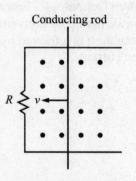

Answer: Clockwise

ELECTRIC GENERATOR

An electric generator is a device that converts mechanical energy into electrical energy. It makes use of the principle of electromagnetic induction. In a sense, the generator works opposite to the electric motor.

In an electric motor, a current-carrying conductor passes through a magnetic field. The interaction between the magnetic fields causes the loop to rotate.

In a generator, there is also a loop of wire, but this loop is mechanically rotated in the magnetic field. This induces a current in the loop by electromagnetic induction. Energy from wind or falling water can be used to rotate the loop.

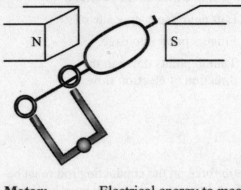

Motor: Electrical energy to mechanical energy
Generator: Mechanical energy to electrical energy

The given generator is an AC generator because the current will alternate back and forth. The alternator in a car is an example of an AC generator. A DC generator uses a split-ring commutator, just like a DC motor. A few years ago, the generators in cars were DC generators.

These principles are important in modern technology. Entertainment systems and computer systems store information by converting electric currents to magnetic fields. This information is retrieved by converting the stored magnetic field back into electric current.

ACTIVITY #1

Purpose: To verify that the magnetic force on a current-carrying conductor varies directly with the electric current flowing through the conductor.

Apparatus:

- PASCO basic current balance apparatus
- Magnet holder
- Ring stand mount
- Conductor
- A gram balance
- A multimeter or ammeter
- A ring stand
- A power supply
- Connecting wires

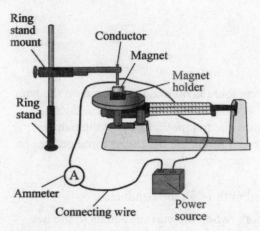

Procedure:

- Set up the apparatus as shown in the given diagram.
- Place the magnet holder on the gram balance pan.
- Adjust the position of the ring stand mount so that the horizontal length of the conductor is just above the top of the magnet. Make sure the apparatus does not interfere with the movement of the gram balance pan.
  (**Note:** Connect the conductor to the power supply so that the magnetic force between the conductor and the magnet is repulsive.)
- Measure the mass of the magnet and the magnet holder at various currents, including a current of 0 A.

Theoretically, when there is no electric current, there will be no magnetic force acting on the system, but when there is an electric current, there will be a magnetic force acting on the system. The conductor is not free to move up or down; however, the balance pan, including the magnet and magnet holder, is free to move. When the scale is adjusted so that it is balanced again, a net force is acting on the pan.

The net force is the sum of the gravitational and magnetic forces acting on the pan. The gravitational force will be down, but the magnetic force on the pan can be either up or down, depending on the direction the electric current flows through the conductor. Set this activity up so that the magnetic force on the magnet is down.

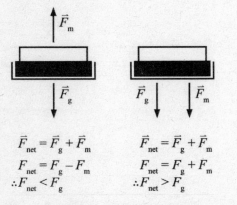

$$\vec{F}_{net} = \vec{F}_g + \vec{F}_m$$
$$F_{net} = F_g - F_m$$
$$\therefore F_{net} < F_g$$

$$\vec{F}_{net} = \vec{F}_g + \vec{F}_m$$
$$F_{net} = F_g + F_m$$
$$\therefore F_{net} > F_g$$

If the net force (balance reading) is equal to the gravitational force, there is no magnetic force on the pan.

If the net force (balance reading) is less than the gravitational force, the magnetic force on the pan is up. If the net force (balance reading) is greater than the gravitational force, the magnetic force on the pan is down.

- Complete the following data table by changing the electric current through the conductor.
- When the current equals 0, there is no magnetic force. Therefore, when the current equals 0, the net force equals the weight of the magnet and holder. Therefore, the magnetic force $\left(\vec{F}_m\right)$ is the difference between the net force $\left(\vec{F}_{net}\right)$ and the weight of the magnet $\left(\vec{F}_g\right)$ and holder (the first value in the third column).

Current (A)	Balance Reading (kg)	Net Force (balance reading × g or sum of $\vec{F}_g$ and $\vec{F}_m$) (N)	Magnetic Force (difference between $\vec{F}_{net}$ and $\vec{F}_g$) (N)
0			

1. Draw a graph of the magnetic force as a function of the electric current.

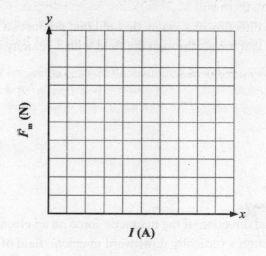

If you were not able to do this activity, use the following data:

• Conductor length = 4.0 cm

• Mass of magnet and holder = 0.076 2 kg

Current (A)	Balance Reading (kg)	Net Force (balance reading × g or sum of $\vec{F}_g$ and $\vec{F}_m$) (N)	Magnetic Force (difference between $\vec{F}_{net}$ and $\vec{F}_g$) (N)
0.0	0.076 2		
1.0	0.073 0		
2.0	0.069 5		
3.0	0.066 4		
4.0	0.063 2		
5.0	0.060 1		

Questions:

1. According to the data, what is the direction of the magnetic force on the pan (magnet and holder)? Explain. (Remember that the balance reading is the net force.)

2. Do your data support the theory that the magnetic force on a current-carrying conductor varies directly with the electric current flowing through the conductor? For example, consider what the shape of your graph should be if your data support the theory. Explain.

3. Use one set of data readings to calculate the magnetic field strength of the magnet used. You will need to determine the length of the conductor.

PRACTICE QUIZ

1. What is the magnitude and direction of a magnetic field that produces a downward force of 7.30×10^{-13} N on a proton that travels through the field with a velocity of 7.80×10^{4} m/s east?

2. Calculate the magnitude and direction of the magnetic force on an electron travelling with a velocity of 7.22×10^{5} m/s west through a vertically downward magnetic field of 3.80×10^{-1} T.

3. A potential difference accelerates an alpha particle from rest, which then travels perpendicularly through a magnetic field of 5.50×10^{-1} T where it experiences a magnetic force of 6.20×10^{-14} N. What is the potential difference through which the particle is accelerated?

4. A potential difference accelerates an electron from rest, which then travels perpendicularly through a magnetic field of 7.20×10^{-1} T where it experiences a magnetic force of 4.1×10^{-13} N. What is the potential difference through which the electron is accelerated?

5. Calculate the downward acceleration on an electron that travels horizontally at a speed of 6.20×10^5 m/s perpendicular to a horizontal magnetic field of 2.30×10^{-1} T.

6. Calculate the downward acceleration on a proton that travels horizontally at a speed of 7.50×10^5 m/s perpendicular to a horizontal magnetic field of 2.70×10^{-1} T.

7. A 0.75 m long conductor carries a conventional current of 2.0 A vertically downward through a magnetic field of 2.7×10^{-3} T directed south. What is the magnitude and direction of the magnetic force acting on the conductor?

8. A 0.35 m long conductor is placed in a magnetic field of 2.9×10^{-2} T east. If it is assumed that the conductor is perpendicular to the magnetic field and the magnetic force acting on the conductor is 4.5×10^{-2} N up, what is the electric current (positive flow) through the conductor?

9. A 0.120 m long copper wire carries an electric current of 2.10 A east through a magnetic field of 5.20×10^{-4} T directed vertically downward. What is the magnitude and direction of the magnetic force acting on the wire?

Use the following information to answer the next question.

A current balance is used to determine the magnetic field intensity in the core of a solenoid. The current balance and the solenoid are described in the given diagram.

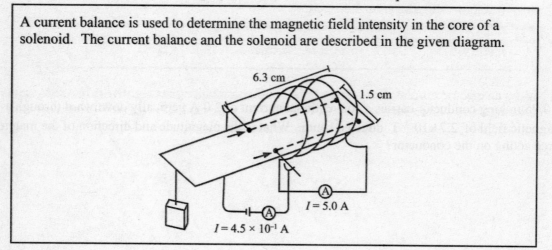

10. If the current balance is balanced by a 2.3×10^{-5} kg mass, what is the magnetic field strength in the solenoid core?

Use the following information to answer the next question.

A student is studying the relationship between the magnetic force on a current-carrying conductor and the length of the conductor by using the apparatus in the given diagram.

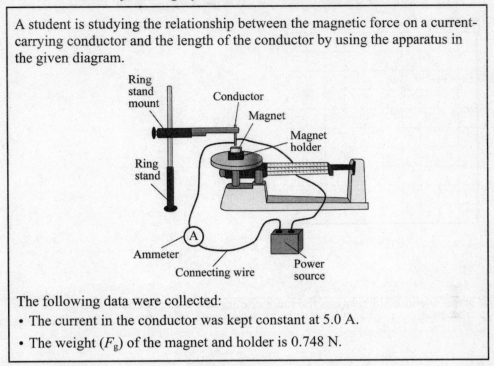

The following data were collected:

• The current in the conductor was kept constant at 5.0 A.

• The weight (F_g) of the magnet and holder is 0.748 N.

11. a) When an electric current flows through the conductor, there is a magnetic force acting on both the conductor and the magnet. In this case, it is the magnet that is free to move (along with the balance pan). In what direction is the magnetic force acting on the magnet?

b) Complete the given data table. Show at least one calculation for each of the magnetic force and the magnetic field.

Length of Conductor (m)	Balance Reading (kg)	Net Force (balance reading × g or sum of $\vec{F}_g$ and $\vec{F}_m$) (N)	Magnetic Force (N)	Magnetic Field Strength (T)
1.0×10^{-2}	0.0794	0.779		
2.0×10^{-2}	0.0828	0.812		
3.0×10^{-2}	0.0854	0.838		
4.0×10^{-2}	0.0886	0.869		
6.0×10^{-2}	0.0950	0.935		
8.0×10^{-2}	0.102	0.998		

c) Draw a graph by plotting the magnetic force as a function of the **conductor** length.

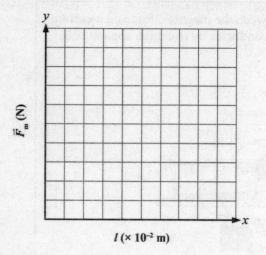

d) What is the relationship between the magnetic force and the conductor length?

REVIEW SUMMARY

- Magnetic interactions in terms of:
  - Forces
  - Fields
- Magnetic fields compared with electric fields
- The discoveries of:
  - Oersted
  - Faraday
- Magnetic fields produced by moving charged particles
- The interaction between a magnetic field and a:
  - Moving charge
  - Current-carrying conductor
- Formulas used in this chapter:
  - $F_m = B_\perp Il$
  - $F_m = qvB_\perp$

PRACTICE TEST

Use the following information to answer the next question.

An electric current is induced in a circuit containing an air core solenoid, as shown in the given diagram, by suddenly pushing a magnet into the coil.

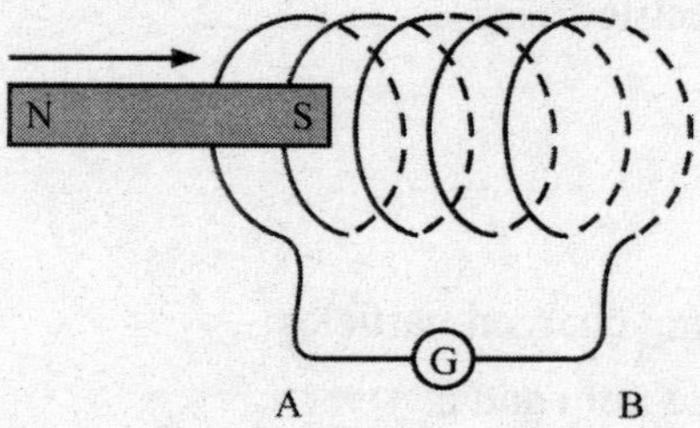

Two students make the following statements about the given setup:
i)   A magnetic field is induced in the solenoid as to attract the magnet.
ii) The current (conventional) will flow from A and B through G.

1. Which of the following statements about **i)** and **ii)** is **true**?

    A. Neither **i)** nor **ii)** is true.

    B. Both **i)** and **ii)** are true.

    C. Only **ii)** is true.

    D. Only **i)** is true.

Use the following information to answer the next question.

The following three characteristics are given:
   i)   Can be produced by moving protons
   ii) Are vector fields
   iii) Can be expressed in $N/A \cdot m$

2. Which of the given characteristics are the characteristics of magnetic fields?

    A. **ii)** and **iii)** only

    B. **i)** and **iii)** only

    C. **i)** and **ii)** only

    D. **i)**, **ii)**, and **iii)**

3. Lenz's law is an example of the conservation of

    A. electric charges

    B. electric energy

    C. energy

    D. forces

Use the following information to answer the next question.

The conducting rod AB decelerates from 3.0 m/s to 1.0 m/s as it slides to the right along conducting rails through a magnetic field, as shown in the diagram.

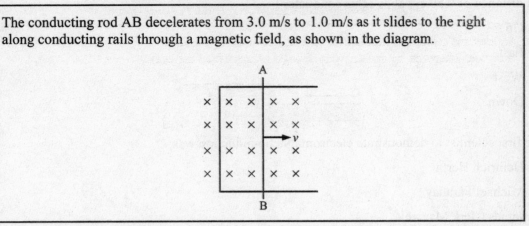

4. Which of the following statements concerning the induced current (electron flow) through the described circuit is **true**?

   A. The current will increase in a clockwise direction.

   B. The current will decrease in a clockwise direction.

   C. The current will increase in a counterclockwise direction.

   D. The current will decrease in a counterclockwise direction.

5. If an alpha particle travels east through a magnetic field directed west, which of the following statements **best** describes the magnetic force on the alpha particle?

   A. It moves up.

   B. It moves north.

   C. It moves down.

   D. There is no force.

6. A proton travels east through Earth's magnetic field at the equator. What is the direction of the magnetic force on the proton?

   A. Up

   B. North

   C. Down

   D. South

7. A conductor carries electrons north. What is the direction of the magnetic field due to this conductor at a distance of 0.50 cm above this conductor?

   A. Up

   B. East

   C. West

   D. Down

8. The first scientist to demonstrate electromagnetic induction was

   A. Heinrich Hertz

   B. Michael Faraday

   C. James Clerk Maxwell

   D. Hans Christian Oersted

Use the following information to answer the next question.

The following three conditions are given:
   i)   The switch is closed.
   ii) The switch is opened.
   iii) The switch is kept closed.

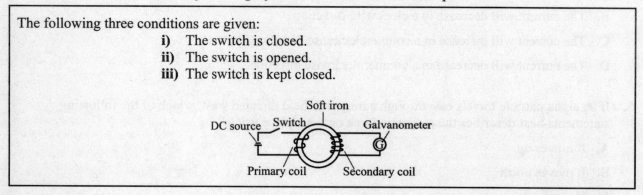

9. Under which of the given conditions will the given galvanometer show a constant reading of zero?

   A. i) only

   B. ii) only

   C. iii) only

   D. i) and ii)

10. The magnetic force acting on a charged particle travelling through a **perpendicular** magnetic field is F. What will be the magnetic force on this particle if both its mass and velocity are halved?

   A. $\dfrac{F}{4}$

   B. $\dfrac{F}{2}$

   C. $2F$

   D. $4F$

11. An ampere is defined in terms of

    A. Lenz's law

    B. Coulomb's law

    C. forces between current-carrying conductors

    D. magnetic fields around current-carrying conductors

Use the following information to answer the next question.

In the given diagram, the magnet's north pole is quickly moved down into the conducting loop and then quickly pulled back up out of the conducting loop.

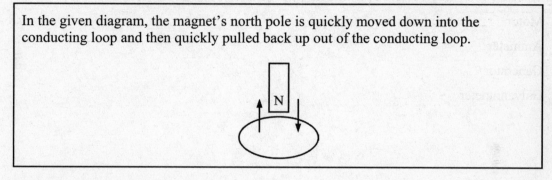

12. As viewed from above, the induced conventional current in the loop is

    A. always clockwise

    B. always counterclockwise

    C. first clockwise, then counterclockwise

    D. first counterclockwise, then clockwise

13. Which of the following devices converts electric energy into mechanical energy?

    A. Motor

    B. Ammeter

    C. Generator

    D. Galvanometer

14. Which of the following devices converts mechanical energy into electric energy?

    A. Motor

    B. Ammeter

    C. Generator

    D. Galvanometer

15. Charged particles are deflected by a magnetic field when they travel perpendicularly to the field. This deflection can be increased by

    A. increasing the mass of the particles

    B. increasing the charge on the particles

    C. decreasing the velocity of the particles

    D. decreasing the strength of the magnetic field

16. Which of the following devices operates on the principle of electromagnetic induction?

    A. Motor

    B. Ammeter

    C. Generator

    D. Galvanometer

ELECTROMAGNETIC RADIATION

When you are finished this unit, you will be able to...

• Describe, qualitatively, how all accelerating charges produce EMR

• Compare and contrast the constituents of the electromagnetic spectrum on the basis of frequency and wavelength

• Explain the propagation of EMR in terms of perpendicular electric and magnetic fields that are varying with time and travelling away from their source at the speed of light

• Explain, qualitatively, various methods of measuring the speed of EMR

• Calculate the speed of EMR, given data from a Michelson-type experiment

• Describe, quantitatively, the phenomena of reflection and refraction, including total internal reflection

• Describe, quantitatively, simple optical systems, consisting of only one component, for both lenses and curved mirrors

• Describe, qualitatively, diffraction, interference and polarization

• Describe, qualitatively, how the results of Young's double-slit experiment support the wave model of light

• Solve double-slit and diffraction grating problems using $\lambda = \dfrac{xd}{nl}, \lambda = \dfrac{d\sin\theta}{n}$

• Describe, qualitatively and quantitatively, how refraction supports the wave model of EMR, using $\dfrac{\sin\theta_1}{\sin\theta_2} = \dfrac{n_2}{n_1} = \dfrac{v_1}{v_2} = \dfrac{\lambda_1}{\lambda_2}$

• Compare and contrast the visible spectra produced by diffraction gratings and triangular prisms

• Explain how blackbody radiation supports energy quantization

• Define the photon as a quantum of EMR and calculate its energy

• Classify the regions of the electromagnetic spectrum by photon energy

• Describe the photoelectric effect in terms of the intensity and wavelength or frequency of the incident light and surface material

• Describe, quantitatively, photoelectric emission, using concepts related to the conservation of energy

• Describe the photoelectric effect as a phenomenon that supports the notion of the wave-particle duality of EMR

• Explain, qualitatively and quantitatively, the Compton effect as another example of wave-particle duality, applying the laws of mechanics and of conservation of momentum and energy to photons

PREREQUISITE SKILLS AND KNOWLEDGE

Prior to starting this unit, you should be able to…
- Use ratios and proportions in a problem-solving context
- Describe a oscillatory motion of a wave in terms of frequency, wavelength, and period
- Describe transverse and longitudinal waves and know the difference between them
- Solve problems using the universal wave equation involving the speed, frequency and wavelength of a propagating wave
- Describe how waves reflect off of surface using the law of reflection
- Understand the concepts of constructive and destructive interference
- Describe the concepts of resonance, standing waves, nodes and antinodes in a closed or open resonating tube
- Understand how the Doppler effect changes the properties of a wave between an observer and a relative sound source that is in motion
- Describe the electric and magnetic fields produced by moving and stationary charges particles
- Understand how electric and magnetic forces interact with charged particles in terms of field strength, charge, and velocity

Lesson 1 ELECTROMAGNETIC RADIATION

Michael Faraday believed in the unity of nature, and he speculated that a relationship existed between light, electricity, and magnetism. Faraday was encouraged by this idea when he demonstrated that the plane of polarization for light travelling through heavy glass could be rotated when a magnetic field was applied to the glass. However, Faraday lacked the mathematical skills needed to prove that light waves could travel by electrical and magnetic fields.

Faraday speculated that there is a relationship between light, electricity, and magnetism.

MAXWELL'S THEORY

In the 1860s, James Clerk Maxwell developed a mathematical theory to express Faraday's speculation; this is known as the theory of electromagnetic radiation (EMR).

Maxwell developed the EMR theory.

Oersted and Faraday established the two basic principles of electromagnetism. Oersted stated that an electric current will produce a magnetic field (the motor effect), and Faraday stated that a magnetic field can produce an electric current (the generator effect).

Maxwell added to and generalized these principles so that they apply to electric and magnetic fields in conductors, insulators, and free space. Maxwell's work demonstrated the dependence of electric and magnetic fields on each other, forming the building blocks for understanding electromagnetism:

• A changing electric field in space produces a magnetic field.
  The magnitude of this magnetic field is proportional to the rate at which the electric field changes.

$$B \propto \frac{\Delta E}{\Delta t}$$

A changing electric field produces a magnetic field.

• A changing magnetic field in space produces an electric field.
  The magnitude of this electric field is proportional to the rate at which the magnetic field changes.

$$E \propto \frac{\Delta B}{\Delta t}$$

A changing magnetic field produces an electric field.

To explain how a changing electric field creates a magnetic field, Maxwell used the concept of displacement current. Imagine an atom or molecule suspended between two horizontal, parallel plates. If these plates are connected to a voltage source (battery) so that the top plate is positive and the bottom plate is negative, the electrons are displaced to the top of the atom (molecule). In order to obtain this displacement, the electrons had to move; this is called displacement current. This movement of the electrons, or current, does not last very long. In order to maintain this current, the charges on the plate can be increased, decreased, or reversed. This can be done by constantly changing the voltage (potential difference) between the two plates. If the voltage changes, the electric field must

change because $E = \dfrac{V}{d}$. Therefore, a changing electric field results in a

displacement current (moving electrons), which in turn produces a magnetic field.

Maxwell assumed that this model, developed for matter, applied to free space as well. This is the basis for Maxwell's theory.

According to this theory, a changing magnetic field produces a changing electric field, which produces a changing magnetic field. Once this process is started, it will set up an unending sequence of events.

Remember that the strength of the magnetic field depends on the electric current.

$$B \propto I \text{ or } B = \frac{\mu_0 I}{2\pi r}$$

The magnetic field around a current-carrying conductor depends on the current, or the rate of flow of charged particles. For a constant current, the magnetic field is constant; if the current changes, so does the magnetic field. Therefore, according to Maxwell's theory, an accelerating charged particle will produce a changing magnetic field, which will produce a changing electric field.

Accelerating charged particle $\quad \Delta\vec{B} \quad \Delta\vec{E} \quad \Delta\vec{B} \quad \Delta\vec{E} \quad \Delta\vec{B} \quad \Delta\vec{E} \quad \Delta\vec{B} \quad \Delta\vec{E}$

An accelerating charged particle will produce a changing magnetic field, setting up an unending sequence of events: EMR.

Maxwell called this unending sequence of changing magnetic and electric fields the electromagnetic wave, which is radiated by an accelerating charged particle. It consists of vibrating electric and magnetic fields that generate each other. At any point on the wave, the electric field is perpendicular to the magnetic field.

Electric field

Magnetic field

Direction of propagation

An accelerating charged particle is required to initiate this electromagnetic wave. Maxwell calculated the speed of the propagation, or the rate at which the magnetic field produces an electric field and vice versa.

Maxwell calculated this rate to be 3.00×10^8 m/s. Maxwell discovered this just a few years after the speed of light was also measured to be 3.00×10^8 m/s! From this calculation, Maxwell concluded that light is a form of EMR. This is what Faraday had also speculated. Maxwell had developed a theory that combined the principles of light, electricity, and magnetism.

Maxwell predicted that electromagnetic waves of many different frequencies could exist. All such waves would travel through space at the speed of light and have the same properties as light. That is, they would reflect, refract, diffract, interfere, and be polarized.

HEINRICH HERTZ

Maxwell never produced or detected these waves; he only predicted their existence. In 1886, Hertz successfully produced and detected these electromagnetic waves.

Using a spark gap across which electric charges move rapidly back and forth (accelerating charged particles), Hertz generated electromagnetic waves that had a frequency of about 10^9 Hz. He was able to detect these waves some distance away by using a loop of wire as a receiver (antenna). Hertz was able to show that these waves travelled at a speed of 3.00×10^8 m/s and that they have characteristics of light waves: reflection, refraction, diffraction, interference, and polarization. Hertz called the waves that he had produced radio waves. His discovery of radio waves was used by Guglielmo Marconi, who in 1901 became the first person to transmit radio waves across the Atlantic Ocean.

THE ELECTROMAGNETIC SPECTRUM

There is a broad range of continuous frequencies for EMR called the electromagnetic spectrum. EMR may also be described in terms of wavelength and energy, as well as frequency. It should be noted that frequency, wavelength, and energy are mathematically related.

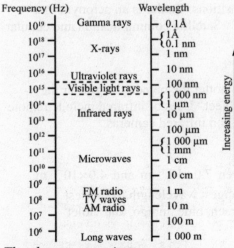

The electromagnetic spectrum

From the electromagnetic spectrum, you should notice that visible light is a very small part of the electromagnetic spectrum. Visible light has a range of wavelengths between 7.0×10^{-7} m and 4.0×10^{-7} m.

Recall the universal wave equation:

Maxwell calculated the speed of EMR to be 3.00×10^8 m/s.

Maxwell predicted that light was a form of EMR.

Hertz used an induction coil to detect EMR.

Hertz produced the first radio wave.

NOTES

$$v = \lambda f \text{ or } c = \lambda f$$

where v = speed of the wave

λ = wavelength

f = frequency

The speed of an EMR wave is c, which is 3.00×10^8 m/s.

The greater the frequency of EMR, the greater its energy.

All EMR is produced by accelerating charged particles. Radio waves (including television signals) and microwaves (radar) are produced by the oscillations of electric current. Infrared radiation is produced by molecular vibrations. Visible light and ultraviolet waves are produced by the transitions of electrons in atoms. X-rays are produced by high-energy electrons undergoing rapid deceleration by hitting a target. Gamma rays are produced by the decaying nuclei of unstable atoms.

Radio Waves

Radio waves are mainly used in communication. They are used in radio, television, and cellular phones.

Microwaves

Microwaves are extremely high-frequency radio waves. Microwave ovens produce wavelengths of 12.2 cm and operate at a frequency of 2.45×10^9 Hz. This frequency causes water molecules to vibrate. Since temperature is the measurement of the average kinetic energy within a substance, the increase in vibration results in an increase in temperature. Radar signals are high-frequency microwaves. Radar was developed to detect objects and determine their positions. Radar is an acronym that means "radio detection and ranging." Satellite communication and cellular phones use microwaves.

Infrared

Infrared is associated with heat. The hotter the object, the greater the infrared radiation coming from the object. Uses of infrared include remote controls, heat lamps, burglar alarms, and infrared cameras.

Visible Light

Visible light has a wavelength between 7.0×10^{-7} m and 4.0×10^{-7} m. The spectrum of visible light from longest wavelength to shortest wavelength is red, orange, yellow, green, blue, indigo, and violet (**ROYGBIV**).

Ultraviolet

Ultraviolet (UV) means "beyond violet." The wavelengths of ultraviolet rays range from 4.0×10^{-7} m to 0.10×10^{-7} m. UV waves cause sunburn and skin cancer. Some UV is blocked by the ozone layer in the atmosphere.

X-Rays

X-rays are used in medicine and airport security. X-rays can also cause cell damage.

Gamma Radiation

Gamma radiation is produced by the nuclei of unstable atoms. It carries the most energy of all forms of EMR; therefore, it is the most dangerous and can cause the most damage. Its high energy can cause cancer, but gamma radiation is also used in medicine to destroy cancer cells (radiotherapy).

SPEED OF EMR (MICROWAVES)

Microwave ovens produce electromagnetic waves by accelerating electrons in a device called a magnetron. Remember, all EMR is produced by accelerating electric charges. In a microwave oven, the electrons are accelerated back and forth at a frequency of 2.45×10^9 Hz (2.45 GHz). Also, the reflection of the waves within the microwave oven produces standing waves.

You can determine the wavelength of a microwave by placing a slice of cheese in a microwave oven and microwaving it for approximately 10 s. You may have to experiment with the time a bit. If the microwave oven has a rotating plate, you should remove it.

The cheese will begin to melt only at the antinodes of the standing wave. By measuring the distance between the two adjacent antinodes, you can determine the wavelength. (Remember, wavelength equals double the distance between antinodes.)

A more precise method for measuring the wavelength and the speed of microwaves uses a microwave transmitter and a microwave detector.

The distance between alternating nodes of a standing wave is $\frac{1}{2}\lambda$.

A standing wave gets its name from the fact that the wave pattern does not move.

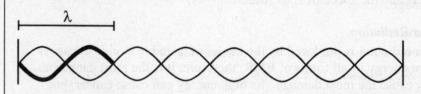

Standing waves are produced by the reflecting wave interfering with the incident (incoming) wave.

A standing wave results when two wave patterns of equal wavelength and amplitude travel in opposite directions through the same medium. A standing wave can be produced when a wave is reflected from a fixed object. The reflecting wave interferes with the incident, or incoming, wave. Standing waves have alternating nodes and antinodes.

Node: region of medium where the standing waves have zero amplitude.

The distance between nodes is $\frac{1}{2}\lambda$.

Antinode: region of medium where the standing waves have maximum amplitudes.

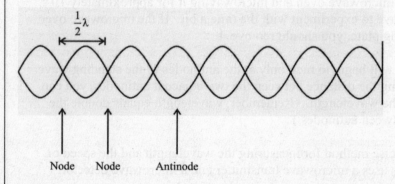

Node   Node   Antinode

Interference can be constructive or destructive. Constructive interference of the incident and reflected waves results in antinodes, while destructive interference of the incident and reflected waves results in nodes.

ACTIVITY #8

Purpose:
To determine the speed of EMR (microwaves)

Apparatus:
- Microwave transmitter with known frequency
- Microwave detector (receiver and probe)
- Reflector
- Ruler

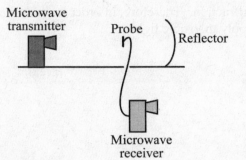

Procedure:
- Set up the apparatus as shown in the given diagram.
- Turn on the transmitter, and direct the microwaves so that they are perpendicular to the reflector. (When the microwaves reflect from the reflector, a standing wave will be produced.)

- Place the microwave detector probe between the transmitter and the reflector. Slowly move it between the transmitter and the reflector. The probe should pick up the microwave signal, which is converted into sound by the receiver. As you move the probe, the signal should increase and decrease as the probe moves from nodes to antinodes of the standing waves. (You may have to adjust the controls of the receiver and the position of the reflector. Also, make sure the receiver horn is directed away from the microwave transmitter horn.)
- Measure the distance between 10 nodes of the standing waves.

Data:
- Record the following data:
- Frequency of microwave transmitter _____
- Distance between 10 nodes _____
- Microwave wavelength _____
- Speed of EMR (microwave) _____
- Percent error _____

If you were not able to do this activity, use the following data:

- Frequency of microwave transmitter: 1.05×10^{10} Hz

- Distance between 10 nodes: 14.5 cm

- Microwave wavelength _____

- Speed of EMR (microwave) _____

- Percent error _____

PROPERTIES OF EMR

EMR has the same properties as light; however, wave properties vary according to wavelength. An example of this is that the longer the wavelength, the greater the diffraction. Therefore, in order to study the properties of EMR, focus on the following properties as they apply to visible light:

- Reflection
- Refraction
- Diffraction
- Interference
- Polarization

Lesson 2 REFLECTION

When a wave reaches a boundary between two media, some or all of the wave reflects. Both waves and particles will reflect according to the law of reflection. The law of reflection states that the angle of reflection equals the angle of incidence.

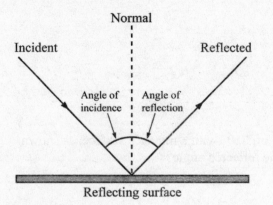

$$\left(\angle r = \angle i \right)$$

Law of reflection: the angle of reflection equals the angle of incidence.

The incident ray is the incoming ray. The normal is a line perpendicular to the reflecting surface. Note that the angles of incidence and reflection are both measured with respect to the normal.

Light obeys this law because light is a form of energy, and energy can travel by particles and waves. Therefore, it makes sense that light obeys the law of reflection. However, although light obeys the law of reflection, this property does not help determine whether light is a wave or a particle.

Questions:
1. What length of a mirror do you need to obtain a full-length view of yourself?

2. What is the reason that you cannot see an image of yourself in paper?

3. How does the frequency of reflected light compare with the frequency of incident light?

Answers:
1. In order to obtain a full-length view of yourself, you need a mirror one half your height. It is important how you position the mirror.

2. You cannot see an image of yourself in paper because paper is rough and gives irregular reflections.

3. The frequency of reflected light is equal to the frequency of the incident light.

NOTES

Example

If the angle of reflection from a mirror is 25.0°, what is the angle of incidence?

Solution

$\angle r = \angle i$

$25.0° = \angle i$

Example

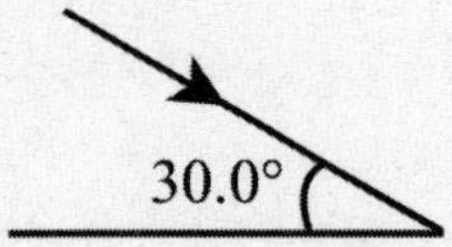

If a ray of light makes an angle of 30.0° with a mirror's surface, as shown in the given diagram, what is the reflected angle?

Solution

$\angle r = \angle i$

$\angle i = 90.0° - 30.0° = 60.0°$

$\angle r = 60.0°$

PRACTICE EXERCISES

Formula: $\angle r = \angle i$

1. If the angle of incidence of a ray of light to a mirror is 50.0°, what is the angle of reflection from the mirror?

2. If the angle of incidence of a ray of light to a mirror is 20.0°, what angle does the reflected light ray make with the mirror?

3. If an incident ray of light makes an angle of 58° with a mirror, what is the angle between the incident ray and the reflected ray?

Use the following information to answer the next question.

A ray of light is reflected in series off two mirrors, A and B, as shown in the given diagram.

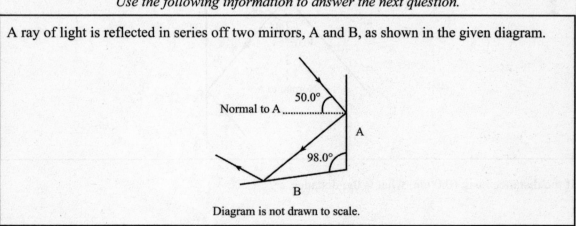

Diagram is not drawn to scale.

4. What is the angle of reflection from mirror B?

Use the following information to answer the next question.

A ray of light is reflected in series from two mirrors, A and B, as shown in the given diagram.

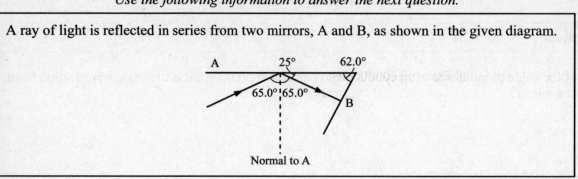

5. What is the angle of reflection from mirror B?

Use the following information to answer the next question.

A ray of light reflects off two mirrors in series, as shown in the given diagram.

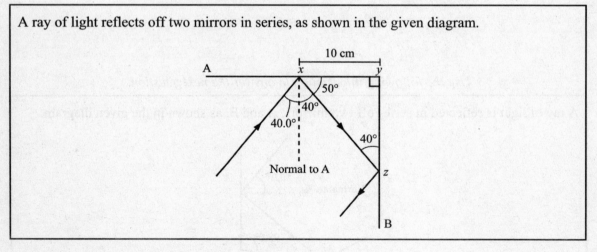

6. If the distance *xy* is 10.0 cm, what is the distance *xz*?

Use the following information to answer the next question.

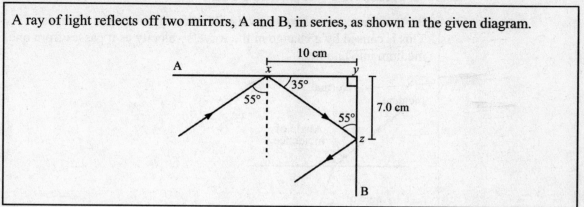

7. If the distance *xy* is 10.0 cm and the distance *yz* is 7.0 cm, what is the angle of incidence of the light ray to mirror A?

Use the following information to answer the next question.

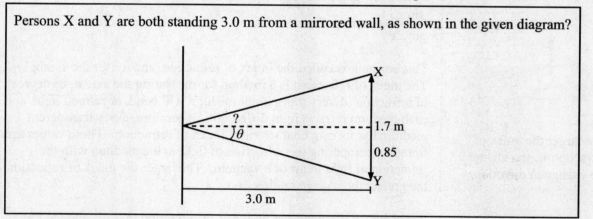

8. If person X sees an image of person Y when they stand 1.7 m apart, what is the angle of reflection of the light from person Y that reaches person X?

Lesson 3   REFRACTION

Refraction occurs when a wave's direction of movement changes. This is caused by a change in the wave's velocity as it passes from one medium into another.

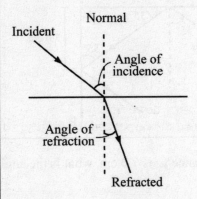

As with reflection, the angle of incidence and angle of refraction are measured with respect to the normal. However, is there any relationship between the refracted angle and the incident angle?

The relationship between the refracted angle and the incident angle is Snell's law.

Although the relationship between these two angles is not easy to see, it was calculated by Willebrord Snell, a Dutch mathematician. This relationship is referred to as the law of refraction, or Snell's law.

Snell's law gives the following equation:

$$\frac{\sin \angle i}{\sin \angle r} = \text{constant} = n$$

This constant is called the index of refraction, and it uses the symbol n. The index of refraction is a method for measuring the extent, or degree, of refraction. Every transparent medium will bend, or refract, light, and each medium refracts light differently. Therefore, every transparent medium has its own characteristic index of refraction. These values are found by comparing the refraction of light in the medium with the refraction of light in air or a vacuum. The larger the index of refraction is, the greater the change in direction.

The larger the index of refraction is, the greater the change in direction.

For example, diamond has an index of refraction of 2.42, and ice has an index of refraction of 1.31.

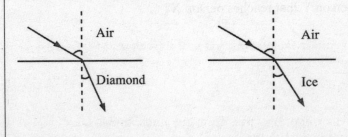

What causes refraction? Refraction is caused by the change of the wave's velocity. If a toy car rolls along a smooth floor and onto a carpeted floor, the car will slow down when it begins to travel on the carpet.

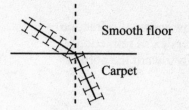

Refraction is caused by a change in velocity.

Note that the front right wheel of the car will slow down first. This happens because the front right wheel is on the carpet and the front left wheel is still on the smooth floor.

Waves behave in the same manner.

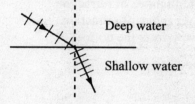

Light also behaves in the same manner.

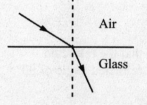

Measurements show that the ratio of the velocities of wheels, waves, or light in the first medium compared with the velocities in the second medium is equal to the ratio of the sine of the angles.

$$\frac{\sin\theta_1}{\sin\theta_2} = \frac{v_1}{v_2}$$

In the case of waves, it can also be shown that the wavelength decreases when the waves slow down.

$$\frac{\sin\theta_1}{\sin\theta_2} = \frac{v_1}{v_2} = \frac{\lambda_1}{\lambda_2}$$

These ratios are also equal to the inverse ratio of their index of refraction.

$$\frac{\sin\theta_1}{\sin\theta_2} = \frac{v_1}{v_2} = \frac{\lambda_1}{\lambda_2} = \frac{n_2}{n_1}$$

Note that when waves or light rays pass from one medium into another, the direction, speed, and wavelength change.

NOTES

$$\frac{\sin \theta_1}{\sin \theta_2} = \frac{v_1}{v_2} = \frac{\lambda_1}{\lambda_2} = \frac{n_2}{n_1}$$

Note that when light travels from one medium to another, its frequency does not change.

When light slows down, it bends toward the normal.

When light speeds up, it bends away from the normal.

The critical angle is the incident angle that produces a refracted angle of 90°.

Question: What happens to the frequency of light or waves when they pass from one medium to another?

Answer: The frequency does not change.

When light passes from a medium that has a low index of refraction (such as air) into a substance that has a higher index of refraction (such as water), the light slows down and bends toward the normal.

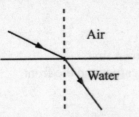

When light passes from a medium that has a high index of refraction (such as water) into a substance that has a lower index of refraction (such as air), the light speeds up and bends away from the normal.

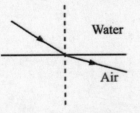

As a result, an angle of the incidence can occur such that the refracted angle is 90°. The angle of incidence that results in a refracted angle of 90° is called the critical angle.

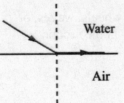

Question: What will happen if the angle of incidence increases beyond the critical angle?

Answer: The light will not refract at all. It will completely reflect off the surface. This is called total reflection.

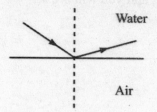

Water

Air

Total reflection never occurs when light passes from a medium with a low index of refraction to a medium with a higher index of refraction.
For example, when light passes from air into water, there will not be a critical angle.

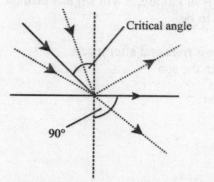

Critical angle

90°

The following situations are examples of refraction of light:

A pool of water is always deeper than it appears. This is because the light waves in the water are shorter than they are in the air.

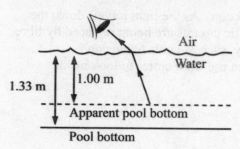

Air
Water

1.33 m

1.00 m

Apparent pool bottom

Pool bottom

The actual depth of the water is 1.33 times greater than the apparent depth.

NOTES

When you are driving your car, the highway ahead of you may appear to be wet. However, you never reach the wet road; this is a mirage. The image that you see is a reflection of the sky on the hot layer of air above the road. The index of refraction of hot air is less than the index of refraction of cool air; therefore, the light passes from cool air (high index) into hot air (low index). In this situation, total reflection can occur, and you will see a reflection of the sky.

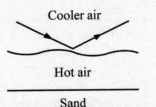

Cooler air

Hot air

Sand

The twinkling of stars is caused by refraction.

The twinkling of stars or distant lights is caused by refraction. The direction the light travels changes as the light passes through air of different temperatures. Because this air is in motion, it will slightly change the position that the star or light appears to be.

Earth's atmosphere refracts light from the sun.

You see the sun for a few minutes before it rises and after it sets. Earth's atmosphere refracts the light from the sun.

Fibre optics uses total internal reflection to transmit many types of information.

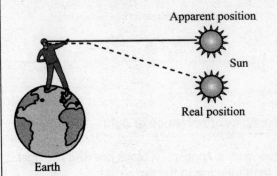

Apparent position

Sun

Real position

Earth

Fibre optics uses total internal reflection. As the light travels down the glass fibres, it cannot escape. Electric circuits are being replaced by fibre optics in communication technology, such as cable television and telephones. Physicians can even use fibre optics to look inside your body.

ACTIVITY #9

Purpose:

To study the angle of refraction and critical angle for two materials with different refractive indices on both plane (flat) and curved surfaces.

Apparatus:

- A ray box
- A semicircular Lucite block
- A semicircular dish, $\frac{2}{3}$ full of water
- A 360° protractor, stencilled on a sheet of paper (there is one at the back of this book)

Procedure:

- Place the Lucite block on top of the 360° protractor so that the flat surface is on the *x*-axis of the protractor and its centre is at the *xy*-intercept.

- Shine a light ray onto the flat surface of the Lucite block at various angles so that the ray enters the block at the *xy*-intercept.

- Complete the following diagram showing your observations:

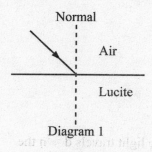

Diagram 1

- Describe your observations in words.

- Shine a light ray onto the curved surface of the Lucite block at various angles so that the ray strikes the flat surface at the *xy*-intercept, as shown in the following diagram:

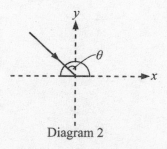

Diagram 2

• Complete the following diagram showing your observations when $\theta = 30°$:

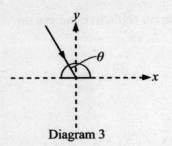

Diagram 3

• Complete the following diagram showing your observations when $\theta = 70°$:

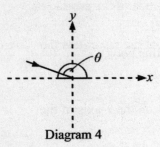

Diagram 4

• Define the term critical angle.

• Measure the critical angle for Lucite.

Question: Is there a critical angle when the light ray passes from air into Lucite, as in Diagram 1? Explain.

Repeat this activity using the semicircular dish $\frac{2}{3}$ full with water.

ACTIVITY #10

Purpose:
To determine the index of refraction of Lucite and water.

Apparatus:
- A ray box
- A semicircular Lucite block
- A semicircular dish, 2/3 full with water
- A 360° protractor, stencilled on a sheet of paper (there is one at the back of this book)

Procedure:
- Place the Lucite block on the 360° protractor so that the flat surface is on the x-axis of the protractor and its centre is at the xy-intercept.
- Shine a light ray onto the flat surface of the Lucite block at various angles so that the ray enters the block at the xy-intercept, as shown in the given diagram.

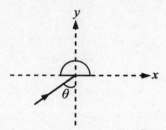

- Complete the following data table:

$\angle i$	$\sin \angle i$	$\angle r$	$\sin \angle r$	n

If you were not able to do this activity, use the following data:

		Lucite		
$\angle i$	sin $\angle i$	$\angle r$	sin $\angle r$	n
30		20		
40		25		
50		31		
60		35		
70		39		
80		41		

Analysis:

Draw a graph by plotting sin $\angle r$ versus sin $\angle i$.

Question: Using only your graph, what is the index of refraction of Lucite?

Repeat this activity using the semicircular dish 2/3 full of water.

$\angle i$	sin $\angle i$	$\angle r$	sin $\angle r$	n

If you were not able to do this activity, use the following data:

Water				
$\angle i$	$\sin \angle i$	$\angle r$	$\sin \angle r$	n
30		22		
40		29		
50		35		
60		41		
70		45		
80		48		

Analysis:

Draw a graph by plotting $\sin \angle r$ versus $\sin \angle i$.

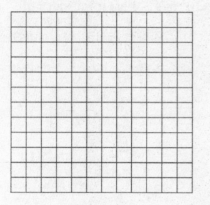

Question: Using only your graph, what is the index of refraction of water?

Example

A ray of light strikes the surface of a block of glass ($n = 1.50$) at an incident angle of 72.0°. What is the angle of refraction?

Solution

$$\frac{\sin \theta_a}{\sin \theta_g} = \frac{n_g}{n_a}$$

$$\frac{\sin 72.0°}{\sin \theta_g} = \frac{1.50}{1.00}$$

$$\sin \theta_g = 0.634$$

$$\theta_g = 39.3°$$

Example

The speed of light through water is 2.26×10^8 m/s. What is the index of refraction of water?

Solution

$$\frac{v_a}{v_w} = \frac{n_w}{n_a}$$

$$\frac{3.00 \times 10^8 \text{m/s}}{2.26 \times 10^8 \text{m/s}} = \frac{n_w}{1.00}$$

$$n_w = 1.33$$

Example

What is the critical angle for an air-Lucite interface if the index of refraction of Lucite is 1.51?

Solution

Light must be travelling from Lucite into air in order for there to be a critical angle. The angle of refraction is 90.0°, and the angle of incidence is the critical angle.

$$\frac{\sin \theta_l}{\sin \theta_a} = \frac{n_a}{n_l}$$

$$\frac{\sin \theta_l}{\sin 90.0°} = \frac{1.00}{1.51}$$

$$\sin \theta_l = 0.662$$

$$\theta_l = 41.5°$$

PRACTICE EXERCISES

Formulas: $\dfrac{\sin\theta_1}{\sin\theta_2} = \dfrac{v_1}{v_2} = \dfrac{\lambda_1}{\lambda_2} = \dfrac{n_2}{n_1}$ $\qquad v = \lambda f$

1. What is the speed of light in a clear plastic that has an index of refraction of 1.40?

2. The speed of light in a clear liquid is 2.30×10^8 m/s. What is the clear liquid's index of refraction?

3. A beam of light in air strikes the surface of a block of glass ($n = 1.50$) and produces a refracted angle of 10.0°. What is the incident angle?

4. What is the wavelength of light in water ($n = 1.33$) if its wavelength in air is 5.30×10^{-7} m?

5. Monochromatic light (light of one frequency) has a wavelength of 6.0×10^{-7} m in air and 5.0×10^{-7} m in a clear liquid. What is the clear liquid's index of refraction?

6. Monochromatic light has a wavelength of 5.75×10^{-7} m in air and 4.32×10^{-7} m in a clear liquid. If a ray of light enters this clear liquid at an angle of incidence of 25.0°, what is the angle of refraction?

7. Monochromatic light has a wavelength of 5.20×10^{-7} m in air and 3.91×10^{-7} m in a clear liquid. What is the speed of light in the clear liquid?

8. What is a substance's index of refraction if the angle of incidence in air is 53.0° and the angle of refraction in this substance is 41.0°?

9. A ray of light in air strikes the surface of water ($n = 1.33$) at an incident angle of 60.0°. What is the angle of refraction?

10. What is the critical angle for an air-glass interface if the index of refraction of glass is 1.50?

11. What is the critical angle for a water-Lucite interface if the index of refraction is 1.33 for water and 1.51 for Lucite?

12. The critical angle for a certain liquid-air interface is 48.8°. What is the liquid's index of refraction?

13. What is the critical angle in air for a substance in which the index of refraction is 1.81?

14. What is the index of refraction for a substance for which the critical angle in air is 42.0°?

15. The speed of light in a clear liquid is $\frac{3}{4}$ the speed of light in air. What is the critical angle in air for the liquid?

Use the following information to answer the next question.

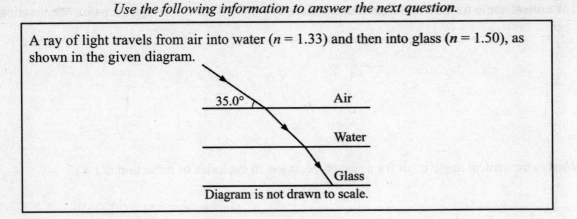

A ray of light travels from air into water ($n = 1.33$) and then into glass ($n = 1.50$), as shown in the given diagram.

Diagram is not drawn to scale.

16. Find the angle of refraction in the glass.

Use the following information to answer the next question.

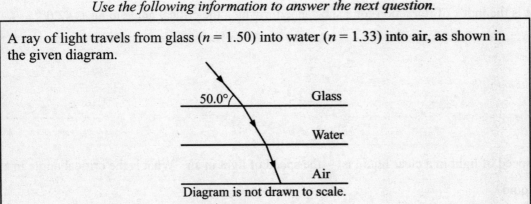

A ray of light travels from glass ($n = 1.50$) into water ($n = 1.33$) into air, as shown in the given diagram.

Diagram is not drawn to scale.

17. Find the angle at which the light leaves the water-air interface.

Use the following information to answer the next question.

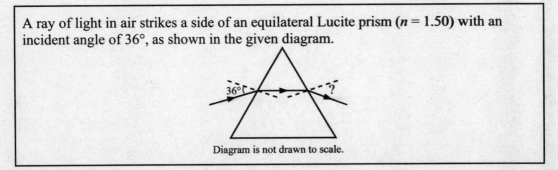

A ray of light in air strikes a side of an equilateral Lucite prism ($n = 1.50$) with an incident angle of 36°, as shown in the given diagram.

Diagram is not drawn to scale.

18. Find the angle at which the light leaves the prism back into the air.

Use the following information to answer the next question.

A ray of light in air strikes a Lucite prism (*n* = 1.50) at 50°, as shown in the given diagram.

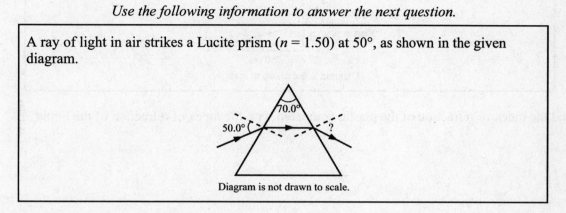

Diagram is not drawn to scale.

19. Find the angle at which the light leaves the prism back into the air.

Use the following information to answer the next question.

A ray of light in air reflects off a mirror onto the surface of a clear liquid, as shown in the given diagram.

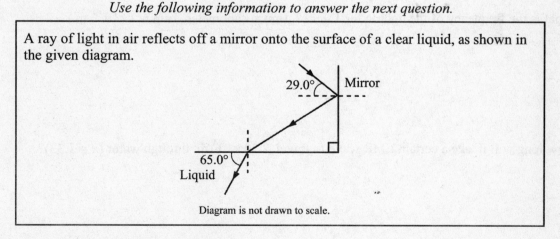

Diagram is not drawn to scale.

20. Determine the liquid's index of refraction.

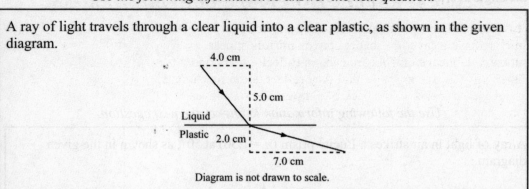

Use the following information to answer the next question.

A ray of light travels through a clear liquid into a clear plastic, as shown in the given diagram.

4.0 cm

5.0 cm

Liquid

Plastic   2.0 cm

7.0 cm

Diagram is not drawn to scale.

21. Find the index of refraction of the plastic compared with the index of refraction of the liquid.

22. What is the frequency of light in diamond ($n = 2.42$) if the frequency in air is 6.20×10^{14} Hz?

23. Monochromatic light of a wavelength of 6.22×10^2 nm enters into Lucite ($n = 1.51$). What is the frequency of the light in the Lucite? (nm = nanometer, $1 \text{nm} = 1 \times 10^{-9}$ m)

24. How long will it take a certain EMR wave to travel 2.50×10^4 m through water ($n = 1.33$)?

25. A certain EMR wave travels 1.0×10^2 m through water. In the same time it took the EMR to travel this distance through water ($n = 1.33$), how far could it have travelled through air?

Lesson 4   REFLECTION FROM CURVED MIRRORS

There are two types of curved mirrors: concave and convex. Concave mirrors have a caved-in shape; convex mirrors appear to bulge outward. Concave mirrors are used in reflector telescopes. Satellite dishes are concave in shape, and they reflect television signals rather than light. The mirror in the back of a drugstore is a convex mirror. Rear-view mirrors on some vehicles may also be convex.

Two types of mirrors:
• Concave
• Convex

CURVED MIRRORS (TERMS)

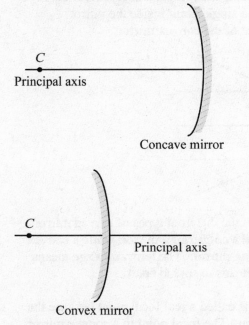

Concave mirror

Principal axis

Convex mirror

Principal axis

When you draw a concave or convex mirror, include the centre of curvature (point C). The centre of curvature is the location that would be the centre of the sphere if the mirror were part of a whole sphere; that is, the centre of the curve. A line drawn through the centre of curvature and through the centre of the mirror is called the principal axis.

Note: Any line drawn through the centre of curvature to the mirror is an axis, but only the line drawn through the centre of curvature to the centre of the mirror is called the principal axis.

Concave mirrors converge light.

NOTES

Rays of light drawn parallel to the principal axis will reflect from the concave mirror in such a way that they will reflect through a single point on the principal axis. This point is called the principal focal point (*f*). The focal point is the midpoint between the centre of curvature and the mirror.

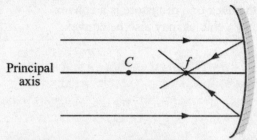

In the same way, rays of light parallel to the principal axis will reflect off a convex mirror as if they came from a single point inside the mirror. This point is the principal focal point of the convex mirror.

Convex mirrors diverge light.

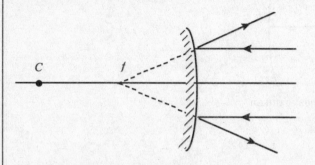

As a result of how light reflects from the different types of curved mirrors, a concave mirror is sometimes called a converging mirror, while a convex mirror is sometimes called a diverging mirror. The term *converge* means to come together; the term *diverge* means to spread apart.

The focal point of a concave mirror is called a real focal point because the light rays really converge at this point. The focal point in a convex mirror is called a virtual focal point because the light only appears to diverge from this point.

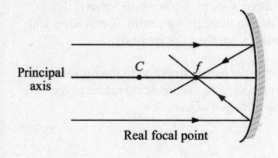

Real focal point

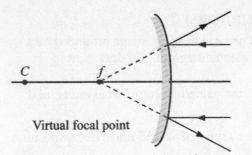

Virtual focal point

The image produced by a mirror can be described as either a real image or a virtual image. A real image is an image that can be projected onto a screen, while a virtual image cannot. Instead, a virtual image appears to be behind the mirror.

The radius of curvature is the distance from the mirror to the centre of curvature, and the focal length is the distance from the mirror to the focal point.

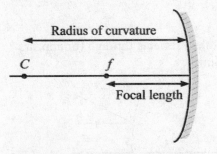

Radius of curvature

Focal length

SPHERICAL ABERRATION

All spherical mirrors have a defect called a spherical aberration. The rays of light parallel to the principal axis that reflect near the edge of the mirror do not reflect through the principal focal point. To correct this problem, the shape of the mirror may be adjusted to a parabolic shape or the size of the mirror is kept relatively small compared with its radius of curvature; here, assume that the mirrors are relatively small spherical mirrors in which the problem is not significant.

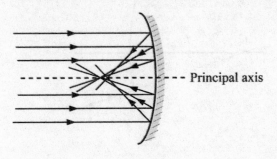

Principal axis

Scale ray diagrams are used to determine the characteristics of an image.

RAY DIAGRAMS (CURVED MIRRORS)

The position, size, and nature (real or virtual) of an image produced by a curved mirror can be found on a scale ray diagram. To draw a scale ray diagram, use the following steps:

1. Draw the mirror, including its principal axis, centre of curvature, and principal focal point.

2. Place a vertical arrow $(\uparrow)$ on the principal axis to illustrate the position and size of the object.

3. Draw two rays from the tip of the object arrow to the mirror. Draw the reflected rays from the mirror. The point at which these reflected rays meet (real image) or appear to diverge from (virtual image) is the position of the image. A vertical arrow can be drawn from the principal axis to the meeting point to represent the position and size of the image.

The two rays that are drawn in step 3 will be selected from three possible rays. The rays selected will depend on the location of the object and the type of mirror used:

• A ray parallel to the principal axis that then reflects through (or appears to diverge from) the principal focal point

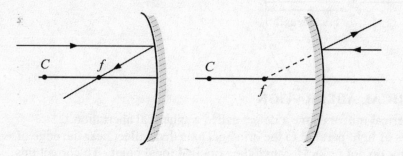

• A ray passing through the centre of curvature and the head of the object that then reflects back along the same path

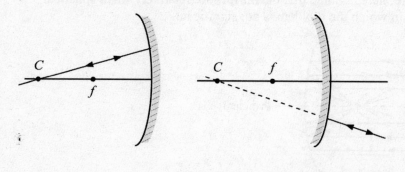

- A ray passing through the focal point that then reflects parallel to the principal axis

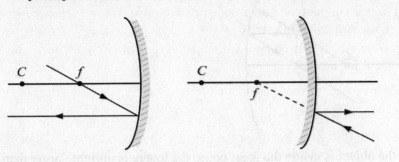

NOTES

The characteristics of images produced by convex mirrors are always the same.

EXAMPLE DIAGRAMS USING CONCAVE MIRRORS

The following ray diagrams depict all possible configurations for a single concave-mirror setup for objects on the principal axis:

When the object is beyond the centre of curvature, the image is inverted, smaller than the object, and real.

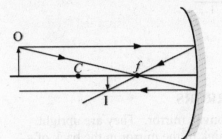

When the object is at the centre of curvature, the image is inverted, the same size as the object, and real.

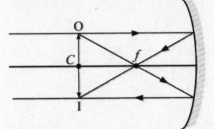

When the object is between the centre of curvature and the focal point, the image is inverted, larger than the object, and real.

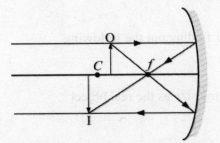

When the object is at the focal point, there is no image.

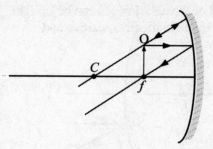

When the object is inside the focal point, the image is upright, larger than the object, and virtual.

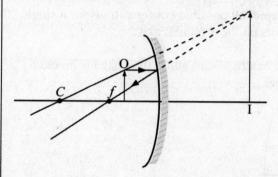

DIAGRAMS USING CONVEX MIRRORS

The images are always the same in a convex mirror. They are upright, smaller than the object, and virtual. Think of the mirror in the back of a drugstore. For a convex mirror, as the object distance increases to infinite, the image distance will approach, but never cross, the virtual focal point.

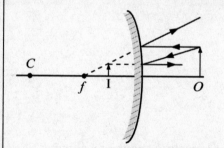

The numerical values produced by ray diagrams may not be as precise as those produced mathematically.

Ray diagrams are best used as an aid for finding out the following characteristics of the image:

• Whether it is upright or inverted

• Whether it is larger, smaller, or the same size as the real object

• Whether it is a real or virtual image

SIGN CONVENTIONS FOR MIRRORS

Both focal points and images can be real or virtual. Images can be upright or inverted. To indicate these opposites mathematically, positive and negative signs are used as follows:

- Real focal points or images are positive (+)

- Virtual focal points or images are negative (–)

- Upright images are positive (+)

- Inverted images are negative (–)

Note that all real images are inverted, and all virtual images are upright.

MATHEMATICS OF CURVED MIRRORS

The position, size, and nature of the image produced by curved mirrors can be described mathematically.

Magnification

Magnification can be described by the following equation:

$$M = \frac{\text{height of image}}{\text{height of object}} = \frac{h_i}{h_o}$$

or

$$= -\frac{\text{distance of image from mirror}}{\text{distance of object from mirror}} = -\frac{d_i}{d_o}$$

so $\dfrac{h_i}{h_o} = -\dfrac{d_i}{d_o}$

A negative magnification indicates that the image is inverted.

Mirrors

Mirrors are described by the following equation:

$$\frac{1}{f} = \frac{1}{d_o} + \frac{1}{d_i}$$

where f = focal length

d_o = object distance from mirror

d_i = image distance from mirror

Real images are always inverted. Virtual images are always upright.

The characteristics of images produced by convex mirrors are always the same.

Example

An object that is 3.00 cm tall is placed 10.0 cm in front of a concave mirror that has a focal length of 3.0 cm. Find the characteristics of the image produced by:

a) Drawing a ray diagram

Solution

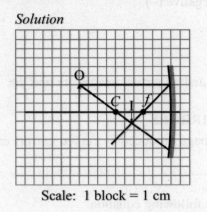

Scale: 1 block = 1 cm

Since the image is inverted and real, $d_i = 4.3$ cm and $h_i = -1.3$ cm.

b) Using the mathematical formulas:

Solution

$$\frac{1}{f} = \frac{1}{d_o} + \frac{1}{d_i}$$

$$\frac{1}{d_i} = \frac{1}{f} - \frac{1}{d_o}$$

$$= \frac{1}{3.0 \text{ cm}} - \frac{1}{10.0 \text{ cm}}$$

$$= \frac{10.0 - 3.0}{30.0 \text{ cm}}$$

$$d_i = \frac{30.0 \text{ cm}}{7.0}$$

$$= 4.3 \text{ cm}$$

$$\frac{h_i}{h_o} = -\frac{d_i}{d_o}$$

$$\frac{h_i}{3.0 \text{ cm}} = \frac{-4.3 \text{ cm}}{10.0 \text{ cm}}$$

$$h_i = -1.3 \text{ cm}$$

The positive value for di indicates that the image is real, and all real images are inverted.

Example

An object that is 2.5 cm tall is placed 9.0 cm in front of a convex mirror that has a focal length of 4.0 cm. Find the characteristics of this image by drawing a ray diagram.

Solution

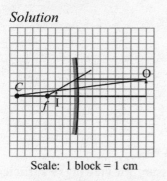

Scale: 1 block = 1 cm

It can be seen from the given diagram that the image is upright and virtual. Therefore, $d_i = -2.8$ cm and $h_i = 0.8$ cm.

Example

An object that is 2.5 cm tall is placed 9.0 cm in front of a convex mirror that has a focal length of 4.0 cm. Find the characteristics of this image by using the mathematical formulas.

Solution

$$\frac{1}{f} = \frac{1}{d_o} + \frac{1}{d_i}$$

$$\frac{1}{d_i} = \frac{1}{f} - \frac{1}{d_o}$$

$$= \frac{1}{-4.0 \text{ cm}} - \frac{1}{9.0 \text{ cm}}$$

$$= \frac{-9.0 - 4.0}{36.0 \text{ cm}}$$

$$= \frac{-13.0}{36.0 \text{ cm}}$$

$$d_i = \frac{36.0 \text{ cm}}{-13.0}$$

$$= -2.8 \text{ cm}$$

$$\frac{h_i}{h_o} = -\frac{d_i}{d_o}$$

$$\frac{h_i}{2.5 \text{ cm}} = \frac{-2.8 \text{ cm}}{9.0 \text{ cm}}$$

$$h_i = 0.78 \text{ cm}$$

The negative value for d_i indicates that the image is virtual, and all virtual images are upright

ACTIVITY #11

Purpose: To determine the focal length and characteristics of images produced by a concave mirror.

Apparatus:
- Concave mirror
- Mirror stand
- Ray box or candle
- White screen
- Ruler

Procedure:
- Set up the concave mirror so the reflective surface is facing the white screen.
- Place the light source along the principal axis (or slightly off-axis if necessary for viewing) a sufficient distance away from the mirror.
- Adjust the mirror or screen until the image from the light source comes into focus (it may be necessary to dim the lights to increase contrast).
- Measure the distance to the image d_i and the distance to the light source (object) d_o.
- Complete the following data table by varying the distance to the light source, do:

d_o (cm)	d_i (cm)	$\dfrac{1}{d_o}$ (cm^{-1})	$\dfrac{1}{d_o}$ (cm^{-1})	f (cm)

- Find the average value of the focal length, f.
- Recall that the centre of curvature C is twice the focal length f. Remember also that for concave mirrors, it is possible to position an object so that no image can be formed. Using this information and your average value of f, complete the chart for the images produced by an object or light source at the following positions:

Position	Size (larger, no change, smaller)	Type (real or virtual)	Orientation (upright or inverted)
Greater than C			
At C			
Between C and f			
At f			
Less than f			

If you were not able to do this activity, use the following data to calculate the average focal length:

d_o (cm)	d_i (cm)	$\dfrac{1}{d_0}$ (cm^{-1})	$\dfrac{1}{d_0}$ (cm^{-1})	f (cm)
15.0	30.2			
20.0	19.8			
25.0	16.8			
30.0	15.3			
35.0	13.8			

1. According to the data, at what position is no image formed by the object? Explain why no image is formed.

2. Why do objects appear to be farther away than they actually are when you look in an external rear-view mirror of some cars? Explain in terms of magnification, image characteristics, and image and object distance.

PRACTICE EXERCISE

Formulas: $M = \dfrac{h_i}{h_o}$ $M = -\dfrac{d_i}{d_o}$ $\dfrac{h_i}{h_o} = -\dfrac{d_i}{d_o}$ $\dfrac{1}{f} = \dfrac{1}{d_o} + \dfrac{1}{d_i}$

1. Complete the following ray diagrams. If an image is produced, state the characteristics of the image. These characteristics include whether the image is real or virtual, upright or inverted, and whether the image is larger than, smaller than, or the same size as the object.

   a)

   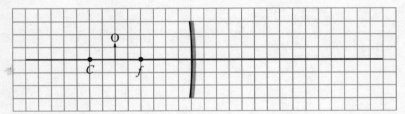

   Characteristics:

   b)

   Characteristics:

   c)

   Characteristics:

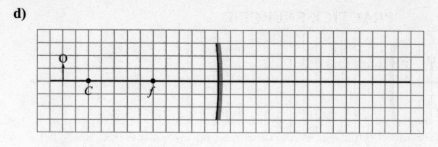

d)

Characteristics:

e)

Characteristics:

f)

Characteristics:

g)

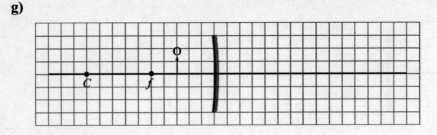

Characteristics:

2. A 5.0 cm tall object is placed 7.0 cm in front of a concave mirror. If a 5.0 cm tall real image is produced, what is the focal length of the mirror?

3. A 3.0 cm tall object is placed 6.0 cm in front of a mirror. If a 1.0 cm tall virtual image is produced, what is the focal length of the mirror? What kind of mirror is used?

4. A 9.0 cm tall object is placed at the focal point of a concave mirror. If the focal length is 5.0 cm, what is the size of the image?

5. A convex mirror produced an image 3.0 cm behind a mirror. If the focal length of this mirror is 5.0 cm, at what distance from the mirror was the object placed?

6. An object is placed 8.0 cm in front of a convex mirror that has a radius of curvature of 8.0 cm. What is the magnification of this object?

7. An object is placed 5.0 cm in front of a concave mirror. The magnification of the object is 2.5. If a real image is produced, what is the radius of curvature of the mirror?

8. A 4.0 cm tall object is placed 8.0 cm in front of a concave mirror. If the real image produced is 6.0 cm tall, what is the focal length of the mirror?

9. A 3.0 cm tall object produces a 2.0 cm tall virtual image. If the image is 2.5 cm behind the mirror, what is the focal length of the mirror? What kind of mirror is used?

10. A 5.0 cm tall object produces an image that is 7.0 cm behind the mirror. If the radius of curvature of this mirror is 10.0 cm, what is the magnification of the object? What kind of mirror is used?

11. A student wishes to place an object in front of a concave mirror to produce an image that is $\frac{1}{2}$ the object's size. If the focal length of the mirror is 5.0 cm, how far from the mirror should the object be placed?

12. An object is placed 2.0 cm beyond the centre of curvature of a concave mirror. If the magnification of this object is –0.30, what is the radius of curvature of this mirror?

Lesson 5   LENSES

As with mirrors, there are two types of lenses: concave and convex. Any lens that is thinner at the centre than at the edges is a concave lens. These lenses are caved in on one or both sides. Any lens that is thicker at the centre than at the edges is a convex lens. These lenses bulge outward on one or both sides.

A concave lens is called a diverging lens because when light passes through it, the light spreads out. A convex lens is a converging lens because when light passes through it, the light comes together. There are different kinds of concave and convex lenses.

CONCAVE LENSES

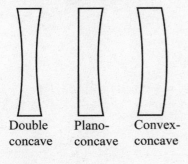

Double concave   Plano- concave   Convex- concave

CONVEX LENSES

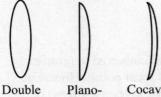

Double convex   Plano- convex   Cocave- convex

This lesson will focus on double-concave and double-convex lenses for simplicity, and they will be referred to as concave and convex lenses, respectively.

LENS TERMS

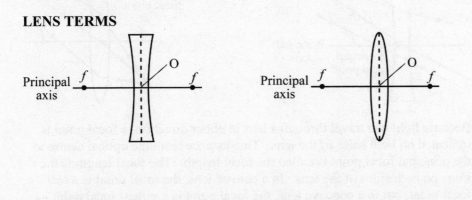

NOTES

The centre of the lens is called the optical centre (O). The line drawn through the optical centre perpendicularly to the surfaces of the lens is called the principal axis. Light rays parallel to the principal axis will be refracted by the lens in such a way that the net result will be the light converging through the principal focal point in a convex lens, or diverging as though coming from the principal focal point in a concave lens.

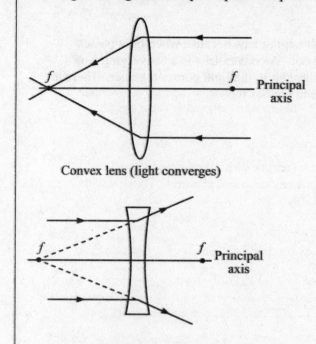

Convex lens (light converges)

Concave lens (light diverges)

Only rays of light parallel to the principal axis will converge to (convex lens) or diverge from (concave lens) the principal focal point. However, parallel rays passing through the lens will converge to (convex lens) or diverge from (concave lens) any point based on the angle of the rays. These points are called focal points, but they are not principal focal points. Consider the following diagrams:

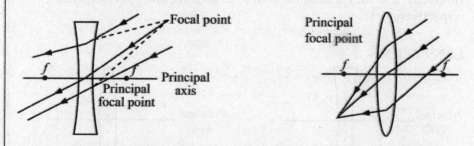

Because light can travel through a lens in either direction, a focal point is indicated on both sides of the lens. The distance from the optical centre to the principal focal point is called the focal length. The focal length is the same on both sides of the lens. In a convex lens, the focal point is a real focal point, but in a concave lens, the focal point is a virtual focal point.

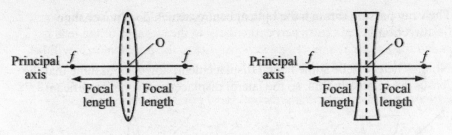

Recall that the focal length in mirrors is half the radius of curvature. In lenses, the material of the lens affects the distance of the focal length from the optical centre. The lower the index of refraction of the material, the longer the focal length. The focal length also depends on the lens's radius of curvature. The greater the radius, the longer the focal length.

RAY DIAGRAMS (LENSES)

The position, size, and nature (real or virtual) of images produced by lenses can be found by a scale ray diagram. To draw a scale ray diagram, use the following steps:

Step 1
Draw the lens, including the principal axis and both principal focal points (points on both sides of lens).

Step 2.
Place a vertical arrow on the principal axis to illustrate the position and size of the object.

A convex lens has a real focal point.

A concave lens has a virtual focal point.

Step 3.
Draw two rays from the tip of the object arrow to the lens.
Draw the refracted rays through the lens. The point at which these refracted rays meet (real image) or appear to diverge from (virtual image) is the position of the image. If a vertical arrow is drawn from the principal axis to the point described, the position and size of the image will be indicated.

The two rays that are drawn in step 3 will be selected from three possible rays. The rays selected will depend on the location of the object and the type of lens used. The following three rays are possible:

1. A ray parallel to the principal axis, refracting through (or appearing to diverge from) the principal focal point

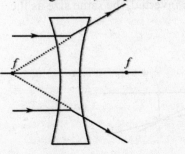
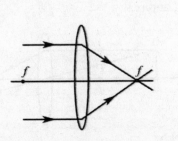

NOTES

2. A ray passing through the optical centre, which does not change direction

Note: There will be some lateral displacement; however, assume that the lenses are relatively thin, so the lateral displacement is not significant.

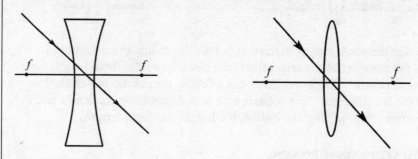

3. A ray passing through the focal point, refracting parallel to the principal axis

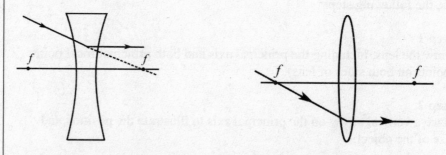

EXAMPLE DIAGRAMS USING CONVEX LENSES

The following diagrams depict all possible configurations for a single convex-lens setup for objects on the principal axis:
When the object is placed at a point greater than 2*f*, the image is inverted, smaller than the object, and real.

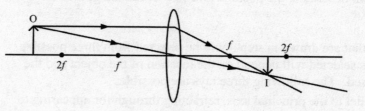

When the object is placed at 2*f*, the image is inverted, the same size as the object, and real.

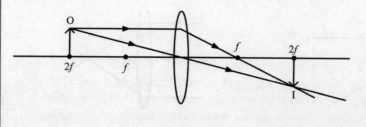

When the object is placed between 2*f* and *f*, the image is inverted, larger than the object, and real.

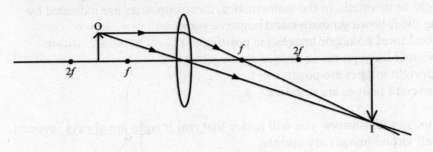

When the object is at *f*, no image is produced.

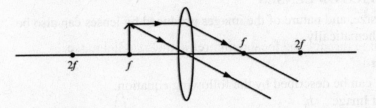

When the object is inside *f*, the image is upright, larger than the object, and virtual.

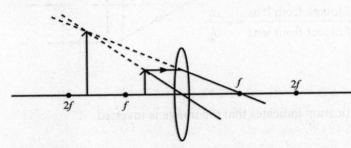

DIAGRAMS USING CONCAVE LENSES

The images are always the same in a concave lens. They are upright, smaller than the object, and virtual. For a concave lens, as the object distance increases to infinite, the image distance will approach, but never cross, the virtual focal point.

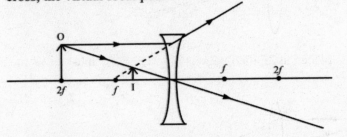

If you compare the images formed by lenses with those formed by mirrors, you will find that the characteristics of images formed by convex lenses are the same as those formed by concave mirrors and the characteristics of images formed by concave lenses are the same as those formed by convex mirrors.

SIGN CONVENTIONS FOR LENSES

The focal points and images can be real or virtual, and the images can be upright or inverted. In the mathematics, these opposites are indicated by using the following positive and negative signs:

1. Real focal points or images are positive (+).
2. Virtual focal points or images are negative (–).
3. Upright images are positive (+).
4. Inverted images are negative (–).

Again, as with mirrors, you will notice that real images are always inverted and all virtual images are upright.

MATHEMATICS OF LENSES

The position, size, and nature of the images produced by lenses can also be described mathematically.

Magnification

Magnification can be described by the following equation:

$$M = \frac{\text{height of image}}{\text{height of object}} = \frac{h_i}{h_o}$$

or

$$= -\frac{\text{distance of image from lens}}{\text{distance of object from lens}} = -\frac{d_i}{d_o}$$

$$\frac{h_i}{h_o} = -\frac{d_i}{d_o}$$

A negative magnification indicates that the image is inverted.

Lenses

Lenses can be described by the following equation:

$$\frac{1}{f} = \frac{1}{d_o} + \frac{1}{d_i}$$

Example

A glowing object that is 2.5 cm tall is placed 15 cm from a convex lens. The lens has a focal length of 7.5 cm. What is the distance of the image from the lens?

Solution

$$\frac{1}{f} = \frac{1}{d_o} + \frac{1}{d_i}$$

$$\frac{1}{d_i} = \frac{1}{f} - \frac{1}{d_o}$$

$$= \frac{1}{7.5 \text{ cm}} - \frac{1}{15 \text{ cm}}$$

$$= \frac{2.0 - 1.0}{15 \text{ cm}}$$

$$d_i = \frac{15 \text{ cm}}{1}$$

$$= 15 \text{ cm}$$

Example

A glowing object that is 2.5 cm tall is placed 15 cm from a convex lens. The lens has a focal length of 7.5 cm. What is the size of the image?

Solution

$$\frac{h_i}{h_o} = -\frac{d_i}{d_o}$$

$$\frac{h_i}{2.5 \text{ cm}} = \frac{-15 \text{ cm}}{15 \text{ cm}}$$

$$h_i = -2.5 \text{ cm}$$

Example

A glowing object that is 2.5 cm tall is placed 15 cm from a convex lens. The lens has a focal length of 7.5 cm.

What are the characteristics of the image?

Solution

The image has the following characteristics:
The image is real since d_i is positive.
The image is inverted since h_i is negative.
The image is the same size since h_i is the same as h_o.

Example

A glowing 4.0 cm tall object is placed 9.0 cm from a concave lens. The lens has a focal length of 5.0 cm.

a) What is the distance of the image from the lens?

Solution

$$\frac{1}{f} = \frac{1}{d_o} + \frac{1}{d_i}$$

$$\frac{1}{d_i} = \frac{1}{f} - \frac{1}{d_o}$$

$$= \frac{1}{5.0 \text{ cm}} - \frac{1}{-9.0 \text{ cm}}$$

$$= \frac{-9.0 - 5.0}{-45 \text{ cm}}$$

$$d_i = \frac{45 \text{ cm}}{-14.0}$$

$$= -3.2 \text{ cm}$$

b) What is the size of the image?

Solution

$$\frac{h_i}{h_o} = -\frac{d_i}{d_o}$$

$$\frac{h_i}{4.0 \text{ cm}} = -\frac{-3.2 \text{ cm}}{9.0 \text{ cm}}$$

$$h_i = 1.4 \text{ cm}$$

c) What are the characteristics of the image?

Solution

The image has the following characteristics:
The image is virtual since d_i is negative.
The image is upright since h_i is positive.
The image is smaller since h_i is less than h_o.

ACTIVITY #12

Purpose:

To determine the focal length of a thin lens.

Apparatus:

- An optical bench
- A metre stick and holders
- A screen and a holder
- A candle holder
- A thin lens (convex)
- A candle

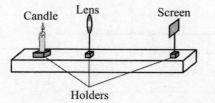

Procedure:

- Set up the apparatus as shown in the given diagram.
- Adjust the position of the candle and screen so that you obtain a sharp image on the screen.
- Using the metre stick, measure the distance between the screen and the lens (d_i).
- Move the candle back, and readjust the position of the screen.
- Measure the distances.
- Repeat this procedure four times.
- Complete the following data table:

d_o (cm)	d_i (cm)	f (cm)

If you were unable to do this activity, use the following data:

d_o (cm)	d_i (cm)	f (cm)
10.0	29.0	
12.0	20.5	
15.0	14.5	
18.0	13.6	
20.0	11.7	

PRACTICE EXERCISE

Formulas:

$$M = \frac{h_i}{h_o} \qquad M = -\frac{d_i}{d_o} \qquad \frac{h_i}{h_o} = -\frac{d_i}{d_o} \qquad \frac{1}{f} = \frac{1}{d_o} + \frac{1}{d_i}$$

Complete the following ray diagrams. If an image is produced, state the characteristics of the image. These characteristics include whether the image is real or virtual, upright or inverted, and whether the image is larger, smaller, or the same size as the object.

1. a)

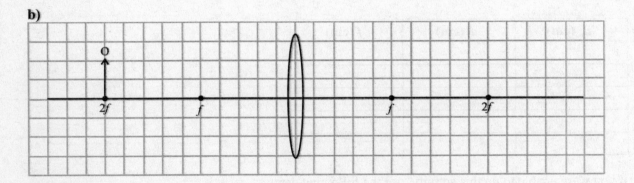

Characteristics:

b)

Characteristics:

c)

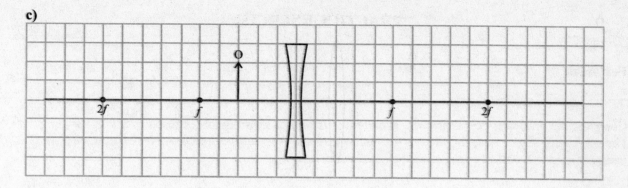

Characteristics:

d)

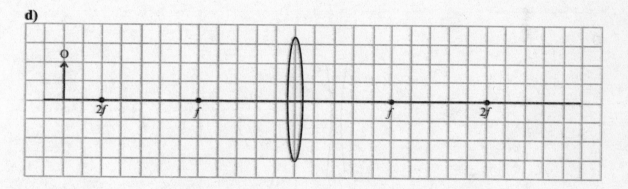

Characteristics:

e)

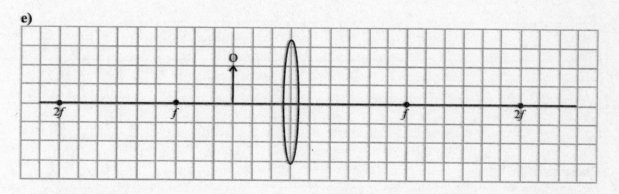

Characteristics:

f)

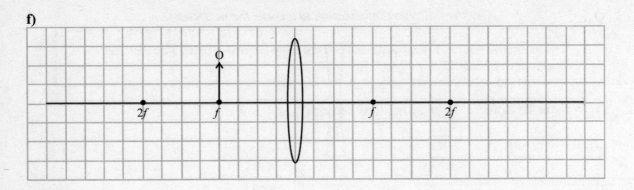

Characteristics:

g)

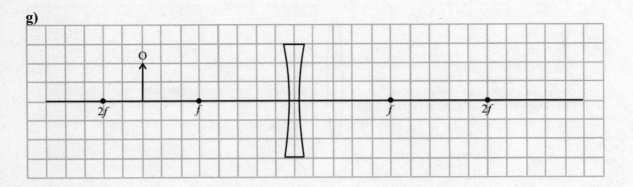

Characteristics:

Use the following information to answer the next question.

> A glowing 6.0 cm tall object is placed 9.0 cm from a convex lens. The lens has a focal length of 8.0 cm.

2. a) What is the distance of the image from the lens?

b) What is the size of the image?

c) What are the characteristics of the image?

Use the following information to answer the next question.

> A glowing 5.0 cm tall object is placed 4.5 cm from a concave lens. The lens has a focal length of 4.5 cm.

3. a) What is the distance of the image from the lens?

b) What is the size of the image?

c) What are the characteristics of the image?

4. A glowing 3.0 cm tall object is placed 6.0 cm from a concave lens. If a virtual image is produced that is 1.0 cm tall, what is the focal length of the lens?

5. A glowing 2.0 cm tall object is placed 5.0 cm from a lens. If a virtual image is produced that is 4.0 cm tall, what is the focal length of the lens? What kind of lens is used?

6. A glowing 8.0 cm tall object is placed 11.0 cm in front of a convex lens. If the focal length is 5.5 cm, what is the magnification of the object?

7. A concave lens produces an image that is 2.5 cm from the lens. If the focal length of this lens is 6.0 cm, at what distance from the lens is the object?

8. A glowing object is 8.0 cm from a concave lens that has a focal length of 4.0 cm. What is the magnification of this object?

9. A glowing object is 7.0 cm from a convex lens. If a real image is produced that is 2.0 times larger than the object, what is the focal length of the lens?

10. A glowing 4.0 cm tall object is 9.0 cm from a convex lens. If the real image produced is 6.0 cm tall, what is the focal length of the lens?

11. A glowing 3.0 cm tall object is 7.0 cm from a convex lens. If the virtual image produced is 6.0 cm tall, what is the focal length of the lens?

12. A glowing 3.0 cm tall object produces a virtual image 2.0 cm tall. If the image is 3.0 cm from the lens, what is the focal length of the lens? What kind of lens is used?

13. A glowing 6.0 cm tall object produces a virtual image 6.0 cm from the lens. If the focal length of the lens is 4.0 cm, what is the magnification of the object? What kind of lens is used?

14. A student wishes to place a glowing object at a distance from a convex lens to produce an image $\frac{1}{3}$ the size of the object. If the focal length of the lens is 6.0 cm, how far from the lens should the object be placed?

15. A compound microscope has two convex lenses that are 10.0 cm apart: the objective lens ($f = 1.6$ cm) and the eyepiece ($f = 3.0$ cm). If the object being studied is 1.5 cm tall and is placed 2.0 cm from the objective lens, what is the magnification produced by this instrument?

Lesson 6   THE WAVE NATURE OF LIGHT

In the seventeenth century, there was debate in the scientific community about the nature of light. Light is a form of energy, and energy can be transmitted by means of particles or by means of waves. Sir Isaac Newton believed that light travelled by particles, while Christiaan Huygens believed that it travelled as waves.

During the first half of the nineteenth century, the following developments supported the wave theory:

• Young's double-slit experiment

• The discovery of Poisson's spot

• The measurement of the speed of light in water

• Polarization

DIFFRACTION

Diffraction and wave interference are fundamental properties of waves. Neither diffraction nor wave interference can be explained using the particle model. Particles do not diffract or show constructive or destructive interference.

Diffraction is a phenomenon in which the energy bends (or spreads out) as it passes through a small opening or when it moves past an obstacle. Diffraction is a fundamental property of waves. Particles do not diffract. Therefore, if it could be shown that light diffracts, that would be conclusive evidence that light travels as a wave.

From studies of water waves in ripple tanks, it is known that the extent of the diffraction (bending or spreading) depends on the wavelength and the width of the opening. In fact, it depends on the following ratio of the two:

$$\frac{\text{wavelength}}{\text{width}} \text{ or } \frac{\lambda}{w}$$

The longer the wavelength is, the greater the diffraction; the smaller the opening is, the greater the diffraction.

Light has a wavelength in the order of 10^{-7} m, which is a very small wavelength. You have to use a very small opening, or slit, in order to observe significant diffraction.

INTERFERENCE

Wave interference is another fundamental property of waves. Particles do not interfere constructively or destructively. Consider the following types of wave interference:

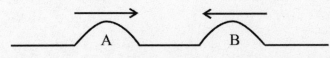

Diffraction: the spreading out of the wave as it passes through a small opening or around an obstacle.

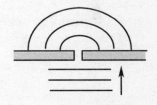

The symbol for wavelength is λ.

NOTES

Two wave crests travel through a rope (or water) toward each other.

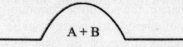

When the pulses meet, they superimpose. This means that their amplitudes combine together when they meet. This is constructive interference.

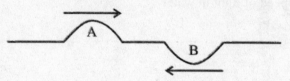

The pulses then pass through each other.

A wave crest and a wave trough travel through a rope toward each other.

$$A + B$$

If the crest and trough have the same amplitude, they cancel out each other's amplitudes at that location. In other words, the amplitude of the trough subtracts from the amplitude of the crest when they meet. This is destructive interference.

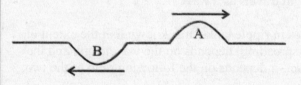

The pulses then pass through each other.

In general, when a crest from one source meets a crest from another source, their energies combine to displace the medium (the energies add together). When one trough meets another trough, the same thing happens. This is constructive interference.

When a crest and trough meet, their energies combine to work against each other and they cancel each other out. In this case, the energies of the crest and trough pass through each other, affecting each other only where they meet. This is destructive interference.

Particles do not behave like this. In water, two point sources for waves will produce an interference pattern as shown in the following diagram of water waves in a ripple tank:

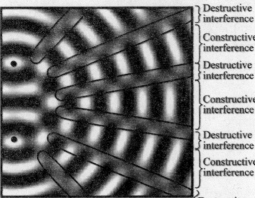

Destructive interference
Constructive interference
Destructive interference
Constructive interference
Destructive interference
Constructive interference
Destructive interference

Destructive interference

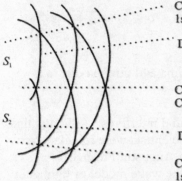

S_1

S_2

Constructive interference
1st order maximum

Destructive interference

Constructive interference
Central maximum

Destructive interference

Constructive interference
1st order maximum

If this ripple tank had glass sides and you could look into the glass side at the right of the given picture, you would see the ends of these lines.

① Constructive interference (1st order maximum)

② Destructive interference

③ Constructive interference (central maximum)

④ Destructive interference

⑤ Constructive interference (1st order maximum)

This is a diffraction pattern. The maxima (1, 3, 5) and minima (2, 4) occur in alternating patterns.

Thomas Young applied the concept of the diffraction pattern to light. In 1803, he demonstrated the diffraction of light and showed how light interferes both constructively and destructively. Young's experiment consisted of the following procedure:

1. He blackened a glass slide and put two very narrow scratches (S_1 and S_2) on the slide.

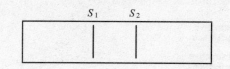

2. He passed monochromatic light through these scratches.

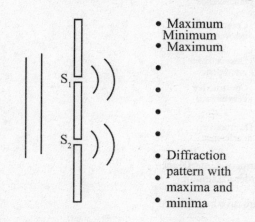

- Maximum
  Minimum
- Maximum

-
-
-
-
- Diffraction
  pattern with
  maxima and
  minima

3. From this setup, Young observed the maxima and minima due to a diffraction pattern on a screen.

Young demonstrated that light both diffracts and interferes. Although this is evidence that light travels as waves, some scientists were reluctant to accept the wave nature of light. The works of Augustin Fresnel, Siméon Poisson, and François Arago helped the wave model of light gain prominence.

POISSON'S SPOT

In 1818, Fresnel wrote a paper about the diffraction of light using the wave model. After reading the paper, Poisson argued that if light travelled as a wave, then the shadow of a sphere illuminated by monochromatic light should have a bright spot at the centre.

Poisson did not support the wave model. He argued that it was ridiculous to believe that an object's shadow could have a bright spot, as predicted by the wave model of light.

However, Arago agreed with Poisson's prediction. Arago tested Poisson's prediction and experimentally demonstrated the existence of this bright spot. He concluded that when light travels around spherical or circular objects, the centre of the shadow is an equal distance from all points on the circumference of the object (that is, the path difference is zero). Therefore, light waves should reach the centre of the shadow from all around the circumference in phase, resulting in constructive interference (a maxima). This spot is known as Poisson's spot or Arago's spot.

This dialogue among the three scientists is an example of how the scientific model helps build and support scientific theory.

MATHEMATICS OF DIFFRACTION

To understand the mathematics of wave diffraction, consider the following diagrams. They will explain how the mathematics was derived.

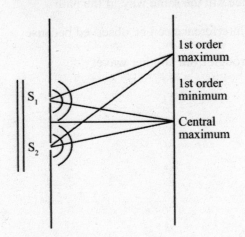

Note that the central maximum is the same distance from both sources (path difference = 0). The first order maximum is 1λ closer to one source than the other.

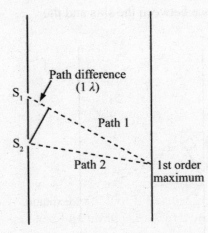

To obtain the nth order maximum, the path difference will be $n\lambda$, in which n is a whole number.

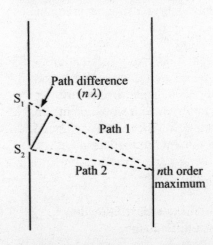

When the path difference is $n\lambda$, a maximum is observed.

Any time the path difference is a whole number of wavelengths, constructive interference (a maximum) can be observed. This is because a crest from one wave meets with a crest from the other wave, setting the conditions for constructive interference. In the same way, if the path difference is $\left(n - \dfrac{1}{2}\right)\lambda$, destructive interference can be observed because a crest from one wave meets with a trough from another wave.

When the path difference is $\left(n - \dfrac{1}{2}\right)\lambda$, a minimum is observed.

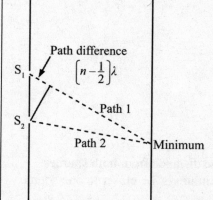

The distance between slits is d. The distance between the slits and the screen is l.

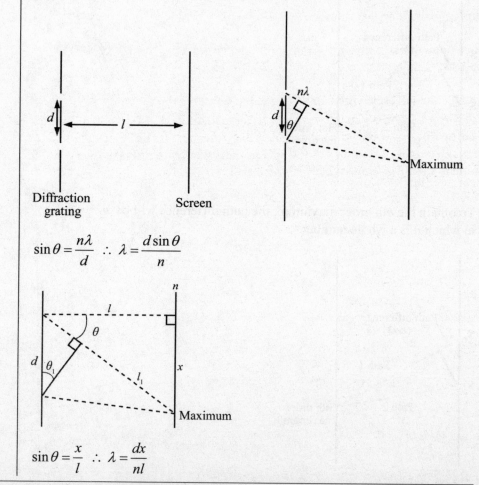

$$\sin\theta = \frac{n\lambda}{d} \quad \therefore \quad \lambda = \frac{d\sin\theta}{n}$$

$$\sin\theta = \frac{x}{l} \quad \therefore \quad \lambda = \frac{dx}{nl}$$

In these equations, x represents the distance between the fringes in the interference pattern.

Visible light has a range of 7.0×10^{-7} m to 4.0×10^{-7} m.

```
2nd order maximum
2nd order minimum
1st order maximum
1st order minimum
Central maximum
```

In deriving these equations, it is assumed that d is very small in comparison with l. It is also assumed that $\sin\theta = \dfrac{x}{l}$; however, in reality, $\tan\theta = \dfrac{x}{l}$. For small angles, $\sin\theta = \tan\theta$; therefore, $\sin\theta = \dfrac{x}{l}$ for small angles only. Because of this, the equation $\lambda = \dfrac{dx}{nl}$ is limited to problems involving small angles as well.

Many spectrometers use diffracting gratings (many closely spaced parallel slits) rather than prisms to disperse light into colour.

Young calculated the wavelength of visible light to be in the range of 7×10^{-7} m to 4×10^{-7} m. Even though Young had demonstrated that light has properties of waves (diffraction and interference) and had calculated the wavelengths of various colours of light, his work was not taken very seriously by the scientific establishment until years later.

ACTIVITY #13

Purpose:

To determine the wavelength of a light source using a diffraction grating.

Apparatus:

• Diffraction grating of known grating

• Laser light source

• Ring stand and clamp

• Screen

• Metre stick

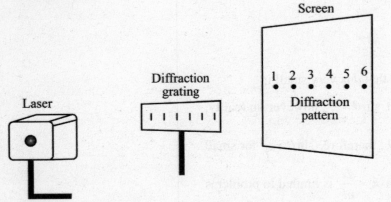

Procedure:

• Set up the apparatus as shown in the given diagram.

• Adjust the level of the grating so that the laser passes through it.

• Adjust the direction of the laser beam so that it strikes both the grating and the screen at 90°.

• Collect the following data:

Grating (lines/m): _____

Distance between the grating and screen: _____

Distance between first order maxima: _____

Central maximum

1st order maxima

Questions:

1. Using the collected data, calculate the wavelength of the laser light source.

212

2. If you use a helium-neon (red-coloured) laser, the wavelength will be 632.8 nm. What is the percent error in your calculating value?

If you were not able to do this activity, use the following data:
- Grating (lines/m): 900 grooves/mm
- Distance between the grating and screen: 0.85 m
- Distance between first order maxima: 0.96 m

ACTIVITY #14:

Background:

The equation $\lambda = \dfrac{dx}{nl}$ can be expressed as $x = \dfrac{n\lambda l}{d}$. This equation uses the following variables:
- x = interference pattern (distance between maxima and minima)
- λ = wavelength
- l = distance between grating and screen
- d = distance between grooves
- n = number of maxima (minima)

The values of λ, d, and l are all manipulated variables. The value of x is always a responding variable. That is, it cannot be changed without first changing one of λ, d, or l.

Purpose:
To observe what happens to x (pattern) when d is changed and when l is changed.

Apparatus:
- 1 200 grooves/mm grating
- 900 grooves/mm grating
- 600 grooves/mm grating
- Laser light source
- Ring stand and clamp
- Screen
- Metre stick

Procedure A:

The equation $x = \dfrac{n\lambda l}{d}$ shows that $x \propto \dfrac{1}{d}$ (x is inversely proportional to d).

- Set up the apparatus as shown in Activity #13.
- Measure and record the distance between the first order maxima at any distance (l) you choose, using the 1 200 grooves/mm grating.

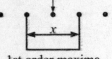

Central maximum

x

1st order maxima

- Repeat step 2 by changing the grating to the 900 grooves/mm grating and the 600 grooves/mm grating. Measure and record the distance between the first order maxima for each grating.
- Record your observations using the following data table:

Grating (grooves/mm)	$d\left(d = \dfrac{1}{\text{grating}}\right)$ (m)	x (m)
1 200		
900		
600		

Question:

1. Do the data verify that $x \propto \dfrac{l}{d}$?

Procedure B:

The equation $x = \dfrac{n\lambda l}{d}$ also shows that $x \propto l$ (x is directly proportional to l).

- Use one of the gratings in the apparatus (you will not change it this time).
- Measure the distance between the first order maxima at any distance (l) you choose.
- Change the distance between the grating and screen, l, to the value of $\dfrac{3}{4}l$. Measure the distance between the first order maxima.

- Repeat step 3 again by changing l to the value of $\frac{1}{2}l$. Measure the distance between the first order maxima. Record this in the following data table:

Distance between Grating and Screen in Terms of l	Actual Distance between Grating and Screen (m)	x (m)
l		
$\frac{3}{4}l$		
$\frac{1}{2}l$		

Question:
1. Do the data verify that $x \propto l$?

If you were unable to do this activity, use the following data:

Grating (grooves/mm)	d (m)	x (m)
1 200		0.92
900		0.60
600		0.45

Distance between Grating and Screen in Terms of l	Actual Distance between Grating and Screen (m)	x (m)
L	1.00	1.14
$\frac{3}{4}l$	0.75	0.84
$\frac{1}{2}l$	0.50	0.58

NOTES

Example

Calculate the angle of deviation of the second order maximum produced by directing monochromatic light $\left(\lambda = 4.30 \times 10^{-7} \text{ m}\right)$ through a diffraction grating ruled with 2.00×10^5 lines/m.

Solution

Change 2.00×10^5 lines/m to d.

$$\frac{2.00 \times 10^5 \text{ lines}}{1 \text{ m}} = \frac{1 \text{ line}}{d}$$

$$d = 5.00 \times 10^{-6} \text{ m}$$

$$\sin \theta = \frac{n\lambda}{d} = \frac{2\left(4.30 \times 10^{-7} \text{ m}\right)}{5.00 \times 10^{-6} \text{ m}}$$

$$= 0.172$$

$$\theta = 9.90°$$

Example

Light passes through a pair of slits 1.28×10^{-5} m apart. The maxima are 4.11×10^{-2} m apart, and the screen is 1.00 m from the slits. What is the wavelength of the light?

nm = nanometre
$1.00 \text{ nm} = 1.00 \times 10^{-9} \text{ m}$

Solution

$$\lambda = \frac{dx}{nl}$$

$$= \frac{\left(1.28 \times 10^{-5} \text{ m}\right)\left(4.11 \times 10^{-2} \text{ m}\right)}{(1)(1.00 \text{ m})}$$

$$= 5.26 \times 10^{-7} \text{ m}$$

Example

A student performing a diffraction experiment using light with a wavelength of 6.00×10^2 nm found that the distance between the first and fourth dark bands was 0.120 m on a screen placed 1.40 m away. What was the diffraction grating ruling?

Solution

$$\lambda = \frac{dx}{nl}$$

$$d = \frac{n\lambda l}{x}$$

$$= \frac{(3)\left(6.00 \times 10^{-7} \text{ m}\right)(1.40 \text{ m})}{(0.120 \text{ m})}$$

$$= 2.10 \times 10^{-5} \text{ m}$$

$$\frac{1 \text{ line}}{\left(2.10 \times 10^{-5} \text{ m}\right)} = \frac{x \text{ lines}}{1 \text{ m}}$$

$$x = 4.76 \times 10^4 \text{ lines/m}$$

PRACTICE EXERCISES

Formulas: $\lambda = \dfrac{d \sin \theta}{n}$ $\qquad$ $\lambda = \dfrac{dx}{nl}$ $\qquad$ $1nm = 1 \times 10^{-9}$ m

1. Calculate the angle of deviation of the first order maximum produced by directing monochromatic light $\left(\lambda = 4.10 \times 10^2 \text{ nm} \right)$ through a diffraction grating in which the slits are 6.00×10^{-6} m apart.

2. If the third order maximum is observed to be deviated 24.0° from the central maximum when a monochromatic light of wavelength 6.30×10^2 nm is used, how far apart are the slits of the diffraction grating that was used?

3. If the second order minimum occurs at an angle of deviation of 16.0° when light with a wavelength of 5.30×10^2 nm is used, how many lines per metre does the diffraction grating have?

4. Calculate the wavelength of monochromatic light used in a diffraction experiment if the first order maximum occurs at an angle of deviation of 26.0° when a diffraction grating ruled with 1.00×10^6 lines/m is used.

5. Monochromatic light is directed at a diffraction grating ruled with 5.00×10^4 lines/m. The maxima on a screen 1.50 m away are 3.11×10^{-2} m apart. What is the wavelength of the light?

6. A student used light with a wavelength of 5.10×10^2 nm in a diffraction experiment. The student found that the distance between the second order minimum and the central maximum was 1.02×10^{-1} m on a screen 1.00 m away from the grating. What was the separation between the slits on the grating?

7. A diffraction grating has 5.00×10^5 lines/m. How many orders of maxima can be observed if the grating is illuminated with monochromatic light with a wavelength of 5.80×10^{-7} m?

8. White light contains wavelengths from 4.00×10^{-7} m to 7.00×10^{-7} m. This white light is directed on a diffraction grating ruled with 5.50×10^4 lines/m. How wide is the first order spectrum on a screen that is 1.25 m away from the grating?

9. Monochromatic light with a frequency of 6.50×10^{14} Hz is directed through a diffraction grating ruled with 4.00×10^4 lines/m. An interference pattern is produced on a screen 1.10 m from the grating. How far is the first order maximum from the central maximum?

10. Monochromatic light with a frequency of 5.50×10^{14} Hz is directed through a diffraction grating ruled with 6.00×10^3 lines/m. What is the distance between the third bright band and the fifth dark band of the interference pattern formed on a screen 2.50 m from the grating?

11. A diffraction grating with lines 0.030 mm apart produces an interference pattern on a screen 1.00 m away. If the maxima are 1.7 cm apart, what is the frequency of the light used?

12. A student used a diffraction grating ruled with 6.20×10^4 lines/m to measure the frequency of a monochromatic light. If the nodal lines are 0.0 522 m apart at a distance of 1.50 m from the grating, what is the frequency of the light used?

13. If the diffraction grating in question 12 is changed to 9.30×10^4 lines/m and all other variables remain unchanged, determine the distance between nodal lines.

14. If the distance between the grating and the screen is increased to a distance of 3.00 m while all the other variables in question 12 remain unchanged, determine the distance between the nodal lines.

15. If the frequency of the light is changed to $\dfrac{4}{5}$ of its original frequency and all other variables in question 12 remain unchanged, determine the distance between nodal lines.

16. A student produced an interference pattern using microwaves by placing a double-slit grating in front of a microwave generator. If the slits are 5.00 cm apart and the maxima of the pattern are 14.5 cm apart at a distance of 1.50 m from the slits, at what frequency are the microwaves generated?

Lesson 7 POLARIZATION

There is evidence that supports the wave model of light, and there is also evidence that shows that light waves travel by transverse waves rather than by longitudinal waves. Only transverse waves can be polarized; light can be polarized.

Transverse waves vibrate the particles of a medium perpendicularly to the direction of energy flow.

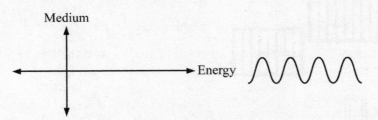

Longitudinal waves vibrate the particles of a medium parallel to the direction of energy flow.

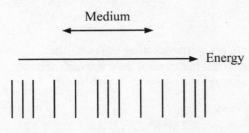

A transverse wave can vibrate in any plane.

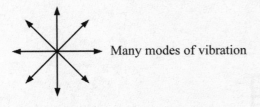

A longitudinal wave has only one mode of vibration (back and forth), so it vibrates only on one plane.

When light waves vibrate in all planes, it is non-polarized light. When non-polarized light shines on a polarizing filter, the light that passes through the filter is polarized. The filter has a polarizing axis, which only allows light to pass through that is vibrating in the same direction as this axis; all other vibrations are absorbed by the filter. If two such filters are used in combination, the light passing through can be made dark and bright by rotating the filters.

notes

If the polarizing axes of both filters are in the same direction, then the light that passes through the first filter will also pass through the second filter.

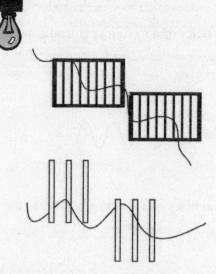

If the polarizing axes of the two filters are perpendicular to each other, then the light that passes through the first filter cannot pass through the second filter.

Light can be polarized.

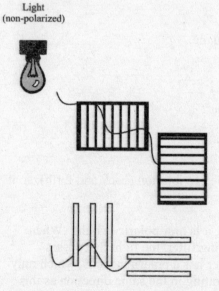

The fact that light can be polarized indicates that light is a transverse wave.

Much of the glare reflected from horizontal surfaces is polarized horizontally. This is why polarized sunglasses are used to reduce glare. The polarization axis of these sunglasses is vertical, which greatly reduces the glare.

Three-dimensional movies also use polarization to give the appearance of depth. Two pictures are taken from slightly different angles. The video is then projected using two projectors. One of these projectors is fitted with a vertical polarizer, and the other projector is fitted with a horizontal polarizer. When you wear polarized glasses to watch the pictures, one of the lenses is vertical and the other is horizontal.

This allows your two eyes to observe the original scene from slightly different angles.

The explanation for polarization was given by Young and Fresnel in 1820. Up until that time, the wave model of light supported the concept that light travelled by longitudinal waves.

Lesson 8   SPEED OF LIGHT

Galileo attempted to measure the speed of light.

The first recorded attempt to measure the speed of light was made by Galileo Galilei in the late sixteenth century. Galileo and his assistant measured the distance across a large field. That night, they each took a shuttered lantern to opposite sides of this field. Galileo would open the shutters on his lantern and start the timing process. When his assistant saw the light from Galileo's lantern, he would then quickly open the shutters on his lantern. Galileo would then stop the timing process when he saw the light from his assistant's lantern. This attempt to measure the speed of light was not successful, however, because light travels very fast and the reaction times of Galileo and his assistant were too great.

However, this attempt does illustrate how speed can be measured. The speed of any object (including light) can be determined by measuring the distance the object travels and the time it takes to travel this distance.

$$v = \frac{d}{t}$$

Rømer observed a moon of Jupiter.

The first successful measurement of the speed of light was performed by Ole Rømer and Christiaan Huygens in 1675. During this period, many scientists were building telescopes and making observations of the stars, planets, and other astrological phenomena. Rømer was interested in the planet Jupiter and one of its moons, Io. When Earth was closest to Jupiter, Rømer observed the period of Io around Jupiter. After he found this period, he could predict when Io would disappear behind Jupiter. His predictions were essentially correct, but Rømer noticed that eclipses became shorter as Earth in its orbit moved closer to Jupiter and longer as Earth in its orbit moved farther from Jupiter. When Earth was closest to Jupiter, eclipses were 11 minutes early. Six months later, when Earth was farthest from Jupiter, eclipses were 11 minutes late. The total discrepancy was 22 minutes. What caused his prediction to be wrong?

Huygens interpreted this as the time required for the light to travel across Earth's orbit.

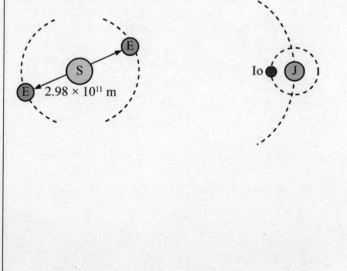

At the end of six months, Earth was approximately 2.98×10^{11} m farther away from Jupiter. This is the distance of Earth's orbit. Huygens interpreted that it takes 22 min for light to travel this distance.

$$v = \frac{d}{t}$$

$$v = \frac{2.98 \times 10^{11}\,\text{m}}{(22\,\text{min})(60\,\text{s/min})}$$

$$= 2.26 \times 10^{8}\ \text{m/s}$$

Huygen's calculation did not produce an accurate measurement of the speed of light. It was the first measurement, however, that showed that light had a finite speed. Astronomers today have determined that the time delay is approximately 16 min, not 22 min.

$$v = \frac{d}{t}$$

$$v = \frac{2.98 \times 10^{11}\ \text{m}}{(16\,\text{min})(60\,\text{s/min})}$$

$$= 3.1 \times 10^{8}\ \text{m/s}$$

$$\text{speed of light} = \frac{\text{extra distance light travels}}{\text{extra time required to travel}}$$

To measure the speed of light, long distances (such as those Rømer and Huygens used) or a method for measuring very short time periods were required. In 1849, Hippolyte Fizeau measured the speed of light using short time periods, and he was able to obtain relatively accurate measurements. Fizeau used rotating, slotted wheels to measure the speed of light.

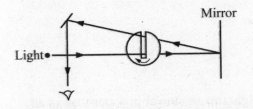

The distance between the slotted wheel and the mirror was measured. He was able to determine how fast the wheel must rotate for the observer to see the returning light. For the light to be observed, the wheel must turn one revolution while the light travels from the wheel to the mirror and back. With the RPM or RPS (revolutions per minute or second) known, the time for the light to pass from the wheel to the mirror and back again could be determined.

e.g., 1 000 RPS

$$\frac{1\,000}{1\ \text{s}} = \frac{1\ \text{rev}}{t}$$

$$t = \frac{1}{1\,000}\ \text{s}$$

Fizeau also measured the speed of light in water.

Therefore, it takes the light 1/1 000 s to travel back and forth between the wheel and mirror.

$$\text{speed of light} = \frac{2 \times d\,(\text{distance between wheel and mirror})}{t\,(\text{time of one revolution})}$$

Fizeau also used this method to measure the speed of light in water. This measurement had great significance. When Fizeau made this measurement in 1850, many still believed that light travelled by particles. The particle supporters believed that light travelled faster in water than in air. This is because the particles bend toward the normal when they speed up.

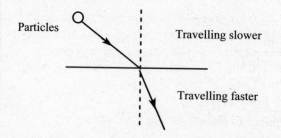

For example, try rolling a marble along a flat surface at an angle to an incline. As the marble rolls down the incline, it speeds up and bends toward the normal.

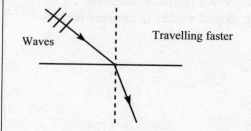

The wave supporters believed that light travels slower in water than in air. This is because waves bend toward the normal when they slow down.

Fizeau measured the speed of light in water and found it to be slower than in air, just as predicted by the wave theory supporters. Most observations of light supported the wave nature of light.

In 1880, A. A. Michelson measured the speed of light using a rotating mirror and a fixed mirror, as shown in the following diagram:

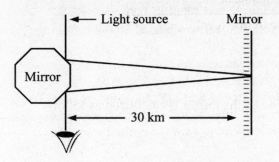

Light reflected from the eight-sided mirror to a fixed mirror 30 km away and returned to the eight-sided mirror. When the eight-sided mirror was rotated, the fixed mirror would receive only flashes of light (a scanning action). This flash would return to the eight-sided mirror, and it would be picked up by the viewing instrument.

In order for the light to be picked up by the viewing instrument, the eight-sided mirror had to rotate $\dfrac{1}{8}, \dfrac{2}{8}, \dfrac{3}{8}, \dfrac{4}{8}$, and so on, of a revolution while the light travelled from the eight-sided mirror to the fixed mirror and back. With the speed of rotation for the eight-sided mirror known, the speed of light could be calculated. The distance was multiplied by 2 because the light had to travel to the fixed mirror and then back to the eight-sided mirror.

$$\text{speed of light} = \frac{\text{distance between wheel and mirror} \times 2}{\text{time of } \dfrac{1}{8} \text{ revolution}}$$

Michelson received a Nobel Prize in physics for this experiment.

Example

The radius of Earth's orbit is 1.49×10^{11} m. Assume Ole Rømer made his initial observation of Jupiter's moon when Earth was in its closest approach to Jupiter and his second observation was six months later. If the light from Jupiter's moon was 22 min "late," what was the speed of light calculated from this information?

Solution

The distance the light travels in the 22 min is twice the radius of Earth's orbit.

$$v = \frac{d}{t}$$
$$= \frac{2.98 \times 10^{11} \text{ m}}{(22 \text{ min})(60 \text{ s/min})}$$
$$= 2.26 \times 10^{8} \text{ m/s}$$

Example

If Michelson used an eight-sided mirror to measure the speed of light and obtained an image when the mirror was rotating 6.10×10^2 RPS, what is the speed of light if the fixed mirror was placed 30.0 km from the rotating mirror?

Solution

The time of $\dfrac{1}{8}$ of a revolution of the mirror is calculated as follows:

$$\frac{6.10 \times 10^2 \, \text{R}}{1 \, \text{s}} = \frac{\frac{1}{8}\text{R}}{t}$$

$$t = 2.05 \times 10^{-4} \, \text{s}$$

$$v = \frac{d}{t}$$

$$= \frac{(2)(30.0 \times 10^3 \, \text{m})}{2.05 \times 10^{-4} \, \text{s}}$$

$$= 2.93 \times 10^8 \, \text{m/s}$$

Example

If light takes 2.5 s to travel to the moon and back, how far away is the moon?

Solution

The time for the light to travel to the moon and back is 2.5 s. It requires 1.25 s to travel to the moon.

$$v = \frac{d}{t}$$

$$d = vt$$

$$= (3.00 \times 10^8 \, \text{m/s})(1.25 \, \text{s})$$

$$= 3.7 \times 10^8 \, \text{m}$$

PRACTICE EXERCISES

Formula: $v = \dfrac{d}{t}$

1. The sun is 1.49×10^{11} m away. How long does it take light from the sun to reach Earth?

2. If an eight-sided mirror makes 4.20×10^2 RPS, how long does it take to make $\dfrac{1}{8}$ of a revolution?

3. If an eight-sided mirror makes 5.40×10^2 RPS, how far does light travel in the time of $\dfrac{1}{8}$ of a revolution?

4. A high school teacher replicated Michelson's experiment using an eight-sided mirror to measure the speed of light. The fixed mirror was placed 35.0 km from the rotating mirror. An image was obtained when the mirror was rotating 3.12×10^4 RPM. What will be the calculated speed of light as a result of this experiment?

5. Michelson's eight-sided mirror and his fixed mirror are 30.0 km apart. What is the minimum angular velocity in revolutions per second that the eight-sided mirror would have to rotate in order for light to be reflected to the observer?

Use the following information to answer the next question.

In a Michelson experiment to determine the speed of light, a mirror rotating 1.20×10^3 RPS was found to produce an image for the observer.

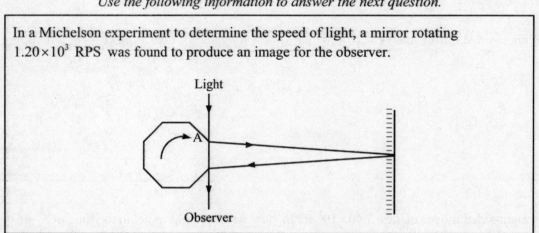

6. Light reflects from side A of the rotating mirror, as shown in the given diagram. If the light from the fixed mirror also reflects to the observer from side A, what is the calculated speed of light if the rotating mirror and fixed mirror are 30.0 km apart?

(**Hint:** The mirror makes $\dfrac{2}{8}$ of a revolution.)

Use the following information to answer the next question.

7. If Michelson had used a six-sided mirror to measure the speed of light and obtained an image when the mirror was rotating 4.88×10^4 RPM, what would be the calculated speed of light if the fixed mirror was placed 30.0 km from the rotating mirror?

8. A spectacular event occurred deep in space. This event was in a direct line with a manned space vehicle and Earth, as shown in the given diagram. If the event was observed from the space vehicle 7.82 s before it was observed on Earth, how far is the space vehicle from Earth?

9. The radius of Earth's orbit is 1.49×10^{11} m. Assuming Rømer made his initial observation of Jupiter's moon when Earth was in its closest approach to Jupiter and his second observation six months later, how "late" should the light from Jupiter's moon have been?

10. It is known that a space vehicle is 6.4×10^8 m from Earth. An event occurs in deep space in a direct line with the vehicle and Earth. This event is observed 2.2 s earlier on the vehicle than on Earth. Using this information, what is the speed of light?

11. Light travels to a distant object and reflects directly back along the same path. How far away is the object if the time the light travels is 1.5×10^4 s?

12. The distance to a planet is measured using EMR. If the time between the transmission of the signal and the reception of the reflected signal is 8.70 s, how far away is the planet?

Lesson 9 DISPERSION OF LIGHT

White light is composed of seven component colours of light: red, orange, yellow, green, blue, indigo, and violet. The dispersion of light is the separation of white light into these components. White light can be separated into its components by means of refraction or diffraction.

ACTIVITY #15:

Purpose: To study the dispersion of white light by means of refraction and diffraction.

Apparatus:
Ray box
Triangular Lucite block
Multi-slit diffraction grating
Sheet of white paper

Procedure: Part 1
1. Place the triangular Lucite block on the sheet of paper.
2. Beam a light ray into the block, as shown in the given diagram.

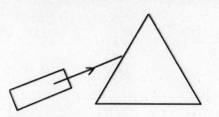

3. Record the order of the colours produced by the spectrum.

Questions:
1. Which colour is refracted the most?

2. Which colour is refracted the least?

Procedure: **Part 2**
1. Place a diffraction grating with its grooves vertical directly in front of the single opened slit of the ray box.
2. Place the sheet of paper 10 to 20 cm in front of the ray box, as indicated in the given diagram.

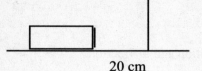

20 cm

Question:
1. Which colour is diffracted the most?

2. Which colour is diffracted the least?

Conclusion:
If you were unable to do this activity, use the following diagrams for your data:

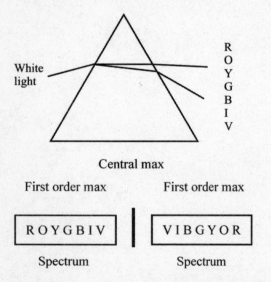

By the end of the nineteenth century, most scientists accepted that light travels as an electromagnetic wave. However, in the late nineteenth century, Heinrich Hertz discovered the photoelectric effect, which could not be explained by the wave model of light. The photoelectric effect can only be explained by assuming that light exists as massless particles of energy called photons.

Some radical ideas were needed to explain the photoelectric effect. However, these explanations have changed not just how scientists view the nature of light, but also the nature of all matter in general.

Lesson 10 WAVE-PARTICLE DUALITY

An ideal incandescent object is called a blackbody. A blackbody is a perfect radiator and absorber of all frequencies of EMR. According to classical physics, the radiation emitted from a blackbody, or any incandescent object, is caused by the oscillation of the atoms and molecules that make up the object. The spectrum analysis of the radiation emitted from a blackbody shows that the intensity of the radiation emitted depends on both the frequency of the radiation and the temperature of the object, as shown in the following graph:

A blackbody is a perfect radiator as well as a perfect absorber of all frequencies.

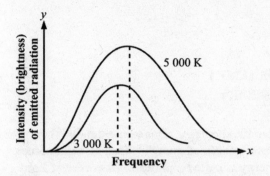

A mathematical relationship between the intensity, frequency, and temperature could not be developed using classical physics. According to classical physics, the spectrum analysis should be described by the following graph:

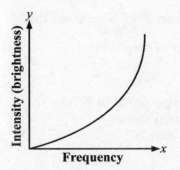

In 1900, Max Planck derived an equation to describe blackbody radiation; in order to derive this equation, however, Planck had to propose a hypothesis that was extremely radical. Planck hypothesized that an oscillator, including vibrating atoms and molecules, is quantized. That is, the oscillator can only have certain values of energy. The energies allowed are given by the following formula:

$$E = nhf$$

where $E =$ energy

$n =$ positive integer

$h =$ Planck's constant $\left(6.63 \times 10^{-34}\,\text{J}\cdot\text{s}\right)$

$f =$ frequency of vibration

Planck's hypothesis marked the beginning of the quantum theory.

Planck's hypothesis was the beginning of quantum theory.

However, it should be noted that Planck's hypothesis seemed too radical at the time and was not generally accepted—not even by Planck himself. This hypothesis was similar to saying that a swinging pendulum could have only certain energies and could increase in height only in steps, rather than through a smooth arc.

In 1905, Albert Einstein used Planck's hypothesis to include light energy. Einstein explained that the energy in light was not continuous but quantized. The energy of a quantum depended on the frequency of the light. A quantum of light energy is now called a photon.

$$E = hf \quad \text{or} \quad E = \frac{hc}{\lambda}$$

where E = energy of photon

h = Planck's constant

f = frequency of the light (EMR)

λ = wavelength of light (EMR)

Planck introduced the idea of quantized energy. Einstein extended this concept to include light energy as a quantized energy. That is, light comes in bundles. A bundle of light energy is called a photon. However, if light energy is quantized, so is the entire EMR spectrum. Therefore, the various regions of the electromagnetic spectrum can be classified according to their photon energies.

The formula $E = hf$ indicates that the higher the frequency of the EMR, the greater the energy of the photon. The formula $E = \frac{hc}{\lambda}$ indicates that the longer the wavelength, the lower the energy of the photon.

Example

A 25 g mass vibrates at the end of a vertical spring ($k = 0.11$ N/m). What is the difference between the allowed energy values? (That is, what is the energy of the spring's quantum?)

Solution

$$T = 2\pi\sqrt{\frac{m}{k}} = 2\pi\sqrt{\frac{25 \times 10^{-3} \text{kg}}{0.11 \text{N/m}}}$$

$$= 3.00 \text{ s}$$

$$f = \frac{1}{T} = \frac{1}{3.00 \text{ s}}$$

$$= 0.333 \text{ Hz}$$

$$E = hf$$

$$= (6.63 \times 10^{-34} \text{ J} \cdot \text{s})(0.33 \text{ Hz})$$

$$= 2.2 \times 10^{-34} \text{ J}$$

Note: This is a very small value.

Example

If the mass in example 1 vibrates to a maximum displacement of 1.0 cm, what is the maximum potential energy of the mass?

Solution

$$E_p = \frac{1}{2}kx^2$$
$$= \frac{1}{2}(0.11 \text{ N/m})(1.0 \times 10^{-2} \text{ m})^2$$
$$= 5.5 \times 10^{-6} \text{ J}$$

According to Planck's hypothesis, the energy in this system changes in very small amounts.

Example

An atom vibrates at its natural frequency of 2.32×10^{13} Hz. What is the difference between the allowed energy values? (In other words, what is the energy of the quantum?)

Solution

$$E = hf$$
$$= (6.63 \times 10^{-34} \text{ J} \cdot \text{s})(2.32 \times 10^{13} \text{ Hz})$$
$$= 1.54 \times 10^{-20} \text{ J}$$

At the atomic level, the energy of the quantum is significant and is observed as light (EMR). At the macro level, quantum effects are not observed.

Example 4

What is the energy of a photon that has a frequency of 5.7×10^{14} Hz?

Solution

$$E = hf$$
$$= (6.63 \times 10^{-34} \text{ J} \cdot \text{s})(5.7 \times 10^{14} \text{ Hz})$$
$$= 3.8 \times 10^{-19} \text{ J}$$

A quantum of light energy is now called a photon. The energy of a photon can be calculated if you know the frequency or wavelength of the light.

PRACTICE EXERCISES

Formulas: $E = hf$ $E = \dfrac{hc}{\lambda}$

1. A pendulum swings back and forth with a frequency of 0.100 Hz. What is the difference between the allowed energy values? (That is, what is the energy of the quantum?)

2. If the pendulum in the first problem has a mass of 25 g, what is the minimum allowed change in height for the pendulum?

Use the following information to answer the remaining questions.

Vibrating atoms or molecules will produce energy in the form of EMR (infrared, visible, and ultraviolet light). A quantum of light (EMR) energy is called a photon. Einstein first used the concept of photons to describe light.

3. A helium-neon laser produces light with a frequency of 4.74×10^{14} Hz. What is the energy of a photon produced by this laser?

4. What is the energy of a photon that has a wavelength of 6.00×10^{-7} m?

5. What is the wavelength of a photon that has 1.50 eV of energy?

6. How many photons are emitted from a 1.50×10^{-3} W laser each second if the frequency of the laser light is 4.75×10^{14} Hz?

7. Approximately 5.0% of the electric energy supplied to an incandescent light bulb converts into light energy. Assuming the average wavelength of the photons is 5.5×10^{-7} m, how many photons are emitted each second by a 40.0 W light bulb?

8. A doctor uses a 2.0 W laser $\left(f = 5.8 \times 10^{14} \text{ Hz} \right)$ to perform eye operations. How many photons are emitted by the doctor's laser if it operates for 0.12 s?

9. If a laser $\left(\lambda = 625 \text{ nm} \right)$ emits 2.0×10^{19} photons each second, what is its power?

Lesson 11 PHOTOELECTRIC EFFECT

NOTES

Generally, the term *light* in this section can be read as *EMR*.

Some unexpected observations were made with the photoelectric effect.

Toward the end of the nineteenth century, a number of experiments were performed that showed the emission of electrons from a metal surface when it was illuminated with light. This phenomenon is known as the photoelectric effect. It appears that electrons on the metal could gain enough energy from the light striking the metal surface to become totally free of the metal itself. This seems simple enough. Light was believed to be wavelike. Therefore, electrons could be expected to be emitted as soon as they gained enough energy from the light to free themselves. To follow this through, it would be expected that the brighter the light, the sooner the electron would have enough energy to escape (the brighter the light, the greater the energy of the light). This did not happen. In fact, some very unexpected things happened.

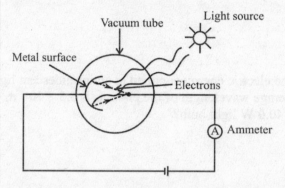

When light was shone on the metal surface (the photoelectric surface), electrons were emitted and travelled across the gap to the anode. From this experiment, the following observations were made:

Electrons are emitted immediately when light hits the photoelectric surface.

• Electrons are emitted immediately when light hits the surface. There is no time for the electrons to build up energy.

• There is a threshold frequency. If the frequency of the light shining on the photoelectric surface is below a certain value, no electrons will be emitted, regardless of how bright the light is. If the frequency of the light is at or above this point, electrons are emitted immediately, even if low-intensity light is used. This certain point is called the threshold frequency.

Every metal has its own characteristic threshold frequency.

• Every metal has its own characteristic threshold frequency.

• If the light is at or above the threshold frequency, the energy of the emitted electrons will increase as the frequency of the light is increased.

• If the light is at or above the threshold frequency and the intensity (brightness) of the light is increased, the current (number of electrons emitted per second) will increase.

The photoelectric effect cannot be explained using the wave model of light.

These are puzzling results. It is not what would have been expected if light were wavelike. If light were wavelike, it would be expected that the intensity (brightness) of the light would determine when the electrons were emitted. However, it was not the intensity that determined when the electrons were emitted, but the frequency.

Einstein gave the explanation of the photoelectric effect, for which he received a Nobel Prize in 1921. Einstein explained the photoelectric effect by extending Planck's quantum hypothesis. Einstein said that light energy was not transferred continuously and evenly as the energy of a wave would be; Einstein suggested that light energy was transferred in bundles.

The energy in this bundle is called a quantum or photon (a tiny particlelike quantum of light energy). Einstein went on to say that the energy of these bundles varied directly with the frequency of the light.

Energy of photon   Frequency of light

$$E \alpha f \quad \text{or } E = hf$$

The variable h represents Planck's constant $(6.63 \times 20^{-34} \ \text{J} \cdot \text{s})$. This is named in honour of Max Planck, who proposed that energy in an atom is not continuous but occurs in quanta (a certain quantity). Einstein extended this idea of quanta to include light as well as atoms.

$$E = hf \quad \text{or} \quad E = \frac{hc}{\lambda}$$

The given equations allow the energy of a photon (light) to be calculated, given either the wavelength or the frequency.

The absorption of a photon by an electron in the metal surface is an all-or-nothing process. One—and only one—photon is absorbed by each electron emitted from the metal. This means that the intensity of light (the number of photons that hit the photoelectric surface) has nothing to do with whether an electron will be emitted. If the energy of the photon is too low, then the electron cannot obtain enough energy to escape, and no electrons are emitted. This explains the threshold frequency.

The electrons require a characteristic amount of energy to escape. If the photon does not provide this energy, the electron does not escape. This explains why the electron is emitted without a time delay. It also explains why the brightness of the light affects the current (the number of electrons emitted). The brighter the light, the more photons emitted. That is, more electrons can absorb photons and escape.

SUMMARY

In a photoelectric investigation, the light will be the manipulated variable. However, there are two ways to vary the light: frequency and intensity. The electrons ejected from the photoelectric surface will be the responding variable. If the frequency of the light is changed, the energy of the ejected electrons is changed. If the intensity of the light is changed, the number of ejected electrons is changed.

Manipulated Variable (Light)	Responding Variable (Electrons)
1. Frequency	1. Energy
2. Intensity (brightness)	2. Number (current)

NOTES (sidebar):

Einstein explained the photoelectric effect by extending Planck's quantum hypothesis.

The word *quantum* is derived from the same word as *quantity*. It means a certain and definite quantity.

A photon is light energy of a certain and definite value.

NOTES

Millikan verified Einstein's explanation of the photoelectric effect.

Robert Andrews Millikan (the same man who found the elementary charge) was able to verify experimentally Einstein's explanation of the photoelectric effect.

THE MATHEMATICS OF THE PHOTOELECTRIC EFFECT

The energy of a photon can be found using the following formulas:

$$E = hf \quad \text{or} \quad E = \frac{hc}{\lambda}$$

The energy of the emitted electron can be found using the following formula:

$$E_{kmax} = hf - W$$

where E_{kmax} = energy of emitted photon

hf = energy of photon

W = work function (the energy required by the electron to escape from the metal)

The work function is the energy required for the electron to escape.

The given equation shows that the energy of the emitted electron is equal to the energy absorbed from the photon minus the energy it uses to escape the metal surface. This equation is an example of the law of conservation of energy.

The energy of the emitted electron can also be calculated using the following formula:

$$E_{kmax} = qV_{stop}$$

where E_{kmax} = energy of emitted electron

q = charge of emitted electron

V_{stop} = voltage required to turn back (stop) the electron from reaching the antenna

The stopping voltage is measured by reversing the polarity of the photoelectric cell and adjusting the voltage until no electron jumps the gap and reaches the antenna.

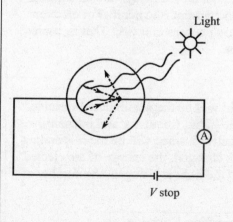

Light

V stop

The energy of the electron is found by calculating the energy required to stop the electron.

The following equation is important for calculating the work function:
$$W = hf_0$$
where W = work function
$\quad h$ = Planck's constant
$\quad f_0$ = threshold frequency

This equation is simply a special form of the equation $E_{kmax} = hf - W$.

If the energy of the photon is simply equal to the work function (the energy required for the electron to escape), then the energy of the emitted electron is zero. This is the situation at the threshold frequency ($W = hf_0$).

You will note that when the energy of the emitted electron is being referred to, the term *maximum energy* (E_{kmax}) is used. Because of the electron's location in (or on) the metal, different electrons require different energies to escape.

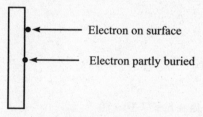

Electron on surface

Electron partly buried

The electron on the surface will require less energy to escape than the partly buried or buried electron. Electrons with a range of energies will escape. Only the energies of the most energetic electrons are calculated.

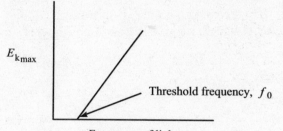

E_{kmax}

Threshold frequency, f_0

Frequency of light

The given graph is obtained by plotting the maximum kinetic energy of the emitted electrons versus the frequency of the light-causing emission. As you can see, there is a minimum frequency (threshold frequency, f_0), and the energy of the electron varies directly with the frequency once the threshold is reached.

The kinetic energy of the emitted electrons can be found by determining the stopping voltage.

Example

What is the energy of a photon that has a wavelength of 4.60×10^{-7} m?

Solution

$$E = \frac{hc}{\lambda}$$

$$= \frac{\left(6.63 \times 10^{-34} \text{ J} \cdot \text{s}\right)\left(3.00 \times 10^{8} \text{ m/s}\right)}{\left(4.60 \times 10^{-7} \text{ m}\right)}$$

$$= 4.32 \times 10^{-19} \text{ J}$$

Example

A photoelectric surface has a work function of 2.00 eV. What is the threshold frequency of this surface?

Solution

$$W = hf_0$$

$$f_0 = \frac{W}{h}$$

$$= \frac{\left(2.00 \text{ eV}\right)\left(1.60 \times 10^{-19} \text{ J/eV}\right)}{6.63 \times 10^{-34} \text{ J} \cdot \text{s}}$$

$$= 4.83 \times 10^{14} \text{ Hz}$$

Example

What is the stopping voltage of an electron that has 7.30×10^{-19} J of kinetic energy?

Solution

$$E_{k_{max}} = qV_{stop}$$

$$V_{stop} = \frac{E_{k_{max}}}{q}$$

$$= \frac{7.30 \times 10^{-19} \text{ J}}{1.60 \times 10^{-19} \text{ C}}$$

$$= 4.56 \text{ V}$$

Example 4

Light with a frequency of 5.00×10^{14} Hz illuminates a photoelectric surface that has a work function of 2.10×10^{-19} J. What is the maximum energy of the emitted electrons?

Solution

$$E_{k_{max}} = hf - W$$

$$= \left(6.63 \times 10^{-34} \text{ J} \cdot \text{s}\right)\left(5.00 \times 10^{14} \text{ Hz}\right) - 2.10 \times 10^{-19} \text{ J}$$

$$= 1.22 \times 10^{-19} \text{ J}$$

ACTIVITY #16

Purpose:
To determine Planck's constant.

Apparatus:
- Sargent-Welch brand self-contained Planck's constant apparatus (includes a photoelectric cell, a variable power supply, and four filters mounted on a filter wheel)
- Mercury lamp
  Note: A mercury light emits light of four prominent wavelengths: 404.6 nm, 435.8 nm, 546.1 nm, and 578.0 nm.
- Microammeter or a very sensitive galvanometer
- Voltmeter

Procedure:
- Turn on the mercury lamp.
- Connect the microammeter and voltmeter to the proper terminals of the Planck's constant apparatus.
- Identify the wavelength transmitted by each of the four filters.
  Note: They will correspond to the wavelengths emitted by the lamp.
- Starting with the filter that transmits the light with the shortest wavelength, move the lamp so that it is in contact with the filter.
- Increase the voltage until the ammeter reads zero.
- Record both the wavelength of the light transmitted by the filter and the voltage required to reduce the current to zero (the stopping voltage).
- Repeat this for the other filters.

Data:

Wavelength (m)	Frequency (Hz)	Stopping Voltage (V)	E_{kmax} (J)
4.05×10^{-7}			
4.36×10^{-7}			
5.46×10^{-7}			
5.78×10^{-7}			

Analysis:

• Plot a graph showing E_{kmax} as a function of frequency.

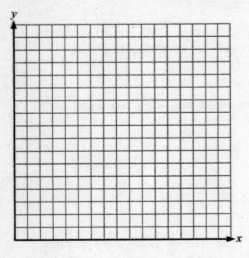

• Using only your graph, determine the following values:

• The threshold frequency

• The work function of the photoelectric surface

• Planck's constant

• The percent error in your measured value for Planck's constant

If you were not able to do this activity, use the following data:

Wavelength (m)	Stopping Voltage (V)
4.05×10^{-7}	1.94V
4.36×10^{-7}	1.75V
5.46×10^{-7}	1.31V
5.78×10^{-7}	1.19V

PRACTICE EXERCISES

Formulas: $E = hf$ $E_{k_{max}} = qV_{stop}$ $E_{k_{max}} = hf - W$

$W = hf_0$ $E = \dfrac{hc}{\lambda}$

1. What is the energy of a photon that has a frequency of 4.50×10^{14} Hz?

2. What is the wavelength of a photon that has 2.1 eV of kinetic energy?

3. Light with a wavelength of 5.30×10^{-7} m illuminates a photoelectric surface that has a work function of 1.70 eV. What is the maximum energy of the emitted electrons?

4. A photoelectric surface has a work function of 3.30×10^{-19} J. What is the threshold frequency of the incident light?

5. What is the energy of a photon that has a wavelength of 4.66×10^{-7} m?

6. A photoelectric surface has a work function of 3.10 eV. What is the maximum wavelength of light that will cause photoelectron emission from this surface?

7. A photoelectric surface has a work function of 2.75 eV. What is the minimum frequency of light needed to cause electrons to be ejected from this surface?

8. Light with a wavelength of 425 nm illuminates a photoelectric surface that has a work function of 2.0 eV. What is the maximum speed of the emitted electrons?

9. Electrons are ejected from a photoelectric surface with maximum energy of 1.20 eV. If the incident light has a wavelength of 4.10×10^2 nm , what is the work function of the surface?

10. A photoelectric surface requires a light of maximum wavelength of 675 nm to cause electron emission. What is the work function of this surface?

11. Electrons are ejected from a photoelectric surface with a maximum speed of 4.20×10^5 m/s. If the work function of this surface is 2.55 eV, what is the wavelength of the incident light?

12. Electrons are emitted from a photoelectric surface with maximum energy of 2.9 eV. If the photons of the incident light have 3.45 eV of energy, what is the minimum frequency of light that can be used to emit the electrons?

13. What is the stopping voltage for an electron that has 5.40×10^{-19} J of kinetic energy?

14. In a photoelectric cell, the minimum voltage required to reduce the current through the cell to zero is 3.0 V. What is the maximum kinetic energy of the electrons emitted from the photoelectric surface in this cell?

15. A photoelectric surface is illuminated with white light ($\lambda = 4.0 \times 10^2$ nm to 7.0×10^2 nm). What is the maximum kinetic energy of the electrons emitted from the photoelectric surface, which has a work function of 2.30 eV?

16. Radiation with a frequency of 7.52×10^{14} Hz illuminates a photoelectric surface in a photoelectric cell. If the work function of this surface is 2.20 eV, what stopping voltage would be required to reduce the current through this cell to zero?

17. In a photoelectric cell, the stopping voltage is 2.00 V. If the voltage applied across this cell is zero, what is the maximum speed of the electrons emitted from the photoelectric surface?

18. What is the wavelength of a 5.7 MeV photon?

Use the following information to answer the next question.

In a photoelectric experiment, a student obtained the data shown.

Frequency of Radiation ($\times 10^{14}$ Hz)	Maximum Kinetic Energy ($\times 10^{-19}$ J)
6.2	2.56
5.3	2.00
4.2	1.31
3.5	0.90
2.9	0.45

19. a) Draw a graph to show the relationship between the frequency of the incident radiation and the maximum kinetic energy of the electrons emitted from the photoelectric surface.

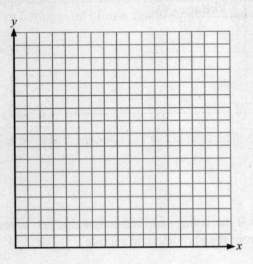

b) Using only your graph, calculate the following values:

i) The threshold frequency of the incident radiation, including error

ii) Planck's constant, including error

20. When radiation with a wavelength of 215 nm illuminates a photoelectric surface in a photoelectric cell, a stopping voltage of 9.11×10^{-1} V is needed to reduce the current through the cell to zero. What is the work function of the surface used in this cell?

Use the following information to answer the next question.

In a photoelectric experiment, a student obtained the data shown.

Frequency of Radiation ($\times 10^{14}$ Hz)	Stopping Voltage (V)
9.9	4.10
7.7	2.95
4.7	1.45
3.2	0.70
2.3	0.15

21. a) Draw a graph that shows the relationship between the frequency of the incident radiation and the stopping voltage.

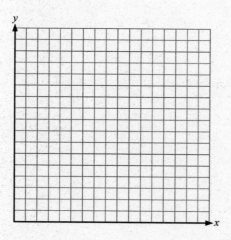

b) Using only your graph, calculate the following values:

i) The threshold frequency of the incident radiation

ii) Planck's constant

Use the following information to answer the next question.

In a photoelectric experiment, a student found that the stopping voltage was 1.40 V when a monochromatic light ($f = 6.00 \times 10^{14}$ Hz) illuminated a certain photoelectric surface and the stopping voltage was 1.10 V when the student illuminated the same surface with a different monochromatic light ($f = 5.20 \times 10^{14}$ Hz). Use these data to calculate the following values:

22. a) Planck's constant

b) The work function of the surface

c) The threshold frequency

Lesson 12 COMPTON EFFECT

The energy of photons can be described by the equations $E = hf$ and $E = \dfrac{hc}{\lambda}$.

Photons are special particles because they do not have a rest mass. However, if they are particles, they should have momentum as well as energy. The Compton experiment demonstrated that photons do have momentum.

In 1923, Arthur Holly Compton performed an experiment in which a beam of X-rays with a known frequency was directed at a graphite crystal. The experiment was similar to photoelectric experiments, but X-rays were used instead of light. As with the photoelectric experiments, electrons were emitted from the graphite surface. However, Compton concentrated his observations on the photons emitted.

Compton observed that the X-rays emitted from the carbon surface were made up of two parts. One part had the same frequency as the incident X-rays, and one part had a lower frequency than the incident X-rays.

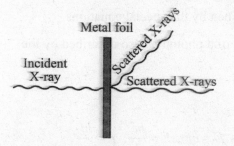

Compton interpreted these observations as the photons having momentum. Remember that the law of conservation of momentum states that the momentum after a collision is equal to the momentum before the collision. When a small object collides with a larger object, the smaller object experiences very little loss in speed; that is, very little momentum or energy is lost. However, when objects of somewhat equal masses collide, there is a significant transfer of momentum and energy.

Using this law of conservation of momentum, Compton concluded that when the incident X-rays collided with the whole atom, the photon lost no momentum or energy, but when the incident X-rays (photons) collided with an electron within the atom, there was a significant transfer of momentum and energy from the photon to the electron. The interpretation of the Compton experiment was that the photon had momentum as well as energy. That is, the photon could be thought of as a particle.

According to classical electromagnetic theory, the X-rays (EMR) will just be reflected by the metal foil; that is, the frequency of the X-rays (EMR) should not change. However, according to the quantum theory, which states that energy in EMR comes in bundles, X-rays (EMR) are made up of photons, and photons have momentum.

NOTES

Graphite crystals can be easily sheared to form extremely thin sheets of pure carbon crystal.

The law of conservation of momentum states that the momentum after a collision is equal to the momentum before the collision.

Compton's experiment demonstrated that photons have momentum.

NOTES

Photons have no rest mass.

Use the formulas $E = hf$, $E = \frac{hc}{\lambda}$, $p = \frac{h}{\lambda}$, and $p = \frac{hf}{c}$ to calculate the energy and momentum of photons.

Use the formulas $E = \frac{1}{2}mv^2$ and $\vec{p} = m\vec{v}$ to calculate the energy and momentum of an object that has rest mass.

The momentum of an object is described as the product of mass and velocity.

$$\vec{p} = m\vec{v}$$

However, a photon has no rest mass. Therefore, the momentum of a photon cannot be described using the formula $\vec{p} = m\vec{v}$. Einstein's mass-energy equivalence equation, $E = mc^2$, can be used to alter the equation as follows:

$$m = \frac{E}{c^2}$$
$$\therefore p = \frac{E}{c^2}v$$

The velocity of a photon is the velocity of light.

$$\therefore p = \frac{E}{c^2}c \text{ or } p = \frac{E}{c}$$

The energy of a photon is described by the equations $E = hf$ or $E = \frac{hc}{\lambda}$.

$$\therefore p = \frac{hf}{c} \text{ or } p = \frac{h}{\lambda}$$

Just as the energy of a photon is described by the special equations $E = hf$ and $E = \frac{hc}{\lambda}$, the momentum of a photon is also described by the special equations $p = \frac{hf}{c}$ and $p = \frac{h}{\lambda}$.

Note that you cannot use the equations $E = hf$, $E = \frac{hc}{\lambda}$, $p = \frac{hf}{c}$, and $p = \frac{h}{\lambda}$, to calculate the energy or momentum of any other particle.

Photons are special particles because they have no rest mass. You will also note that the energy and momentum of a photon is calculated using wave concepts (wavelength and frequency). Knowing the wavelength or frequency of EMR, you can calculate the energy and momentum of a photon.

Using the law of conservation of momentum, $p_{\text{before}} = p_{\text{after}}$, and the law of conservation of energy, $E_{\text{before}} = E_{\text{after}}$, you can calculate the wavelength (λ), frequency, and energy of the scattered photon.

The following equation can be derived from these two conservation laws:

$$\Delta\lambda = \frac{h}{mc}(1 - \cos\theta)$$

where $\Delta\lambda$ = change in the wavelength of the photon
θ = angle of the scattered photon
m = mass of the electron

In part, this theory shows that when an object moves, quantities like momentum and energy change by a factor of $\dfrac{1}{\sqrt{1-\left(\frac{v}{c}\right)^2}}$. You can see that

if v is everyday kinds of speed, then $\dfrac{v}{c}=0$. Therefore, $\dfrac{1}{\sqrt{1-\left(\frac{v}{c}\right)^2}}=1$.

As the speed increases and approaches the speed of light (c), the value of $\dfrac{1}{\sqrt{1-\left(\frac{v}{c}\right)^2}}$ increases.

According to Einstein's special theory of relativity, v can never be larger than c. Also, if v is almost equal to c, the value of $\dfrac{1}{\sqrt{1-\left(\frac{v}{c}\right)^2}}$ is very large.

If relativity is used in the addition of the momenta of the particles in a Compton experiment, it can be assumed that the initial momentum of the electron is zero.

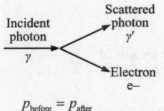

$$p_{\text{before}} = p_{\text{after}}$$
$$p_r + p_{e^-} = p_r' + p_{e^-}'$$

Momentum is a vector quantity; therefore, the directions (angles) have to be considered. To do this, draw a vector diagram (tail to tip).

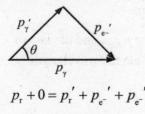

$$p_r + 0 = p_r' + p_{e^-}' + p_{e^-}'$$

To add these vectors, use the cosine law.

$$c^2 = a^2 + b^2 - 2ab\cos\theta$$

$$\left(p_{e^-}{}'\right)^2 = \left(p_r{}'\right)^2 + \left(p_r\right)^2 - 2\left(p_r{}'\right)\left(p_r\right)\cos\theta$$

$$\left[\left(\frac{1}{\sqrt{1-\left(\frac{v}{c}\right)^2}}\right)mv\right]^2 = \left(\frac{h}{\lambda'}\right)^2 + \left(\frac{h}{\lambda}\right)^2 - 2\left(\frac{h}{\lambda'}\right)\left(\frac{h}{\lambda}\right)\cos\theta$$

This is equation 1.

Now, add the energies. Remember, energy is a scalar quantity; therefore, angles are not important.

Use the law of conservation of energy.

$$E_{\text{before}} = E_{\text{after}}$$

$$E_r + E_{e^-} = E_r{}' + E_{e^-}{}'$$

$$\frac{hc}{\lambda} + mc^2 = \frac{hc}{\lambda'} + mc^2\left(\frac{1}{\sqrt{1-\left(\frac{v}{c}\right)^2}}\right)$$

This is equation 2.

Equation 1 (momentum) and equation 2 (energy) are solved simultaneously as follows:

$$\lambda' - \lambda = \frac{h}{mv}(1 - \cos\theta)$$

or

$$\Delta\lambda = \frac{h}{mv}(1 - \cos\theta)$$

Note that the wavelength after the collision in a Compton experiment is always larger than the wavelength before the collision.

Example

Calculate the momentum of a photon with a wavelength of 625 nm.

Solution

$$p = \frac{h}{\lambda}$$
$$= \frac{6.63 \times 10^{-34} \text{ J} \cdot \text{s}}{6.25 \times 10^{-7} \text{ m}}$$
$$= 1.06 \times 10^{-27} \text{ kg} \cdot \text{m/s}$$

Example

Calculate the frequency of EMR for which the photons have a momentum of 2.80×10^{-27} kg·m/s each.

Solution

$$p = \frac{hf}{c}$$
$$f = \frac{pc}{h}$$
$$= \frac{\left(2.80 \times 10^{-27} \text{ kg m/s}\right)\left(3.00 \times 10^8 \text{ m/s}\right)}{6.63 \times 10^{-34} \text{ J s}}$$
$$= 1.27 \times 10^{15} \text{ Hz}$$

Example

Calculate the momentum of a 6.0 MeV proton.

Solution

$$\frac{1 \text{ eV}}{1.60 \times 10^{-19} \text{ J}} = \frac{6.0 \times 10^6 \text{ eV}}{x \text{ J}}$$
$$x = 9.6 \times 10^{-13} \text{ J}$$
$$E_k = \frac{1}{2}mv^2$$
$$v = \sqrt{\frac{2E_k}{m}}$$
$$= \sqrt{\frac{2\left(9.6 \times 10^{-13} \text{ J}\right)}{1.67 \times 10^{-27} \text{ kg}}}$$
$$= 3.4 \times 10^7 \text{ m/s}$$
$$\bar{p} = m\bar{v}$$
$$= \left(1.67 \times 10^{-27} \text{ kg}\right)\left(3.4 \times 10^7 \text{ m/s}\right)$$
$$= 5.7 \times 10^{-20} \text{ kg} \cdot \text{m/s}$$

NOTES

Example

An X-ray with a frequency of 6.00×10^{18} Hz is scattered through an angle of 30.0° in a Compton experiment. What is the wavelength of the scattered X-ray?

Solution

$$c = \lambda f \text{ or } \lambda = \frac{c}{f} = \frac{3.00 \times 10^{8} \text{ m/s}}{6.00 \times 10^{18} \text{ Hz}} = 5.00 \times 10^{-11} \text{ m}$$

$$\Delta \lambda = \frac{h}{mc}(1 - \cos \theta)$$

$$= \frac{\left(6.63 \times 10^{-34} \text{ J} \cdot \text{s}\right)\left(1 - \cos 30.0°\right)}{\left(9.11 \times 10^{-31} \text{ kg}\right)\left(3.00 \times 10^{8} \text{ m/s}\right)}$$

$$= 2.426 \times 10^{-12} \text{ m}\left(1 - 0.866\right)$$

$$= 3.25 \times 10^{-13} \text{ m}$$

$$\Delta \lambda = \lambda' - \lambda$$

$$\lambda' = \Delta \lambda + \lambda$$

$$= 3.25 \times 10^{-13} + 5.00 \times 10^{-11} \text{ m}$$

$$= 5.03 \times 10^{-11} \text{ m}$$

PRACTICE EXERCISES

Formulas: $\quad p = \dfrac{h}{\lambda} \qquad\qquad p = \dfrac{hf}{c} \qquad\qquad \vec{p} = m\vec{v} \qquad\qquad p = \dfrac{E}{c}$

1. Calculate the momentum of a photon with a frequency of 9.65×10^{14} Hz.

2. Calculate the momentum of a photon with a wavelength of 1.25×10^{-10} m.

3. If the momentum of a photon is 7.8×10^{-25} kg·m/s, what is its wavelength?

4. If the energy of a photon is 3.60×10^{-14} J, what is its momentum?

5. If the momentum of a photon is 9.3×10^{-23} kg·m/s, what is its speed?

6. Calculate the momentum of a 4.00 MeV photon.

7. What is the momentum of an electron travelling at $0.110c$?

8. Calculate the momentum of an electron that was accelerated from rest through a potential difference of 2.10×10^3 V.

9. When monochromatic light ($\lambda = 415$ nm) illuminates a photoelectric surface ($W = 3.50 \times 10^{-19}$ J), electrons are emitted.

   a) Calculate the momentum of the incident photon.

   b) Calculate the maximum momentum of the emitted electron.

10. How does the momentum of a photon that has 19.6 eV of kinetic energy compare with the momentum of an alpha particle that has 1.25×10^{-1} eV of kinetic energy?

11. If a photon with a frequency of 2.50×10^{16} Hz collides with an electron at rest and loses 25.0% of its energy, what is the speed of this electron after the collision?

12. An X-ray with a frequency of 3.25×10^{19} Hz is scattered through an angle of 75.0° in a Compton experiment. What is the wavelength of the scattered X-ray?

13. An X-ray with a wavelength of 8.22×10^{-12} is scattered at an angle of 45.0° in a Compton experiment. What is the energy of the scattered photon?

14. A 52.9 keV X-ray is scattered in a Compton experiment. If the scattered photon has a wavelength of 2.40×10^{-11} m, what is the angle of the scattered photon?

15. A 15.0 keV X-ray is scattered in a Compton experiment. If the energy of the scattered photon is 14.8 keV, what is the angle of the scattered photon?

16. A 17.5 keV photon is scattered in a Compton experiment. If the energy of the scattered photon is 17.1 keV, what is the energy of the ejected electron?

PRACTICE QUIZ

Use the following information to answer the next question.

A ray of light is reflected in series from two mirrors (A and B), as shown in the given diagram.

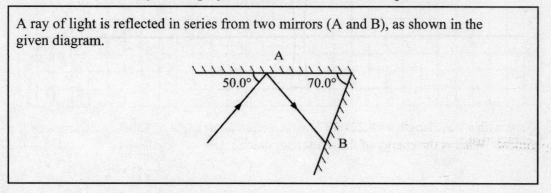

1. What is the angle of reflection from mirror B?

2. A glowing object is 6.00 cm from a convex lens that has a focal length of 4.0 cm. What is the magnification of this object?

3. Complete the following ray diagrams, and state the characteristics of the images.

    a)

    Characteristics:

b)

Characteristics:

4. If light travels 2.00 m through a clear liquid in 8.00×10^{-9} s, what is the index of refraction of the liquid?

5. The speed of light in a clear liquid is 2.66×10^{8} m/s. Calculate the critical angle of this liquid if it has a boundary with air.

6. Calculate the speed of light in diamond ($n = 2.42$).

Use the following information to answer the next question.

Light is incident to a glass-water interface at an angle of 55.0°, as shown in the given diagram.

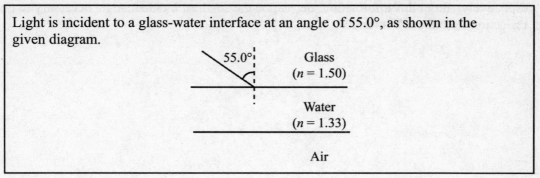

7. Calculate the angle at which the light ray will leave the water-air interface.

8. A glowing object that is 3.0 cm tall is placed 6.0 cm from a concave lens. If a virtual image is produced that is 1.0 cm tall, what is the focal length of the lens?

Use the following information to answer the next question.

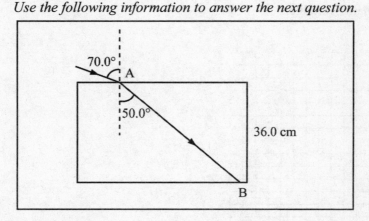

9. A ray of light enters a clear plastic block, as shown in the given diagram. Calculate the time it takes the light to travel along path AB.

10. When light travels from medium X to medium Y, the incident angle and refracted angle are 29° and 42° respectively. From this information, determine the smallest incident angle necessary to obtain total reflection from the XY interface.

Use the following information to answer the next question.

A student was investigating the relationship between the incident angle and the refracted angle. The student recorded the given data.

Incident Angle	Refracted Angle
15.0°	10.5°
30.0°	21.0°
45.0°	30.0°
60.0°	36.0°
75.0°	43.5°

11. a) Draw a graph that shows the relationship between the sine of the responding variable and the sine of the manipulated variable.

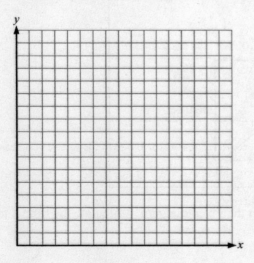

b) Use only your graph to determine the index of refraction of the refracting media, assuming that the incident light was in an air medium.

12. The distance to an object in space was measured by reflecting an EMR signal from this object. If the distance to this object from Earth was found to be 4.80×10^8 m, what is the time between the transmission of the EMR signal and the reception of the reflected signal?

13. What is the period of X-rays that have a wavelength of 5.40×10^{-10} m?

Use the following information to answer the next question.

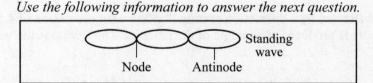

14. A student generated standing microwaves using a microwave generator by reflecting the microwaves directly back to the generator. The distance between the nodes is $\frac{1}{2}\lambda$. If the nodes of this standing wave are 2.1 cm apart, what is the frequency of the waves?

15. Light with a frequency of 4.28×10^{14} Hz is diffracted by a diffraction grating ruled 5.00×10^5 lines/m. On a screen 2.00 m from the grating, the maxima are 7.00×10^{-1} m apart. What is the distance between maxima if the frequency of the light is increased 1.50 times while all other variables remain constant?

16. Calculate the frequency of monochromatic light used in a diffraction experiment if the first order maximum is observed at an angle of deviation of 28.0° when the slits of the diffraction grating are 1.00×10^{-6} m apart.

17. Calculate the wavelength of monochromatic light used in a diffraction experiment if the first order maximum is observed at an angle of deviation of 32.0° when a diffraction grating ruled with 1.10×10^6 lines/m is used.

18. Microwaves are diffracted by a diffraction grating that has a slit separation of 4.50 cm. If the first order maximum is produced at an angle of deviation of 9.60°, what is the wavelength of the microwave?

19. A planet is 6.60×10^{12} m from Earth. How long will it take a radio signal to travel to this planet and back?

20. A student set up standing waves using a microwave generator. If the frequency of the microwaves is 4.60×10^9 Hz, how far apart are the nodes of the standing waves produced?

Use the following information to answer the next question.

Two microwave generators are placed 1.50 m apart. Both of these generators emit signals with a frequency of 1.00×10^9 Hz. A microwave receiver is placed 1.2 m from one of the generators and 0.750 m from the other generator, as shown in the given diagram.

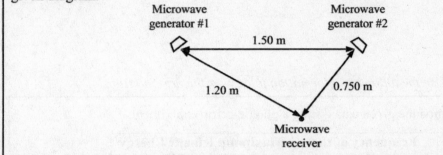

21. a) What is the wavelength of the microwave signal?

b) Will the receiver indicate strong or weak reception? (Clearly show how you arrived at your answer.)

22. Rømer's observations of the moon of Jupiter were originally used by Huygens to calculate the speed of light. However, given that the speed of light is 3.00×10^8 m/s, Rømer's observations could be used to calculate the distance from Earth to the sun. If the time between the predicted and observed eclipses of Jupiter's moon was 22 min, what is the calculated distance from Earth to the sun?

23. How many photons are emitted per second by a 2.0 W helium-neon laser? (The wavelength of light produced by the laser is 633 nm.)

Use the following information to answer the next question.

A student obtained the given data during a photoelectric experiment.

Frequency of the Radiation ($\times 10^{14}$ Hz)	Maximum Kinetic Energy of the Ejected Electrons ($\times 10^{-19}$ J)
7.0	2.0
8.0	3.0
11.0	5.0
14.0	7.0
18.0	10.0

24. a) Draw a graph that shows the relationship between the frequency of the incident radiation and the maximum kinetic energy of the emitted electrons.

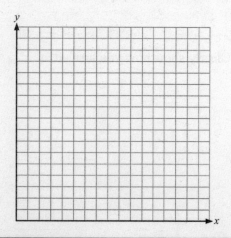

b) Using only your graph, calculate the following values:

i) The threshold frequency of the incident radiation

ii) Planck's constant

25. If an electron is emitted from a photoelectric surface with 11.0 eV of kinetic energy, what is the stopping potential of the electron?

26. Monochromatic light illuminates a photoelectric surface that has a work function of 1.90 eV. If the voltage required to stop the emitted electron is 2.10×10^{-1} V, what is the wavelength of the incident radiation?

27. Monochromatic light with a wavelength of 6.25×10^2 nm illuminated a photoelectric surface. What is the maximum speed of an electron emitted from this surface if the surface has a work function of 1.40 eV?

28. What is the maximum wavelength of light that will cause electrons to be emitted from a photoelectric surface that has a work function of 3.2 eV?

29. Calculate the frequency of a photon if its momentum is 7.60×10^{-29} kg·m/s.

30. Find the momentum of a photon that has a frequency of 9.10×10^{18} Hz.

31. Find the momentum of a photon that has 7.00 eV of energy.

32. Calculate the kinetic energy of a photon that has a momentum of 4.2×10^{-28} kg·m/s.

33. Using the law of conservation of momentum, find the recoil speed of a hydrogen atom (mass $= 1.67 \times 10^{-27}$ kg) when it emits a photon ($\lambda = 486$ nm), assuming the atom was initially at rest.

34. A radioactive nucleus $\left(^{60}_{27}\text{Co} \right)$ emits a photon with a wavelength of 2.7×10^{-13} m. Assuming the nucleus was initially at rest, what is its recoil speed upon emitting this photon?

REVIEW SUMMARY

- Blackbody radiation
- The photoelectric effect
- The Compton effect
- Maxwell's theory of EMR
- An accelerating charge as the source of EMR
- The electromagnetic spectrum, including properties
- An explanation of the properties of EMR, using light as an example
- The following properties of light:
  - Reflection (including curved mirrors)
  - Refraction (including lenses)
  - Interference
  - Diffraction
  - Speed
  - Dispersion
- Formulas used in this chapter:
  - $c = \lambda f$

  - $E = \dfrac{hc}{\lambda}$

  - $f = \dfrac{1}{T}$

  - $E = hf$

  - $\dfrac{\sin \theta_1}{\sin \theta_2} = \dfrac{v_1}{v_2} = \dfrac{\lambda_1}{\lambda_2} = \dfrac{n_2}{n_1}$

  - $E_{k\,max} = hf - W$

  - $\lambda = \dfrac{d \sin \theta}{n}$

  - $E_{k\,max} = qV_{stop}$

  - $\lambda = \dfrac{dx}{nl}$

  - $W = hf_0$

  - $\dfrac{1}{f} = \dfrac{1}{d_o} + \dfrac{1}{d_i}$

  - $p = \dfrac{h}{\lambda}$

  - $M = \dfrac{h_i}{h_o} = -\dfrac{d_i}{d_o}$

  - $p = \dfrac{hf}{c}$

  - $\angle r = \angle i$

  - $\vec{p} = m\vec{v}$

PRACTICE TEST

1. Electromagnetic waves, such as radio waves, are different from mechanical waves in that electromagnetic waves can

   A. demonstrate constructive and destructive interference

   B. demonstrate the Doppler effect

   C. travel through a vacuum

   D. be polarized

Use the following information to answer the next question.

> Light has the following characteristics:
> **i)** It travels at a speed of 3.0×10^8 m/s.
> **ii)** It can travel through space.
> **iii)** It travels as transverse waves.

2. Which of the given characteristics indicate that light travels as an electromagnetic wave?

   A. **i)** and **ii)** only

   B. **i)** and **iii)** only

   C. **ii)** and **iii)** only

   D. **i)**, **ii)**, and **iii)**

3. A diffraction pattern of light is produced by a diffraction grating. If the wavelength of the light is increased, which of the following observations would be expected?

   A. The maxima would become more intense (bright).

   B. The maxima would become less intense (bright).

   C. The maxima would be closer together.

   D. The maxima would be farther apart.

Use the following information to answer the next question.

> Visible light may be dispersed by using a diffraction grating or a prism to refract the light.
>
> Four students make the following statements:
> **i)** Red light diffracts more than blue light.
> **ii)** Blue light diffracts more than red light.
> **iii)** Red light refracts more than blue light.
> **iv)** Blue light refracts more than red light.

4. Which of the given statements are correct?

   A. **i)** and **iii)**

   B. **ii)** and **iv)**

   C. **i)** and **iv)**

   D. **ii)** and **iii)**

5. A diffraction pattern of light is produced by a diffraction grating. If the diffraction grating is changed to one that has a greater number of slits per millimetre, which of the following observations would be expected?

   A. The maxima would be farther apart.

   B. The maxima would be closer together.

   C. The diffraction pattern would be more distinct.

   D. The diffraction pattern would be less pronounced.

6. EMR can be produced by an electric charge that is

   A. at rest

   B. increasing in velocity

   C. moving at a constant velocity

   D. moving at a constant velocity or increasing in velocity

7. Which of the following lists shows radiation in decreasing order of wavelength?

   A. X-rays, blue light, microwaves

   B. Blue light, microwaves, X-rays

   C. Microwaves, X-rays, blue light

   D. Microwaves, blue light, X-rays

8. When light travels from air into water at a 30° angle, which of the following properties of the wave change?

   A. Direction, speed, and wavelength only

   B. Speed, wavelength, and frequency only

   C. Wavelength, frequency, and direction only

   D. Direction, speed, wavelength, and frequency

Use the following information to answer the next question.

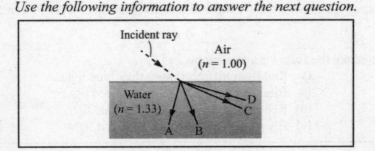

9. When light passes from air into water as shown in the given diagram, which ray could be the refracted ray?

   A. A   B. B

   C. C   D. D

10. Light (frequency in air $= 5.0 \times 10^{14}$ Hz) passes from air ($n = 1.00$) into glass ($n = 1.50$). If the speed of the light in glass is 2.0×10^8 m/s, what is the frequency of the light in glass?

    A. Equal to 5.0×10^{14} Hz

    B. Less than 5.0×10^{14} Hz

    C. Greater than 5.0×10^{14} Hz

    D. The light would be reflected.

Use the following information to answer the next question.

11. A fisher is attempting to spear a fish, as shown in the given diagram. Where should the fisher aim?

    A. Below the fish as the fisher sees it

    B. Above the fish as the fisher sees it

    C. Directly at the fish as the fisher sees it

    D. To the right of the fish as the fisher sees it

12. Which of the following statements about total internal reflection is **true**?

    A. Light must pass from a substance of higher refractive index to one of a lower refractive index at an incident angle greater than the critical angle.

    B. Light must pass from a substance of lower refractive index to one of a higher refractive index at an incident angle greater than the critical angle.

    C. Light must pass from a substance of higher refractive index to one of a lower refractive index at an incident angle less than the critical angle.

    D. Light must pass from a substance of lower refractive index to one of a higher refractive index at an incident angle less than the critical angle.

13. Which of the following characteristics describe an image produced by a convex lens when the object is placed inside the focal point?

    A. Inverted and virtual only

    B. Virtual and enlarged only

    C. Inverted and enlarged only

    D. Inverted, virtual, and enlarged

14. Which of the following characteristics describe an image produced by a concave lens?

A. Virtual and smaller only

B. Inverted and virtual only

C. Inverted and enlarged only

D. Inverted, virtual, and enlarged

Use the following information to answer the next question.

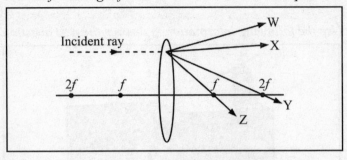

15. If the incident ray is parallel to the principal axis in the given diagram, the light will be refracted by the convex lens along path

A. W

B. X

C. Y

D. Z

Use the following information to answer the next question.

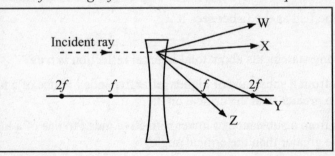

16. If the incident ray passes through the lens as shown in the given diagram, the light will be refracted along path

A. W

B. X

C. Y

D. Z

17. The magnification $\left(\dfrac{h_i}{h_o}\right)$ of an image produced by a convex lens when the object is placed at $2f$ is

A. greater than 1

B. less than 1

C. equal to 1

D. zero

18. The magnification $\left(\dfrac{h_i}{h_o}\right)$ of an image produced by a diverging lens is always

    A. equal to or less than 1
    B. greater than 1
    C. less than 1
    D. equal to 1

19. Which of the following features is **not** a characteristic of an image produced by a plane (flat) mirror?

    A. Real
    B. Upright
    C. Actual size
    D. Laterally inverted

20. A virtual image produced by a lens is always

    A. smaller than the object
    B. larger than the object
    C. inverted
    D. upright

21. The maximum kinetic energy of electrons emitted in a photoelectric cell can be determined by measuring

    A. the work function
    B. Planck's constant
    C. the stopping voltage
    D. the threshold frequency

Use the following information to answer the next question.

Stefanie was describing the photoelectric effect to her friend Kyle. She expressed the following points:
i)   Light consists of photons.
ii) The energy of the emitted electron is the difference between the energy of the incident photon and the energy required to free the electron from the photoelectric surface.
iii) The energy of a photon is directly proportional to the wavelength.

22. Which of these statements about Einstein's theory of the photoelectric effect are **true**?

    A. ii) and iii) only
    B. i) and iii) only
    C. i) and ii) only
    D. i), ii), and iii)

23. When monochromatic light falls on a photoelectric cell, electrons are emitted. If this cell is placed in a circuit, the current through the circuit can be increased by

    A. increasing the intensity of the light

    B. decreasing the intensity of the light

    C. increasing the frequency of the light

    D. decreasing the frequency of the light

24. When a photoelectric cell is illuminated with yellow light, it emits electrons. This photoelectric cell will definitely emit electrons when illuminated with

    A. red light and X-rays

    B. blue light and X-rays

    C. infrared light and X-rays

    D. infrared light and blue light

Use the following information to answer the next three questions.

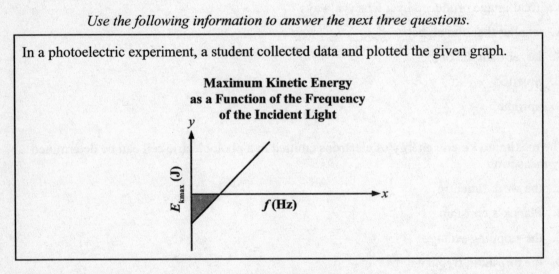

25. To determine the minimum energy of the photons that will cause electrons to flow in the circuit, which of the following features of the graph would be used?

    A. Area of the shaded triangle

    B. Slope of the graph

    C. The y-intercept

    D. The x-intercept

26. To determine the minimum frequency of the incident light that causes electrons to flow in the circuit, which of the following features of the graph would be used?

   A. Area of the shaded triangle

   B. Slope of the graph

   C. The y-intercept

   D. The x-intercept

27. To determine Planck's constant from this experiment, which of the following features of the graph would be used?

   A. Area of the shaded triangle

   B. Slope of the graph

   C. The y-intercept

   D. The x-intercept

28. The collision between high-energy photons with atoms and electrons **cannot** be used to demonstrate

   A. the photoelectric effect

   B. blackbody radiation

   C. the Compton effect

   D. inertia of photons

29. Which of the following graphs **best** represents the relationship between the momentum of a photon and its wavelength?

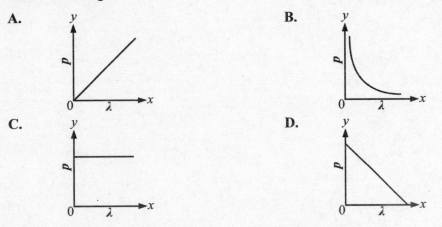

30. The momentum of a photon depends on which of the following physical properties?

   A. Mass

   B. Intensity

   C. Velocity

   D. Frequency

31. Which of the following graphs **best** represents the relationship between the stopping voltage and the frequency in a photoelectric experiment?

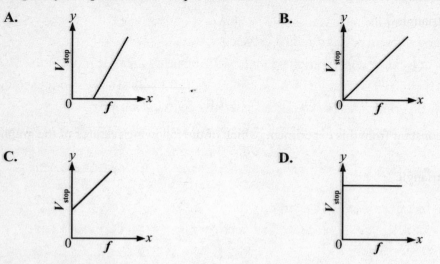

A.

B.

C.

D.

32. Which of the following phenomena could classical physics explain?

   A. The Compton effect

   B. Blackbody radiation

   C. Newtonian mechanics

   D. The photoelectric effect

33. Max Planck developed the quantum hypothesis in order to explain

   A. the photoelectric effect

   B. blackbody radiation

   C. the Compton effect

   D. photons

ATOMIC PHYSICS: ATOMIC STRUCTURE

When you are finished this section of the unit, you should be able to...

• Describe matter as containing discrete positive and negative charges

• Explain how the discovery of cathode rays contributed to the development of atomic models

• Explain J. J. Thomson's experiment and the significance of the results for both science and technology

• Explain Millikan's oil-drop experiment and its significance relative to charge quantization

• Explain, qualitatively, the significance of the results of Rutherford's scattering experiment, in terms of scientists' understanding of the relative size and mass of the nucleus and the atom.

• Explain, qualitatively, how emission of EMR by an accelerating charged particle invalidates the classical model of the atom

• Describe that each element has an unique line spectrum

• Explain, qualitatively, the characteristics of, and the conditions necessary to produce continuous line-emission and line-absorption spectra

• Explain, qualitatively, the concept of stationary states and how they explain the observed spectra of atoms and molecules

• Calculate the energy difference between states, using the law of conservation of energy and the observed characteristics of an emitted photon

• Explain, qualitatively, how electron diffraction provides experimental support for the de Broglie hypothesis

• Describe, qualitatively, how the Rutherford-Bohr model has been further refined by applying quantum concepts to a purely mathematical model based on probability and the de Broglie hypothesis

PREREQUISITE SKILLS AND KNOWLEDGE

Prior to starting this unit, you should be able to...
- Understand centripetal force and acceleration of an object in terms of mass, velocity, and radius
- Understand the relationship between EMR, electric fields, and magnetic fields
- Describe the interaction of positive and negative charges and how they interaction with electric, magnetic and gravitational fields
- Solve problems for motion of a charged particle involving the electric field, magnetic field, gravitational field, mass, voltage (potential difference), speed, and distance between two charged parallel plates
- Explain the dispersion of light through both diffraction gratings and refraction through a prism
- Solve double-slit and diffraction grating problems
- Define the photon as a quantum of EMR and calculate its energy
- Explain how blackbody radiation supports energy quantization
- Describe the photoelectric effect as a phenomenon that supports the notion of the wave-particle duality of EMR
- Classify the different regions that make up the electromagnetic spectrum in terms of photon frequency and wavelength
- Describe, quantitatively, photoelectric emission, using concepts related to the conservation of energy

Lesson 1 ATOMIC STRUCTURE

DALTON'S ATOMIC THEORY

Democritus, an early Greek philosopher, reasoned that matter was composed of tiny particles. However, it was not until 1810 that John Dalton proposed the atomic theory. During the eighteenth century, there had been a lot of activity in the study now called chemistry. During this time, many chemical laws were discovered. Dalton proposed the atomic theory in order to explain some of these chemical relationships.

Dalton's atomic theory consists of the following main points:

- All matter consists of small, indivisible, and indestructible particles called atoms.

- All atoms of a given element are the same.

- Each element's atomic mass is characteristic for that element. That is, it is different from the mass of any other element.

- Atoms combine together to form compounds.

- Atoms are neither created nor destroyed during a chemical reaction; they are only rearranged.

Dalton suggested that atoms were tiny, indivisible chunks of matter. This model is also known as the "billiard ball" model of the atom. This model had no internal or external features.

There were many chemical relationships discovered during the eighteenth century that Dalton's atomic theory successfully explained.

Following Dalton's proposal of the atomic theory, chemists were able to determine which substances were elements and which substances were compounds. They were also able to work out a system of relative atomic masses. Scientists knew that the hydrogen atom is the lightest atom, and they assigned it an atomic mass of 1. Oxygen atoms were 16 times as heavy. Therefore, the atomic mass of oxygen was 16. At first, the standard was hydrogen (atomic mass 1), but it was later changed to oxygen (atomic mass 16). Today, the standard is a particular isotope of carbon (atomic mass 12).

NOTES

John Dalton proposed the atomic theory. This theory has also been called the "billiard ball" model.

Dalton's atomic theory was successful in explaining chemical laws.

Chemists developed a system of relative atomic masses.

PERIODIC TABLE OF ELEMENTS

As more and more elements were discovered, chemists began to search for patterns that would help them understand chemical properties. Mendeleev arranged the 63 known elements in order of their increasing atomic weights (atomic masses). He discovered that the chemical properties of these elements were repeated on a regular basis. Because of this repetition, Mendeleev called his table the periodic table. He further arranged the elements that had the same chemical properties into columns. By doing this, he discovered there were some blank spaces in the table; some elements appeared to be missing. He was able to reason that the blank spaces represented elements that had not been discovered. He was even able to predict the chemical properties of these yet-undiscovered elements.

If you study the periodic table, the elements in the same column have the same chemical properties. The chemical properties repeat on a periodic basis. It should also be noted that on the periodic table today, the elements are listed in order of increasing atomic number (number of protons) rather than atomic mass. However, there are very few differences in the arrangement of elements when they are listed in order of increasing atomic numbers rather than in order of increasing atomic masses.

When the elements are arranged in order of increasing atomic numbers, the chemical properties repeat on a regular basis.

Although Dalton's theory was successful in explaining several phenomena, new questions arose that his model had difficulty answering. These questions suggested that the simple model (the billiard ball model) needed to be amended. Dalton's model had trouble explaining the following questions:

- How do atoms combine to form compounds (molecules)? What holds them together?

- How can the periodic table be explained? What causes the repetition of chemical properties?

Both of these questions suggested that there may be some internal structure to the atom. An atom may not be as simple as a billiard ball.

Lesson 2   CATHODE RAYS AND J. J. THOMSON'S EXPERIMENT

With the invention of highly efficient vacuum pumps in the middle of the nineteenth century by Heinrich Geissler, scientists began investigations that led to the discovery of the electron. Scientists were able to investigate the electric discharge across a spark gap in a vacuum (or in gases at very low pressure).

When an electric discharge takes place in a gas under low pressure, the gas will glow. Different gases will produce different colours. Tubes containing gases under low pressure can be called discharge tubes. Today, discharge tubes are used in spectrum analysis. Another type of discharge tube is the cathode ray tube.

CATHODE RAY TUBE

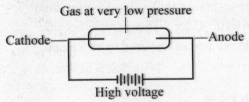

The electrodes of the cathode ray tube (CRT) are connected to a source of high potential difference. The term *cathode ray* is used because it was determined that the discharge originated at the negative electrode (cathode). This was determined because the tube glowed with greater intensity opposite the cathode, as indicated in the following diagram.

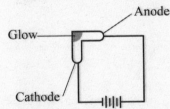

Over several years, a number of scientists discovered the following properties of the discharge that became known as the cathode ray:

• Cathode rays travel in straight lines.

• Cathode rays can be considered to be moving particles.

• They can be deflected by magnetic fields.

• They can be deflected by electric fields.

• The matter the cathode is made of does not affect the properties of the cathode rays.

• Cathode rays can produce chemical reactions similar to those of light.

NOTES

At first, it was speculated that cathode rays were a form of EMR. Remember that cathode rays were discovered shortly after Hertz demonstrated that EMR exists. Cathode rays do have some properties of light (EMR): they both travel in straight lines, and they both can bring about chemical change. However, cathode rays have properties that light (EMR) does not have. Cathode rays can be deflected by electric and magnetic fields, whereas light (EMR) cannot.

Cathode rays are deflected by electric and magnetic fields. EMR is not deflected by electric or magnetic fields.

Many scientists studied cathode rays, but William Crookes and J. J. Thomson were two of the most significant. Crookes discovered many properties of cathode rays. J. J. Thomson is credited with discovering the electron while experimenting with CRTs.

Crookes speculated that cathode rays might be particles. However, J.J. Thomson determined that they were particles, and he showed that they had a characteristic charge-to-mass (q/m) ratio. He measured this charge-to-mass ratio to be 1.76×10^{11} C/kg. This particle became known as the electron. The cathode ray was discovered to be a beam of electrons.

J. J. Thomson determined the charge/mass ratio of the electron.

J. J. THOMSON'S EXPERIMENT

In J. J. Thomson's experiment, cathode rays pass through a magnetic field. The magnetic field was found to deflect the rays.

The cathode ray is a beam of electrons.

The anode is a circular disk with a hole in it. The electrons are accelerated between the cathode and the anode (this part of the tube can be called an electron gun, or accelerator). Under high voltage, the electrons have high kinetic energy (high speed) when they reach the anode.

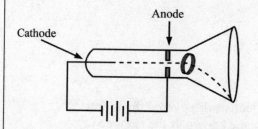

A beam of electrons with high energy first passes through the hole in the anode. Then, it passes through a magnetic field. The electrons may be deflected up or down by the magnetic field. The deflection is in an arc (part of a circle). Remember that the force that causes an object to move in a circle is the centripetal force. The following formula is used for calculating the magnitude of the centripetal force:

Centripetal force is a force causing an object to move in an arc or circle.

$$F_c = \frac{mv^2}{r}$$

where m = mass

r = radius of the circle (arc)

In this case, the force causing the electrons to deflect in an arc (circle) is the magnetic force $\left(\vec{F}_m\right)$. Therefore, $\vec{F}_c = \vec{F}_m$.

$$F_c = \frac{mv^2}{r} \qquad \text{and} \qquad F_m = qvB_\perp$$

$$qvB_\perp = \frac{mv^2}{r} \qquad \text{or} \qquad qB_\perp = \frac{mv}{r}$$

$$\frac{q}{m} = \frac{v}{B_\perp r}$$

The ratio q/m is the charge-to-mass ratio that J. J. Thomson measured. The variables r and $B_\perp$ in these formulas can be measured, but the speed of the electron is difficult to determine. The formula $V = \frac{\Delta E}{q}$ can be used to find the change in energy of the accelerated electron, and the equation $E_k = \frac{1}{2}mv^2$ can be used to find the speed.

However, in order to use these equations, you need the mass and the charge of the electron. J. J. Thomson had neither. He found the speed by passing the electrons through both a magnetic field and electric field. The electric field and magnetic field were adjusted so that the magnetic and electric forces acting on the electrons were equal but acting in opposite directions.

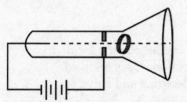

In this case, there is no deflection. The magnitudes of electric and magnetic forces are equal.

$$\therefore F_e = F_m$$
$$qE = qvB_\perp$$
$$\therefore v = \frac{E}{B_\perp}$$

J. J. Thomson obtained the speed of the electron as the ratio of the field strength. Now that he knew the speed of the electrons, he could return to his original formulas:

$$\vec{F}_m = \vec{F}_c \qquad qvB_\perp = \frac{mv^2}{r} \qquad \frac{q}{m} = \frac{v}{B_\perp r}$$

Knowing the values of v, B, and r, Thompson could then calculate the charge-to-mass ratio.

SUMMARY

The following types of forces were used in this section:

Force of gravity: $\vec{F}_g = m\vec{g}$ Electric force: $\vec{F}_e = q\vec{E}$

Magnetic force: $F_m = qvB_\perp$ Centripetal force: $F_c = \dfrac{mv^2}{r}$

J. J Thomson's method involved deflecting electrons of a known velocity using only a magnetic field. This allowed him to equate the magnetic and centripetal forces $\left(qvB = \dfrac{mv^2}{r} \right)$. This equation could be rearranged to

solve for the charge-to-mass ratio $\left(\dfrac{q}{m} = \dfrac{v}{Br} \right)$.

- When Thomson used only a magnetic field, the electrons were deflected.

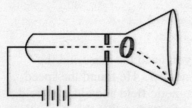

When only a magnetic field is used, there is deflection.

$$\vec{F}_m = \vec{F}_c \qquad qvB_\perp = \dfrac{mv^2}{r}$$

- When Thomson used both a magnetic field and an electric field, he balanced the forces so there was no deflection. This allowed Thomson to determine the velocity of the electrons and solve for the charge-to-mass ratio.

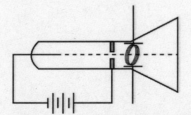

When both a magnetic field and an electric field are used, there is deflection. The magnitudes of electric and magnetic forces are equal.

$$\therefore F_e = F_m \qquad qE = qvB_\perp \qquad v = \dfrac{E}{B_\perp}$$

Example

Charged particles travelling horizontally at 3.60×10^6 m/s enter into a vertical magnetic field of 7.10×10^{-1} T. If the radius of the arc of the deflected particles is 9.50×10^{-2} m, what is the charge-to-mass ratio of the particles?

Solution

$$F_{\text{m}} = F_{\text{c}}$$

$$qvB_{\perp} = \frac{mv^2}{r}$$

$$\frac{q}{m} = \frac{v}{B_{\perp}r} = \frac{3.60 \times 10^6 \text{ m/s}}{(7.10 \times 10^{-1} \text{ T})(9.50 \times 10^{-2} \text{ m})}$$

$$= 5.34 \times 10^7 \text{ C/kg}$$

Example

An electron passes through an electric field of 6.30×10^3 N/C and a magnetic field of 7.11×10^{-3} T undeflected. If the electric and magnetic fields are perpendicular to each other, what is the speed of the electron?

Solution

$$F_{\text{m}} = F_{\text{e}}$$

$$qvB = qE$$

$$v = \frac{E}{B}$$

$$= \frac{6.30 \times 10^3 \text{ N/C}}{7.11 \times 10^{-3} \text{ T}}$$

$$= 8.86 \times 10^5 \text{ m/s}$$

Undeflected means the magnitudes of the electric and magnetic forces are equal.

Example

An electron travelling vertically enters a horizontal magnetic field of 7.20×10^{-2} T. If the electron is deflected in an arc of radius 3.70×10^{-3} m, what is the kinetic energy of the electron?

Solution

$$F_{\text{m}} = F_{\text{c}}$$

$$qvB_{\perp} = \frac{mv^2}{r}$$

$$v = \frac{qB_{\perp}r}{m}$$

$$= \frac{(1.60 \times 10^{-19} \text{ C})(7.20 \times 10^{-2} \text{ T})(3.70 \times 10^{-3} \text{ m})}{9.11 \times 10^{-31} \text{ kg}}$$

$$= 4.68 \times 10^7 \text{ m/s}$$

$$E_{\text{k}} = \frac{1}{2}mv^2$$

$$= \frac{1}{2}(9.11 \times 10^{-31} \text{ kg})(4.68 \times 10^7 \text{ m/s})^2$$

$$= 9.97 \times 10^{-16} \text{ J}$$

PRACTICE EXERCISES

Formulas: Derive your own formulas by equating forces.

$$\vec{F}_e = q\vec{E} \qquad\qquad F_c = \frac{mv^2}{r} \qquad\qquad F_m = qvB_\perp$$

1. An alpha particle travels through a magnetic field of 4.22×10^{-1} T perpendicularly to the field. If the radius of the arc of the deflected particles is 1.50×10^{-3} m, what is the speed of the particles?

2. A proton travels through a magnetic field at a speed of 5.40×10^5 m/s perpendicularly to the field. If the radius of the arc of the deflected proton is 7.20×10^{-3} m, what is the magnetic field strength?

3. Calculate the charge-to-mass ratio of a particle travelling 3.60×10^5 m/s that is deflected in an arc with a radius of 7.40×10^{-2} m as it travels through a perpendicular magnetic field of 6.10×10^{-1} T.

4. Alpha particles travel undeflected through magnetic and electric fields that are perpendicular to each another. The alpha particles have a speed of 7.80×10^5 m/s, and the strength of the magnetic field is 2.20×10^{-1} T. Assuming the alpha particles are travelling perpendicularly to these fields, what is the strength of the electric field?

5. Positively charged particles travel undeflected through magnetic and electric fields that are perpendicular to each other. The magnetic field strength is 6.50×10^{-1} T , and the electric field strength is 2.10×10^5 N/C. Assuming the charged particles travel perpendicularly to these fields, what is the speed of the charged particles?

6. Alpha particles travel through a magnetic field of 3.60×10^{-1} T and are deflected in an arc with a radius of 8.20×10^{-2} m. Assuming the alpha particles travel perpendicularly to the field, what is the energy of each alpha particle?

7. In a CRT, electrons are accelerated from rest by a potential difference of 2.50×10^3 V. What is the maximum speed of the electrons?

8. In a CRT, an electron reaches a maximum speed of 4.75×10^7 m/s. If this electron is accelerated from rest, what is the potential difference across the tube?

9. In a CRT, electrons are accelerated from rest by a potential difference of 1.40×10^3 V. These electrons enter a magnetic field with a strength of 2.20×10^{-2} T. Assuming the electrons travel perpendicularly to the field, what is the radius of the arc of the deflected electrons?

10. Electrons are accelerated from rest in a CRT. These electrons then pass through a magnetic field of 1.40×10^{-2} T and through an electric field of 4.20×10^5 N/C. The fields are perpendicular to each other, and the electrons are not deflected. Assuming the electrons travel perpendicularly to these fields, what is the potential difference across the CRT?

11. A negatively charged particle with a mass of 8.4×10^{-27} kg travels with a velocity of 5.6×10^5 m/s perpendicularly through a magnetic field of 2.8×10^{-1} T. If the radius of the path of the particle is 3.5 cm, how many excess electrons does this particle carry?

12. Alpha particles travel at a speed of 3.00×10^6 m/s through a magnetic field. If the magnetic field strength is 4.2×10^{-2} T, what is the radius of the path followed by the alpha particles when the magnetic field is parallel to the direction the alpha particles travel?

13. A proton travels through a 0.75 T magnetic field in a circle with a radius of 0.30 m. What is the momentum of this proton?

14. Electrons are accelerated from rest through a potential difference. These electrons are then deflected with a radius of 0.77 m when they travel through a 2.2×10^{-4} T magnetic field. What is the accelerating voltage?

15. An ion with a charge-to-mass ratio of 1.10×10^4 C/kg travels perpendicularly to a magnetic field $\left(B = 9.10 \times 10^{-1} \text{ T}\right)$ in a circular path ($r = 0.240$ m). How long does it take the ion to travel one revolution?

16. A positively charged ion $\left(m = 3.34 \times 10^{-26} \text{ kg}\right)$ was accelerated from rest through a potential difference of 1.66×10^4 V. The ion then entered into a magnetic field $\left(B = 3.20 \times 10^{-2} \text{ T}\right)$ perpendicular to the direction of its motion. If the magnetic force on the ion is 5.78×10^{-15} N, what is the charge on the ion?

Lesson 3 MILLIKAN'S OIL-DROP EXPERIMENT

Millikan determined the elementary charge to be 1.60×10^{-19} C.

After J. J. Thomson discovered the electron, Robert Millikan determined the elementary charge through his oil-drop experiment. The elementary charge is the value of the charge on an electron and a proton.

In this experiment, Millikan dropped tiny oil droplets between two horizontal, parallel plates. These plates were connected to a variable voltage source so that one would become positive and the other would become negative. With no charge on the plates, the oil droplets would fall to the lower plate because of the gravitational force. However, when the plates were charged, some of the oil droplets would rise to the top plate.

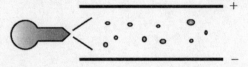

What force caused the oil droplets to rise? This upward force was found to be an electric force. In order for there to be an electric force, the oil droplets must have a charge. Where did this charge on the oil droplets come from? The charge was created by friction when the oil droplets formed. As the droplets slid over one another, some droplets became positive, while others became negative. The negative droplets would be attracted to the positive plate.

When the oil drop is suspended, the gravitational force and the electric force on the drop are equal.

Millikan was able to adjust the voltage so that some oil droplets became suspended. When this happened, he reasoned that the magnitudes of electric and gravitational forces acting on the oil droplets were equal.

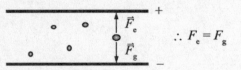

The magnitude of the electric force is given by the equation $F_e = qE$, and the magnitude of the gravitational force is given by the equation $F_g = mg$. If $F_e = F_g$, then $qE = mg$, and q can be calculated using $q = \dfrac{mg}{E}$.

Millikan calculated the mass of the oil droplet using its density (ρ) and the formula $\rho = \dfrac{m}{V}$. Therefore, $m = \rho V$. The volume was obtained by measuring the diameter of the oil droplet and using the formula for the volume of a sphere to find its mass. The gravitational field, g, is a constant, and the magnitude of the electric field, E, can be found using the voltage between the plates.

$$E = \frac{V}{d}$$

Millikan repeated this experiment a number of times, and he found that the charge on the oil droplet was always a multiple of 1.60×10^{-19} C. Millikan concluded that the charge on an elementary particle is 1.60×10^{-19} C.

Example

An oil drop with a mass of 9.80×10^{-16} kg is suspended between two horizontal, parallel, charged plates. If the electric field strength between the plates is 2.0×10^{4} V/m, what is the magnitude of the charge on the oil drop?

Suspended means that the magnitudes of the electric and gravitational forces are equal.

Solution

$$F_e = F_g$$
$$qE = mg$$
$$q = \frac{mg}{E}$$
$$= \frac{(9.80\times10^{-16}\text{ kg})(9.81\text{ N/kg})}{2.0\times10^{4}\text{ V/m}}$$
$$= 4.8\times10^{-19}\text{ C}$$

Example

An oil drop with a weight of 4.80×10^{-14} N is suspended between two horizontal, parallel, charged plates that are placed 5.00 cm apart. If the potential difference between these plates is 3.00×10^{3} V, how many excess electrons does the oil drop carry?

Solution

$$E = \frac{V}{d}$$
$$= \frac{3.00\times10^{3}\text{ V}}{5.00\times10^{-2}\text{ m}}$$
$$= 6.00\times10^{4}\text{ V/m}$$
$$F_e = F_g$$
$$qE = mg$$
$$q = \frac{mg}{E}$$
$$= \frac{4.80\times10^{-14}\text{ N}}{6.00\times10^{4}\text{ V/m}}$$
$$= 8.00\times10^{-19}\text{ C}$$
$$\#e^- = \frac{8.00\times10^{-19}\text{ C}}{1.60\times10^{-19}\text{ C}}$$
$$= 5$$

PRACTICE EXERCISES

Formulas: Using the following equations, derive the relationship to determine the charge on the electron.

$$\vec{F} = m\vec{a} \qquad\qquad \vec{F}_g = m\vec{g} \qquad\qquad \vec{F}_e = q\vec{E}$$

1. An oil drop weighing 3.84×10^{-15} N is suspended between two horizontal, parallel plates where the electric field strength is 1.20×10^4 N/C. What is the magnitude of the charge on the oil drop?

2. An oil drop with a mass of 4.80×10^{-16} kg is suspended between two horizontal, parallel plates that are 6.00 cm apart. If the potential difference between the plates is 5.90×10^2 V, how many excess electrons does the oil drop carry?

3. An oil drop with a mass of 7.20×10^{-16} kg moves upward at a constant speed between two horizontal, parallel plates. If the electric field strength between these plates is 2.20×10^4 V/m, what is the magnitude of the charge on the oil drop?

4. A 3.50×10^{-15} kg oil drop accelerates downward at a rate of 2.50 m/s^2 when placed between two horizontal, parallel plates that are 1.00 cm apart. Assuming the oil drop is negative and the top plate is positive, how many excess electrons does the oil drop carry if the potential difference between the plates is 5.38×10^2 V?

Use the following information to answer the next question.

During a Millikan oil-drop experiment, a student records the weights of five different oil drops. The student also records the electric field intensity necessary to hold each drop stationary between the two horizontal, parallel plates.

Weight $\left(\times 10^{-14} \text{ N} \right)$	$\vec{E}$ $\left(\times 10^5 \text{ N/C} \right)$
1.7	1.1
5.6	3.5
6.1	3.8
2.9	1.8
4.0	2.5

5. a) Using $\vec{E}$ as the manipulated variable, draw a graph showing the relationship between the weight and the electric field.

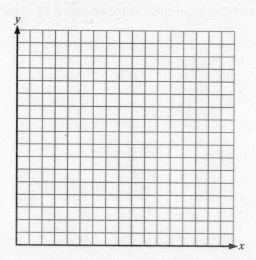

b) Using only your graph, determine the elementary charge.

6. A 5.70×10^{-16} kg oil drop accelerates upward at a rate of 2.90 m/s^2 when placed between two horizontal, parallel plates that are 3.50 cm apart. If the potential difference between the plates is 7.92×10^2 V, what is the magnitude of the charge on the oil drop?

7. In a Millikan oil-drop experiment, a student sprayed oil droplets with a density of 7.8×10^2 kg/m^3 between two horizontal, parallel plates that were 4.0 cm apart. The student adjusted the potential difference between the plates to 4.6×10^3 V so that one of the drops became stationary. The diameter of this drop was measured to be 2.4×10^{-6} m. What was the magnitude of the charge on this oil drop?

8. An oil droplet $(q = 5e^-)$ is suspended between two parallel, charged plates $(V = 175 \text{ V})$. If an oil droplet of the same mass but with a charge of $3e^-$ is to be suspended between the same plates, what potential difference would be necessary?

9. A 6.20×10^{-16} kg oil drop accelerates downward at a rate of 14.0 m/s^2 when placed between two horizontal, parallel plates that are 3.20 cm apart. If the potential difference between the plates is 175 V, what is the magnitude of the charge on the oil drop?

10. In an oil-drop experiment similar to Millikan's, an oil droplet is suspended between two parallel, charged plates. Calculate the magnitude of the charge on the oil droplet if the radius of the oil drop is 4.2×10^{-6} m, the density of the oil is 7.8×10^{2} g/m^3, the distance between the plates is 2.0 cm, and the potential difference between the plates is 99 V.

Lesson 4 ATOMIC MODELS

THOMSON MODEL (RAISIN-BUN MODEL)

Both J. J. Thomson and Millikan equated forces in their experiments. By equating forces, J. J. Thomson was able to derive equations that allowed him to calculate the charge-to-mass ratio of the electron and Millikan was able to find the elementary charge. The model of the atom changed in order to account for this new particle.

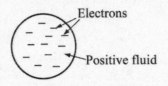

J. J. Thomson proposed a model of the atom in which the electrons were embedded in a positive fluid, like raisins in bread dough. The positive fluid made up the bulk of the mass and volume of the atom. This model was called the raisin-bun model of the atom.

RUTHERFORD'S SCATTERING EXPERIMENT

In 1911, Ernest Rutherford and his laboratory completed a series of experiments that led to a greater understanding of the atomic structure. In these experiments, alpha particles were directed toward a very thin gold foil. Radium in a lead block served as the source of alpha particles.

Rutherford's experiment was like shooting bullets at a piece of tissue paper and finding some of them bouncing back from the paper.

Rutherford found that although most of the alpha particles passed through the gold foil, a few were scattered at various angles. Some even were scattered back along their incident path. This was like shooting bullets at a piece of tissue paper and finding some of them bouncing back from the paper.

Rutherford found that the mass of the atom is concentrated in a small region of the atom. This region is called the nucleus.

Rutherford concluded from these experiments that the mass of the atom is not spread evenly throughout the atom as the Thomson model suggested. Instead, he suggested that the mass is concentrated in a very small region in the centre of the atom, called the nucleus.

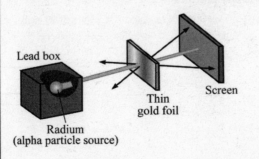

In these experiments, Rutherford's laboratory was also able to determine the size and charge of this nucleus. The nucleus is very small compared with the atom. If the atom could be extrapolated to the size of a football field, the nucleus would be about the size of a small housefly at the centre of the field. Therefore, if the metal foil is three or four hundred atoms thick, most of it is empty space. As a result, the alpha particles pass right through the atom. If there were three or four hundred football fields randomly lined up, what would be the chance of firing a high energy projectile through these fields and hitting a housefly at centre field?

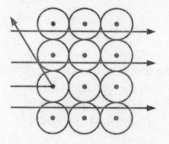

Suppose you wanted to draw a diagram of a gold atom to scale. The radius of the nucleus of a gold atom is about 7.0×10^{-15} m, and its atomic radius is about 1.7×10^{-10} m. If you drew the nucleus with a radius of only 0.50 mm, the radius of your diagram would still be 5.0×10^{4} mm or 50 m.

It was determined that the positive fluid in the atom was contained in the nucleus, and the electrons were external to this nucleus. The positive fluid consisted of protons.

Rutherford determined that the hydrogen nucleus had the smallest charge of any known nucleus and that the charges on other nuclei were whole number multiples of the charge on the hydrogen nucleus. Because of this and the fact that the charge on the hydrogen nucleus was of equal magnitude to the elementary charge, the hydrogen nucleus was determined to be a proton.

RUTHERFORD'S ATOMIC MODEL

There are problems with Rutherford's model of the atom. This model does not explain what keeps the electrons from being pulled into the nucleus or what keeps the atom from collapsing.

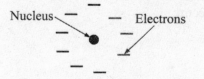

What keeps the electrons from being pulled into the nucleus?

The laws of electric charge (unlike charges attract) predicts that the electrons should be pulled into the nucleus. To deal with this problem, scientists speculated that the electrons orbit the nucleus much like Earth orbits the sun. Earth might be expected to be pulled into the sun, but it is not. This is because of Earth's kinetic energy. If you tie a weight onto the end of a string and twirl it at a certain speed, it will not fall into your hand unless the speed of the weight is decreased.

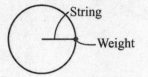

This is the planetary, or solar system, model of the atom.

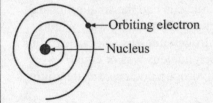

The planetary model of the atom does not properly explain why electrons do not spiral into the nucleus of an atom.

However, there is a problem with this planetary model of the atom as well. According to Maxwell's theory of EMR, an accelerating, charged particle produces EMR. An orbiting electron is an accelerating, charged particle (it does not speed up or slow down, but it changes direction). Energy is emitted, and if energy is emitted, the electron will not be able to maintain its orbit. As it continues to emit energy, the electron will spiral into the nucleus, and the atom would collapse.

Although empirical evidence supported Rutherford's planetary model, his model does not explain why atoms do not collapse.

SPECTRA

One of the major keys to understanding atomic structure was the hydrogen spectrum. There are three categories of spectra:

- Continuous

- Bright line

- Dark line

One of the major keys to understanding atomic structure was the hydrogen spectrum.

Continuous Spectra

When the light from a glowing solid or liquid passes through a diffraction grating or a prism, a continuous spectrum is produced.

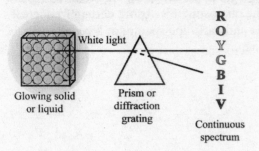

In a continuous spectrum, light of all colours (all frequencies) is present. One colour continues into the next.

Bright-Line Spectra

Bright-line spectra are produced when the light from an excited gas passes through a diffraction grating or through a prism.

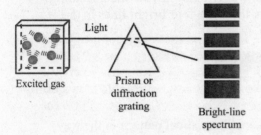

On a bright-line spectrum, there are only certain colours of light (certain frequencies). Every element produces a unique bright-line spectrum when the light it produces passes through a diffraction grating or prism. In 1823, John Herschel suggested that each element had its own characteristic bright-line spectrum and that spectrum analysis could be used to identify elements.

Dark-Line Spectra

Dark-line spectra are produced similarly to how continuous or bright-line spectra are produced. However, the light produced by the glowing solid or liquid passes through an unexcited gas before it passes through the diffraction grating or prism.

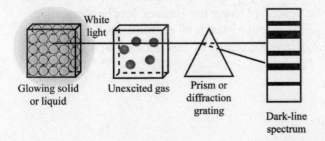

Each element has its own characteristic bright-line spectrum.

Fraunhofer lines

In a dark-line spectrum, light of certain colours (certain frequencies) is missing from the spectrum. There are dark lines through it. The solar spectrum is a dark-line spectrum. The dark lines are called Fraunhofer lines. It appears that the unexcited gases (in this case, the mixture of gases in the sun's outer atmosphere [the photosphere]) absorb certain frequencies of light. Note that the bright-line and dark-line spectra of a certain gas have their lines at the same frequency.

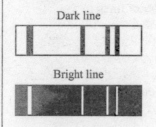

Dark line

Bright line

Continuous and bright-line spectra can be referred to as emission spectra. Dark-line spectra can be referred to as absorption spectra.

HYDROGEN ATOM

The hydrogen bright-line spectrum was a major key to understanding atomic structure. In this spectrum, there are four bright lines in the visible region.

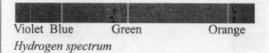

Violet Blue   Green   Orange

Hydrogen spectrum

The bright line spectrum suggests a mathematical pattern in the way electrons gain and lose energy.

Hydrogen bright-line spectrum: A bright line is produced when a hydrogen atom releases energy.

Hydrogen dark-line spectrum: A dark line is produced when a hydrogen atom absorbs energy.

Johann Balmer, a scientist who loved to do puzzles, looked on this as a challenge that could be solved. He searched for a possible mathematical relationship and found that he could calculate the wavelength of each of the four lines visible in the hydrogen spectrum using an empirical mathematical formula which was developed through trial and error. Balmer did not physically understand why the formula worked, but it did yield the correct results.

Modifying the work of Balmer, Johannes Rydberg realized that the equation Balmer had developed was a special case of a more general equation that could mathematically describe a complete series of emission lines. This complete set of hydrogen emissions lines is now known as the Balmer series and can be described using the Balmer-Rydberg equation. This equation can be used to calculate the four visible emission lines corresponding to the emission discovered by Balmer ($n = 3, 4, 5, 6$).

$$\frac{1}{\lambda} = R_H \left(\frac{1}{2^2} - \frac{1}{n^2} \right)$$

$n = 3$ for the red line

$\quad = 4$ for the green line

$\quad = 5$ for the blue line

$\quad = 6$ for the violet line

$R_H = $ Rydberg constant

As well as describing the visible lines of the Balmer series, the Balmer-Rydberg equation can also be used to calculate emission lines beyond the visible spectrum. The complete set of lines is described by the Balmer-Rydberg equation for all possible values of n (n = 3, 4, 5,...). These other lines could not be observed, because they fell in the ultraviolet region of the spectrum. When it became possible to detect ultraviolet radiation, the lines predicted by the Balmer-Rydberg equation were observed. Not only were these lines observed, but other lines in the ultraviolet and infrared regions that could not be calculated with the equation were discovered as well. This is because the Balmer-Rydberg equation describes only a small set of the emission spectrum corresponding to certain changes in energy levels. A more general form of the equation is now known that includes all the possible hydrogen emission spectrum. This more general form of the equation is called the Rydberg formula:

$$\frac{1}{\lambda} = R_H \left(\frac{1}{n_l^2} - \frac{1}{n_u^2} \right)$$

The n_l and n_u values in this equation are any whole numbers in which l is the lower energy value and u is the upper energy value. The Bohr model of the hydrogen atom explains why this works.

When the electron undergoes a transition from a high energy level to a lower energy level, a bright-line spectrum is produced. When the electron undergoes a transition from a low energy level to a higher level, a dark-line spectrum is produced.

The Bohr model of the hydrogen atom shows six energy levels. This model in the given diagram shows all of the possible transitions of electrons from higher levels to lower levels for the first six energy levels. Each time an electron moves to a lower energy level, a photon with a specific amount of energy is emitted. The reverse of these transitions takes place as well, from a lower level to a higher level, and it requires the absorption of a photon with a specific amount of energy.

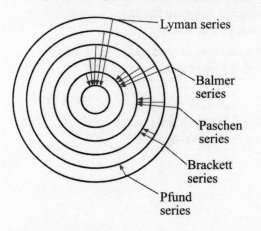

Note that each of these transitions is grouped and that each of these groups is named (Lyman, Balmer, Paschen, Brackett, and Pfund series).

The Balmer-Rydberg formula for calculating the Balmer series of hydrogen emission and absorption lines:

$$\frac{1}{\lambda} = R_H \left(\frac{1}{2^2} - \frac{1}{n^2} \right)$$

To calculate the wavelength of any photon emitted or absorbed as the electron undergoes a transition, use the Rydberg formula. For example, you can calculate the wavelength of emission or absorption in the Lyman series. The Lyman series represents emission and absorption for electrons moving to the first energy level ($n_l = 1$) from any other higher energy level ($n_u = 2, 3, 4,...$) in the Bohr model.

$$\frac{1}{\lambda} = R_H \left(\frac{1}{n_l^2} - \frac{1}{n_u^2} \right)$$

where $n_l = 1$
$n_u = 2, 3, 4,...$

In the same way, the wavelength in the Balmer series can be calculated when $n_l = 2$ and $n_u = 3, 4, 5,....$

NIELS BOHR

Consider again the questions that arose because of Mendeleev's periodic table:

• What can account for the repetition of chemical properties in the periodic table?

• Why do excited gases produce light of only certain values?

• Why do atoms not continuously give off energy and collapse?

Niels Bohr provided the answers to these questions. He became interested in the problem of atomic structure, and after extensive research by him and others, Bohr reached the following conclusions:

• Within the atom are certain allowed orbits around the nucleus, in which the electrons move without giving off energy. In other words, the energy of the electron in an atom is quantized. Recall that Planck was able to correctly describe the relationship between temperature, energy, and the frequency of vibration of blackbody radiation by proposing that the energy of vibration of an atom is quantized. Bohr's model explains why the energy of a blackbody is quantized, because the atom's electrons emit and absorb the energy in quantized amounts.

• In order for the electron to occupy any one of these allowed orbits, it must possess the energy allowed for that orbit.

This model of the atom allows the electrons to move from one orbit to another. The electron cannot be found between the energy levels, or orbits, but it can gain energy and move to a higher energy level.

Consider the analogy of a bookcase. In the bookcase, there are different levels, or shelves, and a book has a certain potential energy with respect to the floor. Because the book can be placed only at certain levels (shelves) away from the floor, it can have only certain potential energies. The book's energy can be increased by moving it to a higher shelf, or its energy can be decreased by moving it to a lower shelf. The book can move across the shelf without losing or gaining any energy. The Bohr model of the atom uses this analogy to describe the electrons in an atom.

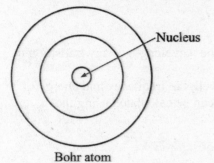

Bohr atom

The Bohr model of the atom allows only certain energy levels.

An electron absorbs a certain amount of light energy (a photon) when it jumps to a higher energy level (orbit) from a lower one.

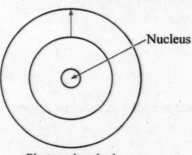

Photon absorbed

An electron emits a certain amount of light energy (a photon) when it drops from a higher energy level (orbit) to a lower one.

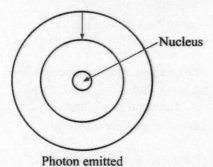

Photon emitted

Lasers work on the principle that atoms can emit light of only certain energy.

This means that photons of only certain frequencies (or wavelengths) can be emitted or absorbed. It also explains why the atom does not collapse: there are only certain allowed orbits.

NOTES

SUMMARY

The following table shows the possible values of *nl* and *nu* for each series:

n_1	n_u	Series Name
1	2, 3, 4, ...	Lyman
2	3, 4, 5, ...	Balmer
3	4, 5, 6, ...	Paschen
4	5, 6, 7, ...	Brackett
5	6, 7, 8, ...	Pfund

Only transitions that leave e^- in the second energy level result in photons being emitted in the visible spectrum.

Using the equation $\dfrac{1}{\lambda} = R_H \left(\dfrac{1}{n_1^{\,2}} - \dfrac{1}{n_u^{\,2}} \right)$, the wavelength of any transition in a hydrogen atom can be calculated. As well, the frequency and energy of the photons involved in these transitions can be calculated using the following formulas:

$$c = \lambda f \qquad \text{and} \qquad E = hf \qquad \text{or} \qquad E = \frac{hc}{\lambda}$$

Bohr was able to calculate the energy and radius of each of the allowed orbits in a hydrogen atom. He calculated the energy of the allowed orbits using the following formula:

$$E_n = \frac{-2\pi^2 k^2 m_e q_e^{\,4}}{h^2 n^2}$$

where E_n = energy of allowed orbit
n = orbit number

All values in this equation are constants, except *n*. If *n* is equal to 1, then $E_1 = -13.6$ eV or -2.18×10^{-18} J.

Energy of allowed hydrogen orbits:

$E_n = \dfrac{E_1}{n^2}$

E_1 = energy of first energy level

n^2 = orbit number

The values -13.6 eV and -2.18×10^{-18} J correspond to the energy of the first energy level in a hydrogen atom. If E_1 is known, the equation may be reduced as follows:

$$E_n = \frac{E_1}{n^2}$$

where E_1 = energy of the first level

Note that the energy levels in a hydrogen atom are not equally spaced. There is a greater energy difference between $n=1$ and $n=2$ (10.2 eV) than between all the other levels put together. Between $n=2$ and $n=\infty$, the energy difference is 3.4 eV. Each level is progressively closer to the next.

The energy levels in a hydrogen atom are not equally spaced.

$n = \infty$ ———— 0
$n = 3$ ———— -1.51
$n = 2$ ———— -3.40

$n = 1$ ———— -13.6

The radius of the allowed orbits in a hydrogen atom can be calculated using the following formula:

$$r_n = \frac{h^2}{4\pi^2 k m_e q_e^2} n^2$$

where r_n = radius of allowed orbit
n = orbit number

All the values in this equation are constants, except n. When n is equal to 1, $r_1 = 5.29 \times 10^{-11}$ m. This is the radius of the first energy level in a hydrogen atom. Therefore, this formula may be reduced as follows:
$$r_n = r_1 n^2$$

If the formula for the energy in each energy level can be calculated from the formula $E_n = \dfrac{E_1}{n^2}$, then the energy absorbed or emitted by an electron transition can be determined using the following formula:

$$E = E_u - E_1$$

where E = energy of the transition
E_u = energy of higher (upper) energy level
E_1 = energy of lower energy level

If the energy of the transition is found using this formula, the wavelength and frequency of the emitted or absorbed photons can be found using the following formula:

$$E = hf \qquad \text{or} \qquad E = \frac{hc}{\lambda}$$

where E = energy of the transition

The energy of the energy level is always negative. This is because the energy of $n = \infty$ is assigned a value of zero. If the greatest energy is zero, then the other energies must be negative. Therefore, the closer the electron is to the nucleus, the less energy it has. However, the energy of a transition, whether the energy of a photon is emitted or absorbed, is never negative.

The energy of the energy
level is always assigned
a negative value.
However, the energy
of an electron is
never negative.

Bohr's model of the atom can be used to understand the periodic table of elements. Bohr suggested that the chemical properties of an element depend on the number of electrons in the outermost occupied orbit (the outside energy level) in an unexcited atom. This orbit is called the valence orbit, and the electrons in it are called valence electrons.

Bohr's model of the
atom can be used to
understand the periodic
table of elements.

Bohr's model of the atom allowed only a certain number of electrons in any energy level at one time. When $n = 1$, there are a maximum of two electrons; when $n = 2$, there are a maximum of eight electrons; when $n = 3$, there are a maximum of eight electrons. According to this pattern, a family of elements from the periodic table (elements that have the same chemical properties) should have the same number of valence electrons.

Note: The symbol for atomic number is z.

Lithium $(z = 3)$ Sodium $(z = 11)$ Potassium $(z = 19)$

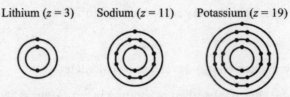

Each of these elements has one valence electron, so all of these elements have the same chemical properties.

Fluorine $(z = 9)$ Chlorine $(z = 11)$

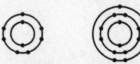

Each member in this chemical family has seven valence electrons.

Strengths of the Bohr Model

The Bohr model explained the repetition of chemical properties in the periodic table. It also explained the hydrogen spectra.

Weaknesses of the Bohr Model

Although the Bohr model generally explained bright-line and dark-line spectra, it could not explain the spectra of atoms containing many electrons. The Bohr model could also not explain why only certain orbits were allowed. Maxwell's theory of EMR argued against orbiting electrons not emitting energy. Bohr's model does not explain the relative intensities of spectra lines or why each spectrum line splits into several lines when placed in a magnetic or electric field.

The Bohr model provided answers to some questions regarding atomic structure, but it could not answer every question. This model, like the J. J. Thomson and the Rutherford models, was part of the development in scientific knowledge about the atomic structure, but it was not the final model of the atom.

Example

Calculate the radius of the second orbit of a hydrogen atom.

Solution

$$r_2 = r_1 n^2$$
$$= (5.29 \times 10^{-11} \text{ m})(2)^2$$
$$= 2.12 \times 10^{-10} \text{ m}$$

Example

Calculate the energy of the second energy level of a hydrogen atom.

Solution

$$E_2 = \frac{E_1}{n^2}$$

$$= \frac{-2.18 \times 10^{-18} \text{ J}}{(2)^2}$$

$$= -5.45 \times 10^{-19} \text{ J}$$

$$\text{or } = \frac{-13.6 \text{ eV}}{(2)^2}$$

$$= -3.40 \text{ eV}$$

Example

An electron undergoes a transition from the third energy level to the second energy level in a hydrogen atom. What is the wavelength of the emitted photon?

Solution

$$\frac{1}{\lambda} = R_H \left(\frac{1}{n_e^{\,2}} - \frac{1}{n_u^{\,2}} \right)$$

$$= \left(1.10 \times 10^7 / \text{m} \right) \left(\frac{1}{2^2} - \frac{1}{3^2} \right)$$

$$= 1.53 \times 10^6 \text{ m}^{-1}$$

$$\lambda = 6.54 \times 10^{-7} \text{ m}$$

or

$$E_3 = \frac{E_1}{n^2} \qquad\qquad E_2 = \frac{E_1}{n^2}$$

$$= \frac{-2.18 \times 10^{-18} \text{ J}}{(3)^2} \qquad = \frac{-2.18 \times 10^{-18} \text{ J}}{(2)^2}$$

$$= -2.42 \times 10^{-19} \text{ J} \qquad = -5.45 \times 10^{-19} \text{ J}$$

Energy lost in transition $= E_3 - E_2$

$$= -2.42 \times 10^{-19} \text{ J} - \left(-5.45 \times 10^{-19} \text{ J} \right)$$

$$= 3.03 \times 10^{-19} \text{ J}$$

$$E = \frac{hc}{\lambda}$$

$$\lambda = \frac{hc}{E}$$

$$= \frac{\left(6.63 \times 10^{-34} \text{ J} \cdot \text{s} \right) \left(3.00 \times 10^8 \text{ m/s} \right)}{3.03 \times 10^{-19} \text{ J}}$$

$$= 6.57 \times 10^{-7} \text{ m}$$

PRACTICE EXERCISES

Formulas: $r_n = r_1 n^2$ $E_n = \dfrac{E_1}{n^2}$ $\dfrac{1}{\lambda} = R_H \left(\dfrac{1}{n_e^2} - \dfrac{1}{n_u^2} \right)$

1. Calculate the radius of the third orbit of a hydrogen atom.

2. Calculate the energy of the third energy level of a hydrogen atom.

3. An electron undergoes a transition from the fourth energy level to the third energy level in a hydrogen atom. What is the wavelength of the radiation emitted?

4. An electron undergoes a transition from the first energy level to the third energy level in a hydrogen atom. What is the wavelength of the radiation absorbed?

5. An electron undergoes a transition from the sixth energy level to the second energy level in a hydrogen atom. What is the frequency of the light emitted?

6. Calculate the energy required to ionize a hydrogen atom in which the electron is in the ground state (the first energy level). (**Note:** To ionize means to move the electron to $n = \infty$.)

7. An unexcited hydrogen atom (the electron is in the ground state) absorbed a photon of light that had a frequency of 3.09×10^{15} Hz. Through what transition did the electron in this atom undergo?

8. A photon of light with a wavelength of 433 nm is emitted from an excited hydrogen atom. Through what transition did the electron in this atom undergo?

9. What orbit (*n*-value) in a hydrogen atom has a radius of 1.90×10^{-9} m?

10. Calculate the frequency of the third line in the Paschen series of spectra lines for a hydrogen atom.

11. What is the shortest wavelength of light emitted by an electron transition in the Brackett series of spectra lines of a hydrogen atom?

12. One of the spectra lines of an unknown element has a wavelength of 523 nm. Calculate the energy of the electron transition that is involved.

13. If the third energy level of a hypothetical hydrogenlike atom is -1.50×10^{-18} J, what is the energy of the second energy level?

14. What is the radius of the orbit of a hydrogen atom that has an energy value of -1.51 eV?

15. Calculate the time required for an electron in the third orbit of a hydrogen atom to make one revolution around the nucleus.

16. Calculate the centripetal force on an electron in the fourth energy level of a hydrogen atom.

17. Calculate the electric force on an electron in the fourth energy level of a hydrogen atom.

18. In a hypothetical hydrogenlike atom, the energy of the second energy level is −13.9 eV. Calculate the momentum of the electron in the third energy level of this atom.

19. A spectrum line in the hydrogen bright-line spectrum (visible region) passes perpendicularly through a diffraction grating $(d = 5.00 \times 10^{-6} \text{ m})$. This spectrum line produces a first-order maximum at an angle of 4.97°. What is the transition of the electron that produces this spectrum line?

Lesson 5   DE BROGLIE

In 1924, Louis de Broglie suggested that if light (EMR) could have particle properties, particles such as electrons, protons, atoms, molecules, billiard balls, and even humans could have wave properties. He suggested that the wavelength of these objects is related to their momentum. The de Broglie equation is as follows:

$$\lambda = \frac{h}{p} \qquad p = mv$$

$$\therefore \lambda = \frac{h}{mv}$$

The wavelength of a particle is often referred to as the de Broglie wavelength. It should be noted that a large mass with an ordinary speed has a very, very small wavelength. However, a small particle (like an electron) travelling at high speed has a detectable wavelength. De Broglie received a Nobel Prize in physics for this theory.

It was suggested that if electrons have a wave nature, they could be diffracted. It was also suggested that crystals could be used as a diffracting grating. Davisson and Germer demonstrated that electrons could be diffracted. G. P. Thomson confirmed Davisson and Germer's results using thin metal foil. G. P. Thomson demonstrated the wave nature of the electron 28 years after his father, J. J. Thomson, discovered it.

G. P. Thomson demonstrated the diffraction of electrons.

An electron microscope makes use of the wave nature of electrons. The wavelengths of electrons are many times shorter than the wavelengths of visible light, and because of this, electron microscopes are able to distinguish details that are not possible to see with microscopes that use light.

Example

Calculate the wavelength of an electron that has a speed of 5.50×10^6 m/s.

Solution

$$\lambda = \frac{h}{mv}$$

$$= \frac{6.63 \times 10^{-34} \text{ J} \cdot \text{s}}{\left(9.11 \times 10^{-31} \text{ kg}\right)\left(5.50 \times 10^6 \text{ m/s}\right)}$$

$$= 1.32 \times 10^{-10} \text{ m}$$

Example

Calculate the wavelength of an electron that has kinetic energy of 3.10×10^{-16} J.

(**Note:** Find the speed first.)

Solution

$$E_k = \frac{1}{2}mv^2$$

$$v = \sqrt{\frac{2E}{m}}$$

$$= \sqrt{\frac{2\left(3.10 \times 10^{-16} \text{ J}\right)}{9.11 \times 10^{-31} \text{ kg}}}$$

$$= 2.61 \times 10^7 \text{ m/s}$$

$$\lambda = \frac{h}{mv}$$

$$= \frac{6.63 \times 10^{-34} \text{ J} \cdot \text{s}}{\left(9.11 \times 10^{-31} \text{ kg}\right)\left(2.61 \times 10^7 \text{ m/s}\right)}$$

$$= 2.79 \times 10^{-11} \text{ m}$$

PRACTICE EXERCISES

1. Calculate the wavelength of an electron that has a speed of 2.25×10^7 m/s.

2. Calculate the wavelength of an electron that has a kinetic energy of 7.50×10^{-3} MeV.

3. What is the frequency of an electron that has a speed of 9.20×10^5 m/s?

4. What is the speed of an electron that has a wavelength of 7.00×10^2 nm?

5. Calculate the wavelength of an electron that is accelerated from rest through a potential difference of 1.00×10^3 V.

6. Calculate the wavelength of a ball that has a mass of 1.30 kg and a speed of 3.2×10^1 m/s.

7. What is the kinetic energy of an alpha particle that has a wavelength of 1.46×10^{-15} m?

8. Calculate the speed of a proton that has a wavelength of 5.88×10^{-12} m.

9. Through what potential difference must an electron be accelerated so that its wavelength is 2.75×10^{-11} m?

10. What is the kinetic energy of an alpha particle whose wavelength is the same as that of a 1.00 MeV photon?

11. What is the kinetic energy of a proton whose wavelength is the same as that of a 1.00 keV electron?

12. If an electron is moving in a circular path ($R = 0.75$ m) through a perpendicular magnetic field $\left(B = 2.3 \times 10^{-4} \text{ T}\right)$, what is the wavelength of the electron?

Lesson 6 STANDING WAVES (ELECTRONS)

One of the difficulties with the Bohr model is that it does not explain why the electron has only certain orbits. This can be understood by considering de Broglie's theory about the wave nature of electrons. De Broglie also suggested that an electron is a circular standing wave within an atom.
In a standing wave, the number of wavelengths is always a whole number. Therefore, the electron will exist only when the circumference of the orbit is equal to a whole number of wavelengths. That is, the wave closes in on itself, as shown in the following diagram. In this way, the wave is reinforced constructively (constructive interference).

The electron can exist only where there is constructive interference.

In order to obtain this constructive interference, the wavelength of the electron must fit evenly into the circumference of the orbit. This means that the wavelength multiplied by a whole number must equal the circumference of the electron's orbit. This relationship is expressed using the following equation:

$$2\pi r = n\lambda$$

where $2\pi r$ = circumference of orbit
n = whole number

If this does not happen, destructive interference occurs.

In this diagram, the wave does not close in on itself. Each cycle does not reinforce the previous cycles, which results in destructive interference. Therefore, the wave cannot exist, and the electron cannot exist at this orbit.

The electron cannot exist where there is destructive interference.

In order for the electron to exist in a given orbit, constructive interference must occur. The circumference of the orbit must be equal to some whole number of wavelength.
$$2\pi r = n\lambda$$

This explains why the electrons have only certain orbits.

Example

What is the wavelength of an electron in the second level of the hydrogen atom?

Solution

$$E_n = \frac{E_1}{n_2}$$

$$E_2 = \frac{-2.18 \times 10^{-18} \text{ J}}{2^2}$$

$$= -5.45 \times 10^{-19} \text{ J}$$

$$E_k = \frac{1}{2}mv^2$$

$$v = \sqrt{\frac{2E_k}{m}}$$

$$= \sqrt{\frac{2(5.45 \times 10^{-19} \text{ J})}{9.11 \times 10^{-31} \text{ kg}}}$$

$$= 1.09 \times 10^6 \text{ m/s}$$

$$\lambda = \frac{h}{mv}$$

$$= \frac{6.63 \times 10^{-34} \text{ J} \cdot \text{s}}{(9.11 \times 10^{-31} \text{ kg})(1.09 \times 10^6 \text{ m/s})}$$

$$= 6.65 \times 10^{-10} \text{ m}$$

or

Find *r* first.

$$r_n = r_1 n^2$$

$$= (5.29 \times 10^{-11} \text{ m})(2)^2$$

$$= 2.12 \times 10^{-10} \text{ m}$$

$$n\lambda = 2\pi r$$

$$\lambda = \frac{2\pi r}{n}$$

$$= \frac{(2)(3.14)(2.12 \times 10^{-10} \text{ m})}{2}$$

$$= 6.65 \times 10^{-10} \text{ m}$$

Example

If the wavelength of an electron in the fourth orbit of a hypothetical hydrogenlike atom is 2.8×10^{-10} m, what is the wavelength of an electron in the first orbit of this same atom?

Solution

$$\lambda = \frac{h}{mv}$$

$$v = \frac{h}{m\lambda}$$

$$= \frac{6.63 \times 10^{-34} \text{ J} \cdot \text{s}}{\left(9.11 \times 10^{-31} \text{ kg}\right)\left(2.8 \times 10^{-10} \text{ m}\right)}$$

$$= 2.60 \times 10^{6} \text{ m/s}$$

$$E_k = \frac{1}{2}mv^2$$

$$= \frac{1}{2}\left(9.11 \times 10^{-31} \text{ kg}\right)\left(2.60 \times 10^{6} \text{ m/s}\right)^2$$

$$= 3.08 \times 10^{-18} \text{ J}$$

$$E_n = \frac{E_1}{n^2}$$

$$E_1 = E_4 n^2$$

$$= \left(-3.08 \times 10^{-18} \text{ J}\right)\left(4^2\right)$$

$$= -4.92 \times 10^{-17} \text{ J}$$

$$E_k = \frac{1}{2}mv^2$$

$$v = \sqrt{\frac{2E_k}{m}}$$

$$= \sqrt{\frac{2\left(4.92 \times 10^{-17} \text{ J}\right)}{9.11 \times 10^{-31} \text{ kg}}}$$

$$= 1.04 \times 10^{7} \text{ m/s}$$

$$\lambda = \frac{h}{mv}$$

$$= \frac{6.63 \times 10^{-34} \text{ J} \cdot \text{s}}{\left(9.11 \times 10^{-31} \text{ kg}\right)\left(1.04 \times 10^{7} \text{ m/s}\right)}$$

$$= 7.0 \times 10^{-11} \text{ m}$$

or

Find radius of fourth orbit first.

$$n\lambda = 2\pi r$$

$$r = \frac{n\lambda}{2\pi}$$

$$r = \frac{4\left(2.8 \times 10^{-10} \text{ m}\right)}{2\left(3.14\right)}$$

$$= 1.8 \times 10^{-10} \text{ m}$$

$\therefore$ radius of first orbit is:

$$r_4 = r_1 n^2$$

$$r_1 = \frac{r_4}{n^2}$$

$$= \frac{1.8 \times 10^{-10} \text{ m}}{\left(4\right)^2}$$

$$= 1.1 \times 10^{-11} \text{ m}$$

Now, find the wavelength in the first orbit.

$$n\lambda = 2\pi r$$

$$\lambda = \frac{2\pi r}{n}$$

$$= \frac{2\left(3.14\right)\left(1.1 \times 10^{-11} \text{ m}\right)}{1}$$

$$= 7.0 \times 10^{-11} \text{ m}$$

PRACTICE EXERCISES

Formulas: $\qquad \lambda = \dfrac{h}{mv}$ $\qquad\qquad\qquad n\lambda = 2\pi r$

1. Calculate the wavelength of an electron in the third energy level of a hydrogen atom.

2. The wavelength of an electron in a hydrogen atom is 1.66×10^{-9} m. What energy level is this electron in?

3. If the wavelength of an electron in the third orbit of a hypothetical hydrogenlike atom is 7.30×10^{-9} m, what is the radius of the first orbit of this atom?

4. The energy of an electron in the first energy level of a hypothetical hydrogenlike atom is 9.6 eV. What is the wavelength of the electron at this level?

5. When an electron orbits the nucleus, it can be thought of as a standing wave. Calculate the frequency of this wave if the electron is in the fourth energy level of a hydrogen atom.

Lesson 7 QUANTUM MECHANICS

The study of the motion of large objects is called mechanics, and this motion can be described by classical physics. The study of motion in the atomic world is quantum mechanics, but this motion cannot be described by classical physics. Classical physics cannot describe the atomic structure, because of the significant wave nature of atomic and subatomic particles. Because of the significance of the wave nature in quantum mechanics, quantum mechanics is also referred to as wave mechanics.

Quantum mechanics was developed in the early twentieth century by a number of scientists. In the mid-1920s, Werner Heisenberg and Erwin Schrödinger developed a quantum-mechanical model to describe atomic structure. This is a mathematical model, and it is described in the Schrödinger equation. This equation defines the wave properties and predicts the particlelike behaviour of electrons in an atom. Similar to the Bohr model, the quantum-mechanical model assumes there are only certain energy levels.

The quantum-mechanical model of the atom cannot be shown as the Bohr model could. This is because the position of the electron within the atom cannot be exactly defined. Instead, it can only be described in terms of probabilities. These probability patterns are referred to as orbitals, not orbits. Think of these orbitals as clouds—if the position of the electron were determined 1 000 times, you would obtain this probability pattern. The shape and dimension of a probability pattern depends on the electron's energy and can be found mathematically.

Keep in mind that the process of science is not static. The understanding of the universe, including atoms, is forever increasing and developing. Einstein believed that the quantum-mechanical model of the atom will later be replaced by a model not based on probability. Currently, however, this probability description (quantum mechanics) is still used to describe the atom.

The reason classical physics does not work for atomic or subatomic particles is because of the significant wave nature of these small particles.

Quantum mechanics is the description of motion in the atomic or subatomic world.

PRACTICE QUIZ

1. Alpha particles travel undeflected through magnetic and electric fields that are perpendicular to each other. If the magnetic field strength is 1.75×10^{-2} T and the electric field strength is 1.94×10^{4} N/C, what is the kinetic energy of the alpha particles?

2. Protons travel with a speed of 5.05×10^{5} m/s perpendicularly to a magnetic field. If the radius of curvature of the proton path is 2.77×10^{-3} m, what is the magnitude of the magnetic force on the protons?

Use the following information to answer the next question.

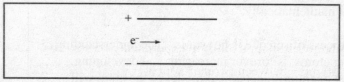

3. Electrons travel horizontally between two parallel, charged plates, as shown in the given diagram. If the plates are 2.00 cm apart and have a potential difference between them of 6.50 V, what is the vertical acceleration on the electrons?

4. A potential difference of 1.00×10^{4} V accelerated an electron from rest. The electron then enters into a perpendicular magnetic field where it experiences a magnetic force of 5.20×10^{-15} N. What is the magnetic field strength?

5. X^{2+} and Y^+ ions travel at the same speed as they enter into a magnetic field. An X^{2+} ion has a mass of 8.35×10^{-27} kg, while a Y^+ ion has a mass of 3.34×10^{-27} kg. If the X^{2+} ions are deflected through an arc with a radius of 0.400 m, what is the radius of the arc through which the Y^+ ions are deflected?

6. In an experiment similar to Millikan's oil-drop experiment, an oil drop with a weight of 2.40×10^{-15} N falls at a constant speed between two horizontal, parallel, charged plates. If the potential difference between the two plates is 1.00×10^2 V and the plates are 6.00 cm apart, what is the magnitude of the charge of the oil drop?

7. In an experiment similar to Millikan's oil-drop experiment, a 3.60×10^{-16} kg oil drop accelerated upward at a rate of 1.60 m/s^2 between two horizontal, parallel plates. If the electric field between the plates is 5.13×10^3 V/m, what is the magnitude of the charge on the oil drop?

8. Using the Bohr model of the hydrogen atom, how many times larger is the radius of the fourth orbit than the radius of the third orbit?

9. If the radius of the fifth energy level of a hypothetical hydrogenlike atom is 9.20×10^{-10} m, what is the radius of the third energy level of this atom?

10. In a hypothetical hydrogenlike atom, the energy of the fourth energy level is -12 eV. Calculate the wavelength of the radiation emitted by this atom as the electron drops from the third energy level to the second energy level.

11. Using the Bohr model of the hydrogen atom, how many times lower is the energy of the fifth energy level than the energy of the second energy level?

12. When white light is shone through hydrogen gas and then through a diffraction grating, a dark-line spectrum is produced. If one of these dark lines corresponds to a wavelength of 654 nm, what is the electron transition in a hydrogen atom?

13. What is the lowest frequency of radiation emitted by an electron transition in the Paschen series of spectra lines of a hydrogen atom?

14. What is the energy of the lowest-energy photon that an unexcited atom of hydrogen will absorb? (**Hint:** If $n_i = 1$, what must n_f be?)

15. A student directed a laser beam through a diffraction grating ruled 2.20×10^5 lines/m and obtained an interference pattern on a screen 7.50×10^{-1} m from the grating. If the first-order maximum was 7.00×10^{-2} m from the central maximum, what is the energy of each photon in the beam?

16. What is the frequency of a wave of an electron that moves with a speed of 5.60×10^7 m/s?

17. Calculate the velocity of an electron that has a wavelength of 4.22×10^{-11} m.

18. What is the wavelength of an electron in the fourth energy level of a hydrogen atom?

19. What is the wavelength of an alpha particle travelling at a speed of 2.00×10^7 m/s?

20. Calculate the frequency of a proton travelling at a speed of 9.00×10^6 m/s.

21. In a hypothetical hydrogenlike atom, the energy of the first energy level is -18.1 eV. Calculate the wavelength of the electron found in the second energy level of this atom.

22. Calculate the wavelength of an alpha particle that has been accelerated from rest through a potential difference of 2.60×10^1 V.

23. A beam of electrons is diffracted by a crystal. The ions in this crystal are separated by a distance of 1.10×10^{-10} m, and the first-order maximum is found 7.30×10^{-2} m from the central maximum. If the crystal is placed 2.50×10^{-1} m from the screen, find the energy of each electron.

24. What is the speed of a proton that has a wavelength of 7.00×10^2 nm?

25. A potential difference accelerated an electron from rest. If the electron has a wavelength of 4.85×10^{-11} m after accelerating, what was the accelerating voltage?

26. Calculate the radius of the arc an electron travels through as the electron, with a wavelength of 2.08×10^{-9} m, travels perpendicularly through a magnetic field $\left(B = 8.00 \times 10^{-6} \text{ T}\right)$.

27. When an electron travelling at a speed of 5.5×10^{7} m/s is diffracted by a crystal, a second-order minimum is produced at an angle of deviation of 5.0°. What is the spacing between the atoms in this crystal?

28. In a hypothetical hydrogenlike atom, the energy of the fourth energy level is −3.5 eV. Calculate the momentum of the photon emitted by this atom as the electron drops from the third energy level to the second energy level.

29. Radiation with a frequency of 6.67×10^{14} Hz illuminated a photoelectric surface $\left(W = 2.50 \text{ eV}\right)$. The emitted electrons were then deflected by a perpendicular magnetic field $\left(B = 3.11 \times 10^{-5} \text{ T}\right)$. What was the maximum radius of deflection of these electrons?

REVIEW SUMMARY

- Various models of the atom
  - Thomson model
  - Planetary model
  - Rutherford-Bohr model
  - Quantum-mechanical model
- The discovery of the electron through:
  - Cathode rays
  - Thomson's experiment
  - Millikan's oil-drop experiment
- The various types of spectra:
  - Bright-line spectra
  - Continuous spectra
  - Dark-line, or absorption, spectra
- The role of the hydrogen spectra in the development of the atomic model
- The de Broglie hypothesis and the diffraction of electrons
- The duality (wave-particle) of the electron and the beginning of the quantum-mechanical model
- Formulas used in this section of the unit:
  - $F_m = qvB_\perp$
  - $E = hf$
  - $n\lambda = 2\pi r$
  - $\vec{F}_e = q\vec{E}$
  - $E = \dfrac{hc}{\lambda}$
  - $c = \lambda f$
  - $\vec{F}_g = m\vec{g}$
  - $E_n = \dfrac{E_1}{n^2}$
  - $F_c = \dfrac{mv^2}{r}$
  - $r_n = r_1 n^2$
  - $\dfrac{1}{\lambda} = R_H \left(\dfrac{1}{n_1^2} - \dfrac{1}{n_u^2} \right)$
  - $\lambda = \dfrac{h}{mv}$

PRACTICE TEST

1. The first line in the Lyman series has a wavelength of 121 nm. What is the wavelength of the second line in this series?

   A. 93.5 nm

   B. 94.7 nm

   C. 102 nm

   D. 654 nm

2. When a charged particle travels undeflected through perpendicular electric and magnetic fields, the ratio of the electric field strength to the magnetic field strength is equal to the

   A. mass of the particle

   B. speed of the particle

   C. charge on the particle

   D. charge-to-mass ratio of the particle

Use the following information to answer the next question.

A student makes the following statements:
i) The energy of an electron in an atom is quantized.
ii) The electrons move within an orbit by emitting energy.
iii) The allowed energy levels are not equally spaced.

3. Which of the given statements about the Bohr model of the hydrogen atom are **true**?

   A. i) and ii) only

   B. i) and iii) only

   C. ii) and iii) only

   D. i), ii), and iii)

4. What is the speed of an electron in the third energy level of a hydrogen atom?

   A. 7.29×10^5 m/s

   B. 1.26×10^6 m/s

   C. 2.19×10^6 m/s

   D. 6.56×10^6 m/s

5. Classical physics could explain

   A. the Compton effect

   B. blackbody radiation

   C. the photoelectric effect

   D. deflection of electrons by a magnetic field

Use the following information to answer the next question.

> The following items each have a de Broglie wavelength:
> i)   An electron accelerated by a potential difference of 1.00×10^4 V
> ii) A ball with a mass of 4.50×10^{-2} kg travelling at a speed of 1.00×10^2 m/s
> iii) An electron in the first energy level of a hydrogen atom

6. When the given items are placed in decreasing order according to their de Broglie wavelengths, the order is

   A. i), ii), iii)

   B. iii), i), ii)

   C. ii), i), iii)

   D. ii), iii), i)

7. An alpha particle may be described as

   A. a high-energy proton

   B. the nucleus of a helium atom

   C. the component of a cathode ray

   D. a particle composed of a neutron and a proton

8. The charge-to-mass ratio of the electron was determined partially by balancing the

   A. electric and magnetic forces

   B. gravitational and electric forces

   C. gravitational and magnetic forces

   D. gravitational, electric, and magnetic forces

9. The elementary charge was determined by balancing the

   A. electric and magnetic forces

   B. gravitational and electric forces

   C. gravitational and magnetic forces

   D. gravitational, electric, and magnetic forces

10. A cathode ray is a beam of

    A. alpha particles

    B. electrons

    C. photons

    D. protons

11. Which of the following statements about cathode rays is **false**?

    A. Cathode rays can be deflected by electric fields.

    B. Cathode rays can be deflected by magnetic fields.

    C. Cathode rays travel at a speed of 3.00×10^8 m/s through a vacuum.

    D. Cathode rays are particles with a characteristic charge-to-mass ratio.

12. The solar spectrum is an example of

    A. a hydrogen spectrum

    B. a bright-line spectrum

    C. a continuous spectrum

    D. an absorption spectrum

13. One of the problems with the Bohr model of the atom was that it

    A. could not explain the dark-line spectra of hydrogen

    B. could not explain why orbiting electrons did not emit EMR

    C. only predicted the Balmer series of spectra lines for hydrogen

    D. predicted that the energy of the electrons in hydrogen atoms was quantized

14. The Thomson model of the atom was formulated in order to explain the

    A. bright-line spectra of hydrogen

    B. existence of electrons in matter

    C. scattering of alpha particles by a gold foil

    D. deflection of cathode rays by magnetic fields

15. Charged particles are deflected by a magnetic field when they travel perpendicularly to the field. This deflection can be increased by decreasing the

    A. mass of the particles

    B. charge on the particles

    C. strength of the magnetic field

    D. number of the particles within the field

16. In a CRT experiment, electrons pass through perpendicular electric and magnetic fields without deflection. Which of the following properties of the electron can be calculated if only the strength of each field is known?

    A. Mass

    B. Speed

    C. Charge

    D. Charge-to-mass ratio

17. According to classical physics, the atom should **not** exist because

    A. electrons travel faster than light

    B. accelerating electrons emit energy

    C. accelerating electrons must gain energy

    D. electrons travel too slow to maintain an orbit

18. A hydrogen atom emits a photon when its electron

    A. collides with its nucleus

    B. makes one complete orbit around the nucleus

    C. moves from a lower energy level to a higher one

    D. moves from a higher energy level to a lower one

19. Which of the following light sources could be used to produce a bright-line spectrum?

    A. Sun

    B. Neon sign

    C. Barbeque lighter

    D. Incandescent light bulb

20. In a Millikan oil-drop experiment, a student wants to determine the relationship between the mass of the oil drop and the strength of the electric field needed to suspend it. If all other variables are kept constant, what is this relationship?

    A. $E \propto m$

    B. $E \propto \dfrac{1}{m}$

    C. $E \propto m^2$

    D. $E \propto \dfrac{1}{m^2}$

21. If you know the speed of an electron, it is possible to calculate its

    A. energy and momentum only

    B. wavelength and energy only

    C. momentum and wavelength only

    D. energy, momentum, and wavelength

Use the following information to answer the next question.

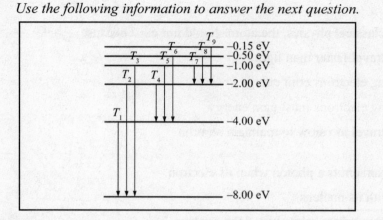

22. The given diagram represents the possible transitions within the gaseous atoms of a hypothetical element, E. If transitions T_5 and T_9 produce light in the visible region, which of the other transitions will also produce light in the visible region?

    A. T_4

    B. T_6

    C. T_7

    D. T_8

ATOMIC PHYSICS: ATOMIC NUCLEUS AND ELEMENTARY PARTICLES

When you are finished this section of the unit, you should be able to…

- Describe the nature and properties, including biological effects, of alpha, beta, and gamma radiation

- Write nuclear equations, using isotope notation, for alpha, beta-negative, and beta-positive decays, including the appropriate neutrino and antineutrino

- Perform simple, non-logarithmic half-life calculations

- Use the law of conservation of charge and mass number to predict the particles emitted by a nucleus

- Compare and contrast the characteristics of fission and fusion reactions

- Relate, qualitatively and quantitatively, the mass defect of the nucleus to the energy released in nuclear reactions, using Einstein's concept of mass-energy equivalence.

- Explain how the analysis of particle tracks contributed to the discovery and identification of the characteristics of subatomic particles

- Explain, qualitatively, in terms of the strong nuclear force, why high-energy particle accelerators are required to study subatomic particles

- Describe the modern model of the proton and neutron as being composed of quarks

- Compare and contrast the elementary fermions and their antiparticles in terms of charge and energy (mass-energy)

- Describe beta-positive $\left(\beta^+\right)$ and beta-negative $\left(\beta^-\right)$ decay, using first-generation elementary fermions and the principle of charge conservation (Feynman diagrams are not required)

PREREQUISITE SKILLS AND KNOWLEDGE

Prior to starting this unit, you should be able to…

- Understand centripetal force and acceleration of an object in terms of mass, velocity, and radius
- Explain charged particle interactions in terms of repulsion, attraction and the law of conservation of charge
- Explain the past theories that led to modern understand of the atomic model
- Describe the experiments of J. J. Thomson, Millikan, and Rutherford and the significance of the results for both science and technology
- Explain, quantitatively, the modern atomic model of the atom
- Describe, quantitatively, photoelectric emission, using concepts related to the conservation of energy
- Calculate the amount of energy absorbed or released when an electron in an atom changes energy levels
- Classify the different regions that make up the electromagnetic spectrum in terms of photon frequency and wavelength
- Solve problems describing the motion of charged particles in terms of centripetal force, centripetal acceleration, speed, mass, and radius in an electric, magnetic, and gravitational field.

Lesson 1 ATOMIC NUCLEUS AND ELEMENTARY PARTICLES

In 1896, Henri Becquerel discovered that certain elements are radioactive; that is, they emit some kind of radiation. These waves of radiation were initially called Becquerel rays. This discovery was the beginning of nuclear physics. Becquerel received a Nobel Prize for his discovery.

When Ernest Rutherford discovered the nucleus, he also determined the size of the nucleus. The approximate size of the nucleus is related to its atomic number, as shown in the following formula:

$$r \approx \left(1.2 \times 10^{-15} \text{ m}\right) A^{1/3}$$

where r = radius of the nucleus

A = mass number (number of nucleons)

The radius of the nucleus is very small in comparison with the radius of the atom. The radius of an atom is approximately 10^{-10} m, while the radius of a nucleus is approximately 10^{-15} m.

Two years after Rutherford discovered the nucleus, Henry Moseley, who was working in Rutherford's lab, discovered that the charge on the nucleus is always a multiple of the charge of an electron, but the charge is positive instead of negative. Moseley's work led to the development of the modern periodic table, in which elements are listed according to atomic number. The atomic number is the number of protons within the nucleus. It was Rutherford who showed that the nucleus contains protons.

Frederick Soddy discovered isotopes while investigating the nature of radioactivity. In order to explain the existence of isotopes, it was suggested that the nucleus also contained some neutral particles in addition to the actual protons in the nucleus, and that each neutral particle had a mass similar to that of a proton. In 1932, James Chadwick discovered this particle and called it the neutron.

Protons and neutrons are collectively called nucleons.

Henri Becquerel discovered that certain elements were radioactive.

Ernest Rutherford discovered the nucleus of the atom.

Atoms that have the same number of protons but a different number of neutrons are called isotopes.

nucleons = protons + neutrons

NOTES

$1\mu = 1.6605 \times 10^{-27}$ kg

The charges and masses of electrons, protons, and neutrons are given in the following table:

	Charge (C)	Mass (kg)	Mass (atomic mass unit $-\mu$
Electrons	-1.60×10^{-19}	9.11×10^{-31}	0.000 548 58
Neutrons	0	1.6749×10^{-27}	1.0087
Protons	$+1.60 \times 10^{-19}$	1.6726×10^{-27}	1.0073

In the given chart, the atomic mass unit (μ) is used.

$1\mu = 1.6605 \times 10^{-27}$ kg

In nuclear physics, the atomic mass unit is used more often than the kilogram. Nuclear physics also focuses on the nucleus of the atom rather than on its external electrons. This nucleus is represented by the following symbol:

$$_Z^A X$$

where   X = symbol of the element
A = mass number (the number of nucleons [protons and neutrons])
Z = atomic number (the number of protons)

Lesson 2 ISOTOPES

Isotopes are different atoms of the same element. They have the same number of protons but a different number of neutrons within the nucleus. Isotopes have the same atomic number but different mass numbers. For example, uranium can have the following isotopes:

$$^{235}_{92}U \qquad ^{238}_{92}U$$

Example

If an oxygen nucleus is represented by the symbol $^{15}_{8}O$, how many protons and neutrons are found in this nucleus?

Solution

The number of protons is found as follows:
Z = number of protons
$\quad = 8$

The number of neutrons is found as follows:
$$A = \text{number of neutrons} + \text{number of protons}$$
$$15 = \text{number of neutrons} + 8$$
$$\text{number of neutrons} = 15 - 8$$
$$= 7$$

Example

Identify the element that has the isotope $^{130}_{56}X$.

Solution

The atomic number, 56 in this example, identifies the isotope.
By looking at a periodic table, you can see that element 56 is barium.

Example

How many protons and neutrons are found in an isotope of radium-226?

Solution

The number 226 is the number of nucleons. If you look up radium on a periodic table, you can see that it is element 88. That is, it has 88 protons.

Therefore, radium-226 has $226 - 88 = 138$ neutrons.

PRACTICE EXERCISES

Formula: $^A_Z X$

1. How many protons and neutrons are found in a nucleus of the following isotopes?

    a) $^{16}_{8} O$

    b) $^{35}_{17} Cl$

    c) $^{234}_{92} U$

    d) $^{234}_{90} Th$

    e) $^{14}_{6} C$

    f) $^{1}_{1} H$

2. Identify the elements that have the following isotopes.

    a) $^{2}_{1} X$

    b) $^{60}_{27} X$

c) $^{56}_{26}X$

d) $^{197}_{79}X$

e) $^{90}_{38}X$

3. How many protons and neutrons are found in a nucleus of the following isotopes?

a) Carbon-14

b) Strontium-90

c) Uranium-238

Lesson 3 MASS SPECTROMETRY

NOTES

A spectroscope is an instrument that separates the components of light according to frequency.

A mass spectrometer is an instrument that separates particles according to mass.

Isotopes are separated using a mass spectrometer. A mass spectrometer is an instrument that separates particles according to mass. There are different kinds of mass spectrometers; however, there are four basic parts that make up all mass spectrometers:

• An ion source

• A velocity selector

• An ion separation region

• An ion detector

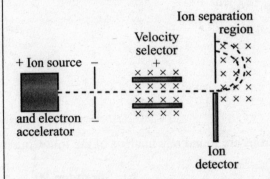

Ions are produced by either heating or electrical discharge. Positive or negative ions may be produced. However, the following examples will consider only positive particles. These ions are accelerated by an accelerating voltage (in an electric field).

$$\Delta E = qV$$

Once the ions leave their source, or the accelerator, they enter a velocity selector (the ions will have slightly different velocities when they leave the accelerator). For precise work, the ions must pass through this velocity selector so that all the ions will have the same velocity. This will limit the error that might occur in observation. The velocity selector is composed of uniform magnetic and electric fields that are perpendicular to each other (similar to the Thomson apparatus).

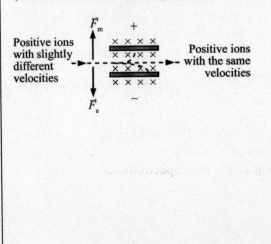

As the positive ions pass through these fields, the magnetic force and the electric force will be equal only for particles that have a certain velocity. For particles with other velocities, these forces will not be equal, so these particles will be deflected and prevented from exiting the velocity selector.

$$F_e = F_m$$
$$qE = qvB_\perp$$
$$v = \frac{E}{B_\perp}$$

After leaving the velocity selector, the charged particles enter a perpendicular magnetic field. In this field, the charged particles are deflected in a circular path by the magnetic force.

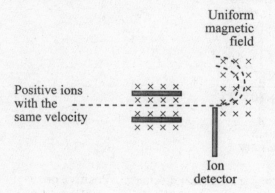

In the given formula, you can see that the radius (r) depends on the mass, velocity, and charge of the ions, as well as the strength of the uniform deflecting magnetic field.

$$F_m = F_c$$
$$qvB_\perp = \frac{mv^2}{r}$$
$$r = \frac{mv}{qB_\perp}$$

Although it is possible to produce ions with charges other than elementary charges, they are easily taken into account. In other words, if the mass of the ions is different, the radius will also be different.
$r \propto m$

This is the principle by which the mass spectrometer separates particles according to mass.

The mathematics of the mass spectrometer is the same as the mathematics for Thomson's cathode rays. Thomson's work on the charge-to-mass ratio of electrons led to the development of the mass spectrometer.

NOTES

Example

A potential difference of 1.66×10^4 V accelerated a positively charged ion $\left(q = 1.60 \times 10^{-19} \text{ C} \right)$ from rest. This ion then entered a magnetic field $\left(B = 3.20 \times 10^{-2} \text{ T} \right)$ perpendicular to the direction of the ion's motion.

If the magnetic force on the ion was 5.27×10^{-15} N, what was the mass of the ion?

Solution

$$\Delta E = qV$$
$$= \left(1.60 \times 10^{-19} \text{ C}\right)\left(1.66 \times 10^4 \text{ V}\right)$$
$$= 2.66 \times 10^{-15} \text{ J}$$
$$F_m = qvB_\perp$$
$$v = \frac{F_m}{qB_\perp}$$
$$= \frac{5.27 \times 10^{-15} \text{ N}}{(1.60 \times 10^{-19} \text{ C})(3.20 \times 10^{-2} \text{ T})}$$
$$= 1.03 \times 10^6 \text{ m/s}$$
$$E_k = \frac{1}{2}mv^2$$
$$m = \frac{2E_k}{v^2}$$
$$= \frac{2\left(2.66 \times 10^{-15} \text{ J}\right)}{\left(1.03 \times 10^6 \text{ m/s}\right)^2}$$
$$= 5.01 \times 10^{-27} \text{ kg}$$

Example

Ions travelling with a velocity of 2.80×10^6 m/s pass undeflected through the velocity selector in a mass spectrometer. If the electric field strength in the velocity selector is 2.87×10^6 V/m, what is the magnetic field strength in the velocity selector?

Solution

$$F_m = F_e$$
$$qvB_\perp = qE$$
$$B_\perp = \frac{E}{v}$$
$$= \frac{2.87 \times 10^6 \text{ V/m}}{2.80 \times 10^6 \text{ m/s}}$$
$$= 1.03 \text{ T}$$

Example

Doubly charged ions $\left(\text{mass} = 4.00 \times 10^{-26} \text{ kg}\right)$ pass undeflected through the velocity selector of a mass spectrometer. This velocity selector has a magnetic field of 0.820 T and an electric field of 4.00×10^{5} V/m perpendicular to each other. These ions then enter into the ion separation region. If the radius of the deflected ions is 5.00×10^{-2} m, what is the magnitude of the magnetic field in this region?

Solution

$$F_e = F_m$$
$$qE = qvB_\perp$$
$$v = \frac{E}{B_\perp}$$
$$= \frac{4.00 \times 10^{5} \text{ V/m}}{0.820 \text{ T}}$$
$$= 4.88 \times 10^{5} \text{ m/s}$$
$$F_m = F_c$$
$$qvB_\perp = \frac{mv^2}{r}$$
$$B_\perp = \frac{mv}{qr}$$
$$= \frac{\left(4.00 \times 10^{-26} \text{ kg}\right)\left(4.88 \times 10^{5} \text{ m/s}\right)}{\left(3.20 \times 10^{-19} \text{ C}\right)\left(5.00 \times 10^{-2} \text{ m}\right)}$$
$$= 1.22 \text{ T}$$

PRACTICE EXERCISES

Formulas:
$$F_e = F_m \qquad\qquad F_m = F_c$$
$$qE = qvB_\perp \qquad\qquad qvB_\perp = \frac{mv^2}{r}$$

1. Ions travelling at a velocity of 3.50×10^7 m/s pass undeflected through the velocity selector in a mass spectrometer. If the magnetic field strength in the velocity selector is 0.500 T, what is the magnitude of the electric field strength in the velocity selector?

2. A velocity selector comprises a uniform magnetic field $\left(B = 4.00 \times 10^{-2} \text{ T}\right)$ and a uniform electric field perpendicular to each other. If the electric field is produced by using parallel plates that are 1.50 cm apart, what is the potential difference between the plates that will permit singly charged ions with a speed of 4.20×10^6 m/s to pass undeflected through the selector?

3. Singly charged ions pass undeflected through the velocity selector of a mass spectrometer. This velocity selector has a magnetic field $\left(B = 2.50 \times 10^{-1} \text{ T}\right)$ and an electric field $\left(E = 7.00 \times 10^3 \text{ V/m}\right)$ perpendicular to each other. These ions then into enter the separation region where the magnetic field is the same as it is in the velocity selector. If the radius of the deflected ions is 8.12×10^{-3} m, what is the mass of each ion?

4. A potential difference of 4.00×10^4 V accelerated a singly charged ^{7}Li ion $\left(\text{mass} = 1.16 \times 10^{-26} \text{ kg} \right)$ from rest. This ion then entered a magnetic field $\left(B = 0.700 \text{ T} \right)$ perpendicular to its motion. What was the radius of the deflected ion?

Use the following information to answer the next question.

An ion source contains two isotopes of magnesium $\left(^{24}\text{Mg and } ^{25}\text{Mg} \right)$. These ions travel undeflected through the velocity selector $\left(B = 0.850 \text{ T}, \text{ E} = 4.60 \times 10^5 \text{ V/m} \right)$ of a mass spectrometer.

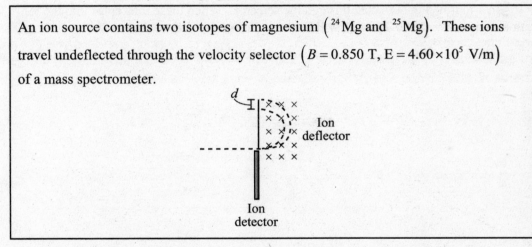

5. If both isotopes are singly charged, how far apart are the lines on the ion detector (*d*)? (Assume the magnetic field strength in the ion separator is 0.250 T.)

6. A singly charged carbon ion travels in a circular path ($r = 11.3$ cm) through the ion separation region of a mass spectrometer. If the velocity selector comprises an electric field $\left(E = 7.50 \times 10^4 \text{ N/C}\right)$ and a magnetic field ($B = 0.300$ T) perpendicular to each other, what is the mass number of the carbon isotope? (Assume that the ion separation region also has a magnetic field of 0.300 T.)

7. In a mass spectrometer, a velocity selector allows singly charged carbon-14 ions with a velocity of 1.00×10^6 m/s to travel undeflected through the selector. When these ions enter into the ion separation region ($B = 0.900$ T), what will be the radius of the path of the ions?

8. In a certain mass spectrometer, the radius of the path for singly charged ^{20}Ne ions is 15.1 cm in the ion separation region. What would be the radius of the path for singly charged ^{16}O ions, assuming identical velocities in the same mass spectrometer?

9. A beam of Pb^{2+} ions $\left(\text{mass} = 3.44 \times 10^{-25} \text{ kg}\right)$ travels through the velocity selector of a mass spectrometer with a velocity of 5.00×10^4 m/s. What is the magnetic field strength required in the ion separation region to cause these ions to travel in a circular path with a radius of 19.6 cm?

10. A potential difference of 2.00×10^3 V accelerated doubly charged neon atoms from rest. The atoms then entered into a perpendicular magnetic field $\left(B = 0.200 \text{ T}\right)$ and moved in a circular path with a radius of 10.2 cm. What was the mass of the neon ion?

11. A potential difference of 2.86×10^6 V in a mass spectrometer accelerated a singly ionized ion from rest. In the ion separation region, a magnetic field of 7.20 T deflected this ion through a radius of 14.0 cm. Calculate the mass of the ion.

Use the following information to answer the next question.

A student using a mass spectrometer with a constant magnetic field studied the relationship between the radius of the circular path of a number of singly charged isotopes and their momentum. The following data were determined:

Momentum $(\times 10^{-20}\ \text{kg} \cdot \text{m/s})$	Radius $(\times 10^{-1}\ \text{m})$
0.83	0.74
1.4	1.2
1.7	1.5
2.6	2.4
3.2	2.8
3.7	3.3

12. a) Draw a graph plotting the radius as a function of momentum.

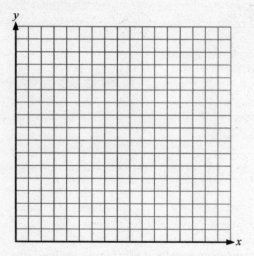

b) Using a suitable averaging technique, determine the magnetic field used in the spectrometer.

Lesson 4 RADIOACTIVE DECAY

NUCLEAR FORCES

Binding protons and neutrons together in a nucleus requires extremely large forces. Scientists have identified only four types of forces:

- Gravitational forces
- Electromagnetic forces (electric and magnetic forces, as well as contact forces)
- Strong nuclear forces
- Weak nuclear forces

The positively charged protons within a nucleus have electrostatic forces between them. Therefore, a nucleus with many protons will have large repulsive forces between them. These large electrostatic forces must be counteracted by strong nuclear binding forces.

Strong nuclear forces are not completely understood, but it is known that the range of these forces is very short $\left(1\times10^{-15}\text{ m}\right)$. Strong nuclear forces do not exist at distances greater than this. It is also known that strong nuclear forces are independent of the charge of the objects.

A nucleus with a large number of protons will have extra neutrons to offset the large electrostatic force. However, situations arise where extra neutrons cannot counteract the repulsive electrostatic force, and the nucleus becomes unstable. When this happens, the nucleus will disintegrate, rearrange itself, or both. Such an unstable nucleus is radioactive.

TYPES OF RADIOACTIVITY

Recall that Becquerel discovered a mysterious radiation emitting from certain elements. These rays were called Becquerel rays. It was later discovered that Becquerel rays were actually three types of rays: alpha rays, beta rays, and gamma rays. Alpha rays are beams of helium nuclei, beta rays are beams of electrons, and gamma rays are beams of high-energy photons. Gamma rays penetrate more than beta rays, which penetrate more than alpha rays.

When an unstable nucleus rearranges itself, it emits these particles. When an alpha ray or beta ray is emitted, the atom changes from one element to another; the atom transmutes or decays.

ALPHA DECAY

Alpha decay occurs in large nuclei where the electrostatic forces in the nucleus become greater than the strong nuclear forces. The nucleus emits an alpha particle to become more stable.

Consider the example of thorium, which decays to form radium and an alpha particle.

$$^{227}_{90}\text{Th} \rightarrow {}^{223}_{88}\text{Ra} + {}^{4}_{2}\alpha$$

Strong nuclear forces do not exist beyond the nucleus.

Electrostatic forces would cause the nucleus to disintegrate.

Strong nuclear forces hold the nucleus together.

Types of radioactivity:
– Alpha rays
– Beta rays
– Gamma rays

To show a nuclear reaction, write the symbols for the nuclei involved.

An alpha particle may be written as $^4_2\alpha$ or ^4_2He.

BETA DECAY

There are two forms of beta decay:

- Beta-negative $\left(^{\ 0}_{-1}\beta\right)$

  – The symbol $^{\ 0}_{-1}\beta$ represents an electron, and it can also be written as $^{\ 0}_{-1}\text{e}$.

- Beta-positive $\left(^0_1\beta\right)$

  – The symbol $^0_1\beta$ represents a positron, and it can also be written as ^0_1e.

Positrons are the antimatter of electrons. This means they have the same mass as electrons but a positive charge instead of a negative charge. Positrons have only transitory existences.

The process that takes place during beta decay is complex; however, on a simplified level, it appears that during beta-negative decay, a neutron transforms into a proton by emitting an electron (a negative beta particle). This can be seen in the beta-negative decay of carbon.
$$^{14}_{6}\text{C} \rightarrow\ ^{14}_{7}\text{N} +\ ^{\ 0}_{-1}\beta$$

Similarly, during beta-positive decay, a proton transforms into a neutron by emitting a positron (a positive beta particle). This can be seen in the beta-positive decay of fluoride.
$$^{19}_{9}\text{F} \rightarrow\ ^{19}_{8}\text{O} +\ ^0_1\beta$$

It seems that if the ratio of neutrons to protons in the nucleus of an atom is too high or too low, the nucleus is unstable. The nucleus becomes stable by changing the ratio.

If the neutron-to-proton ratio is low, a proton changes into a neutron (beta-positive decay). If the neutron-to-proton ratio is high, a neutron changes into a proton (beta-negative decay).

Scientists believe that when a nucleus emits a beta particle, there is also a neutrino or antineutrino emitted. Neutrinos and antineutrinos have zero mass and zero charge. They are symbolized as follows:

neutrino $^0_0\nu$ antineutrino $^{0\ -}_0\nu$

The neutrino was named in 1932, 24 years before it was detected. Scientists were convinced that such particles existed. These particles had to exist to account for the conservation of energy and momentum during beta decay. The beta particle alone could not account for the energy and momentum in these nuclear reactions.

When a neutron changes into a proton and an electron, it is shown by the following equation:

$${}^{1}_{0}n \rightarrow {}^{1}_{1}p + {}^{0}_{-1}\beta + {}^{0}_{0}\overline{\nu}$$

When a proton changes into a neutron and a positron, it is shown by the following equation:

$${}^{1}_{1}p \rightarrow {}^{1}_{0}n + {}^{0}_{1}\beta + {}^{0}_{0}\nu$$

The examples of beta decay in carbon and fluoride can be written to include the neutrino or antineutrino as follows:

$${}^{14}_{6}C \rightarrow {}^{14}_{7}N + {}^{0}_{-1}\beta + {}^{0}_{0}\overline{\nu}$$

and

$${}^{19}_{9}F \rightarrow {}^{19}_{8}O + {}^{0}_{1}\beta + {}^{0}_{0}\nu$$

GAMMA RADIATION

When a nucleus emits gamma rays, it is emitting high-energy photons. In other words, a gamma ray is a high-energy photon.

Unlike alpha and beta decay, the nucleus does not transmute (change to a new element) in gamma decay. Gamma decay is often associated with alpha and beta decay. It appears that, following alpha and beta decay, the nucleus may be left in an excited state, so it drops to a lower state by emitting a gamma ray (photon).

During alpha and beta decay, the initial nucleus is referred to as the parent nucleus and the product is referred to as the daughter nucleus.

Consider the alpha decay of thorium:

$${}^{227}_{90}Th \rightarrow {}^{223}_{88}Ra + {}^{4}_{2}\alpha$$

In this reaction, ${}^{227}_{90}Th$ is the parent nucleus and ${}^{223}_{88}Ra$ is the daughter nucleus.

Photon: Light energy of a certain value.

The nucleus has energy levels (states).

RADIOACTIVE DECAY SERIES

When alpha and beta decay occur with a certain parent isotope, the daughter isotope is also radioactive, which further decays to a new daughter isotope. This might occur a number of times until a stable isotope is produced. This is called a decay series. A decay series is often represented in a graph. An example of such a decay series starts with ${}^{238}_{92}U$ and ends with ${}^{206}_{82}Pb$. This decay series is shown in the following graph:

NOTES

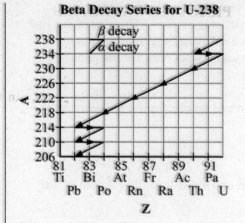

Beta Decay Series for U-238

Example

Complete the following nuclear reaction.

$$^{234}_{90}\text{Th} \rightarrow\ ^{234}_{91}\text{Pa} + \underline{\ ?\ }$$

Solution

The change in the number of nucleons is 234 – 234 = 0.
The mass number of the unknown particle is 0.
The change in the atomic number (number of protons) is 90 – 91 = –1.
The atomic number of the unknown particle is –1.

Therefore, the missing particle that completes the nuclear reaction
is $^{0}_{-1}\beta$.

Example

Complete the following nuclear reaction.

$$^{222}_{86}\text{Rn} \rightarrow\ ^{218}_{84}\text{Po} + \underline{\ ?\ }$$

Solution

The change in the number of nucleons is 222 – 218 = 4.
The mass number of the unknown particle is 4.
The change in the atomic number (number of protons) is 86 – 84 = 2.
The atomic number of the unknown particle is 2.

Therefore, the particle that completes the given nuclear reaction is $^{4}_{2}\alpha$.

Example

Complete the following nuclear reaction.

$$\underline{\ ?\ } \rightarrow\ ^{0}_{-1}\beta + ^{55}_{25}\text{Mn}$$

Solution

The number of nucleons in the unknown particle is 0 + 55 = 55.
The number of protons in the unknown particle is –1 + 25 = 24.
Element 24 on the periodic table is chromium (Cr).

Therefore, the unknown particle in the nuclear reaction is $^{55}_{24}\text{Cr}$.

PRACTICE EXERCISES

1. Complete the following nuclear reactions.

   a) $^{230}_{90}\text{Th} \rightarrow ^{4}_{2}\alpha + \underline{\ ?\ }$

   b) $^{226}_{88}\text{Ra} \rightarrow ^{222}_{86}\text{Rn} + \underline{\ ?\ }$

   c) $^{212}_{82}\text{Pb} \rightarrow ^{0}_{-1}\beta + \underline{\ ?\ }$

   d) $^{214}_{83}\text{Bi} \rightarrow ^{214}_{84}\text{Po} + \underline{\ ?\ }$

   e) $^{239}_{93}\text{Np} \rightarrow ^{239}_{92}\text{U} + \underline{\ ?\ }$

   f) $^{46}_{24}\text{Cr} \rightarrow ^{0}_{1}\beta + \underline{\ ?\ }$

2. In which of the reactions in question **1** is a neutrino emitted?

3. In which of the reactions in question **1** is an antineutrino emitted?

4. What happens to the nucleus of an atom during the emission of a gamma ray?

5. Write the nuclear reaction for the alpha decay of uranium-238.

6. Write the nuclear reaction for the beta-negative decay of cobalt-60.

7. Write the nuclear reaction for the emission of a positron by the nucleus of chromium-51.

Use the following information to answer the next question.

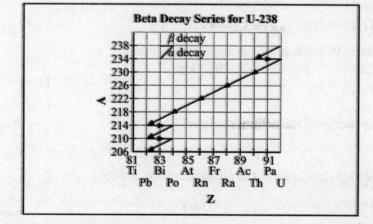

8. Uranium-238 decays to produce lead-206 in a series of reactions (decay steps) by emitting
    alpha $\left(\begin{smallmatrix} 4 \\ 2 \end{smallmatrix}\alpha\right)$ and beta $\left(\begin{smallmatrix} 0 \\ -1 \end{smallmatrix}\beta\right)$ particles. Using the information in the given graph, write each
    of the 14 reactions (decay steps).

Lesson 5   MASS DEFECT AND NUCLEAR BINDING ENERGY

The nuclear binding energy is the energy required to separate the nucleons of a nucleus. It can be determined by finding the mass of the nucleus and the mass of the individual nucleons. This difference is called the mass defect. The nuclear binding energy is the product of this mass defect and the speed of light squared.

binding energy = (mass defect)(speed of light)^2

This is one conclusion that came out of Einstein's special theory of relativity, and it is represented by the following equation:
$E = mc^2$

This equation states that mass and energy are equivalent. Whenever the nucleus undergoes some change, mass converts into energy (heat). The mass converted is the mass defect.

NOTES

Mass defect is the difference in mass between the nucleus and the individual nucleons.

Example

The mass of a helium nucleus $\left({}^4_2\text{He} \right)$ is 6.6443×10^{-27} kg.

a) What is the mass defect of the helium nucleus?

Solution
The mass defect of the helium nucleus can be found as follows:
$$2 \text{ protons} = (2)(1.6726 \times 10^{-27} \text{ kg}) = 3.3452 \times 10^{-27} \text{ kg}$$
$$2 \text{ neutrons} = (2)(1.6749 \times 10^{-27} \text{ kg}) = 3.3498 \times 10^{-27} \text{ kg}$$
$$\text{total mass} = 6.6950 \times 10^{-27} \text{ kg}$$
$$\text{mass defect} = 6.6950 \times 10^{-27} \text{ kg} - 6.6443 \times 10^{-27} \text{ kg}$$
$$= 5.07 \times 10^{-29} \text{ kg}$$

b) What is the binding energy of the helium nucleus?

Solution
$$\text{binding energy} = (\text{mass defect})c^2$$
$$= (5.07 \times 10^{-29} \text{ kg})(3.00 \times 10^8 \text{ m/s})^2$$
$$= 4.56 \times 10^{-12} \text{ J}$$

c) What is the binding energy per nucleon in the helium nucleus?

Solution
There are 4 nucleons.

Therefore, the binding energy per nucleon is calculated as follows:
$$\frac{4.56 \times 10^{-12} \text{ J}}{4} = 1.14 \times 10^{-12} \text{ J}$$

PRACTICE EXERCISE

Formulas:	$E = mc^2$

To complete these problems, use the following masses:
- Proton $= 1.6726 \times 10^{-27}$ kg
- Neutron $= 1.6749 \times 10^{-27}$ kg

1. The mass of a beryllium nucleus $\left({}^{7}_{4}Be \right)$ is 1.1652×10^{-26} kg.

   a) What is the mass defect of the beryllium nucleus?

   b) What is the binding energy of the beryllium nucleus?

   c) What is the binding energy per nucleon in the beryllium nucleus?

2. The mass of a carbon-14 nucleus $\left({}^{14}_{6}C \right)$ is 2.3252×10^{-26} kg.

   a) What is the mass defect of the carbon nucleus?

b) What is the binding energy of the carbon nucleus?

c) What is the binding energy per nucleon in the carbon nucleus?

3. If the mass defect for a boron-11 nucleus $\left(^{11}_{5}\text{B}\right)$ is 1.3184×10^{-28} kg, what is the mass of the nucleus?

4. If the binding energy of a lithium-6 nucleus $\left(^{6}_{3}\text{Li}\right)$ is 4.9118×10^{-12} J, what is the mass of the nucleus?

Lesson 6 HALF-LIFE

NOTES

The rate that a radioactive sample transmutes can be expressed by either its activity or its half-life.

- **Half-life**—the time it takes $\frac{1}{2}$ of a radioactive sample to decay. It is a statistical probability, and every radioactive substance has a characteristic half-life. Consider the following examples:

  – The half-life of ^{14}C is 5.73×10^3 yr.

  – The half-life of ^{214}Po is 1.64×10^{-4} s.

- **Activity**—the number of nuclei that change in a given period of time. The standard SI unit for activity is the becquerel (Bq).

  – 1 Bq = 1 decay/s.

1 Bq = 1 decay/s

However, it is common to express the time in other units when solving problems. The activity of a sample of a radioactive isotope is directly proportional to the number of radioactive nuclei present. As a sample decays, its activity decreases. This can be expressed by the following formula:

$$A \propto N$$

where A = activity

N = number of radioactive nuclei

The relationship between the activity of a sample and the time of decay is given by the following graph:

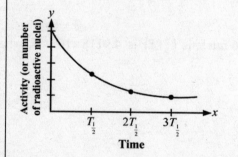

The following formula corresponds to the given graph:

$$N = N_0 \left(\frac{1}{2} \right)^n$$

where N = the number of radioactive nuclei remaining

N_0 = the original number of radioactive nuclei, the original mass of radioactive material, or the original activity of the radioactive material

n = the number of half-lives

However, N may also represent the mass of radioactive material remaining, or it may represent the activity of the radioactive material.

Example

The half-life of a radioactive isotope is 2.5 yr. If the activity of the original sample of this isotope was 3.2×10^3 Bq, what would its activity be after 5.0 yr?

Solution

$$\frac{time}{T_{\frac{1}{2}}} = \frac{5.0 \text{ y}}{2.5 \text{ y}}$$

$$= 2$$

$$N = N_0 \left(\frac{1}{2}\right)^n$$

$$= (3.2 \times 10^3 \text{ Bq})\left(\frac{1}{2}\right)^2$$

$$= 8.0 \times 10^2 \text{ Bq}$$

Example

The half-life of a radioactive isotope is 6.8 yr. If the activity of the original sample of this isotope was 4.9×10^5 Bq, what would its activity be after 100 yr?

Solution

$$\frac{time}{T_{\frac{1}{2}}} = \frac{100 \text{ y}}{6.8 \text{ y}}$$

$$= 14.7$$

$$N = N_0 \left(\frac{1}{2}\right)^n$$

$$= \left(4.9 \times 10^5 \text{ Bq}\right)\left(\frac{1}{2}\right)^{14.7}$$

$$= 18 \text{ Bq}$$

Example

What fraction of a polonium-210 sample will remain after 172 days if it has a half-life of 138 days?

Solution

$$\frac{time}{T_{\frac{1}{2}}} = \frac{172 \text{ d}}{138 \text{ d}}$$

$$= 1.25$$

$$N = N_0 \left(\frac{1}{2}\right)^n$$

$$\frac{N}{N_0} = \left(\frac{1}{2}\right)^{1.25}$$

$$= 0.422$$

Example

A 2.0 g sample of a radioactive isotope undergoes radioactive decay.
If the half-life of this isotope is 45 min, how much of this isotope remains
after 5.0 h?

Solution

$$\frac{time}{T_{\frac{1}{2}}} = \frac{5.0 \text{ h}}{0.75 \text{ h}}$$

$$= 6.67$$

$$N = N_0 \left(\frac{1}{2}\right)^n$$

$$= (2.0 \text{ g})\left(\frac{1}{2}\right)^{6.67}$$

$$= 0.020 \text{ g}$$

PRACTICE EXERCISES

Formula: $N = N_0 \left(\dfrac{1}{2}\right)^n$

1. If a 2.00 g sample of strontium-90 $\left(T_{\frac{1}{2}} = 28.5 \text{ yr}\right)$ is produced, what mass of strontium-90 will remain after 1.00 yr?

2. If the half-life of an isotope is 3.0 days, what percentage of the isotope remains after 2.5 days?

3. If the half-life of an isotope is 2.7 yr, how would the original activity of the sample of this isotope compare with the activity of the sample after 9.5 yr?

4. A 2.0 g sample of a radioactive isotope undergoes radioactive decay. If the half-life of this isotope is 45 min, how much of this isotope remains after 5.0 h?

5. The activity of a sample of a radioactive isotope is 1.8×10^3 Bq. If this isotope has a half-life of 16 days, what is the activity of this sample after 16.0 days, 24.0 days, and 60.0 days?

6. A sample of a radioactive isotope $\left(T_{\frac{1}{2}} = 24.0 \text{ min} \right)$ contains 5.00×10^{16} radioactive nuclei. Draw a decay curve for this isotope.

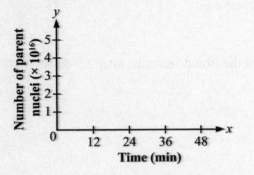

7. If a radioactive sample contains 52.5 g of polonium-210 (half-life = 138 days), how many grams of polonium-210 does it contain 27.0 days later?

8. A radioactive sample of an isotope $\left(T_{\frac{1}{2}} = 1.0 \text{ days} \right)$ has an activity of 3.0×10^5 Bq when delivered to a physics lab. What is the activity of this isotope exactly 14 h later when it is to be used in an experiment?

9. The half-life of thorium-234 is 24.1 days. How many grams of thorium-234 will remain in a 8.50×10^{-3} g sample of thorium-234 after 3 half-lives?

10. A radioactive isotope $\left(T_{\frac{1}{2}} = 4.50 \text{ days} \right)$ was prepared for an experiment that took place 14.0 days after preparation. The sample had an activity of 6.00×10^6 Bq when it was used in the experiment. What was the activity of this isotope when it was initially prepared?

11. A radioactive source contains 2.00×10^{18} nuclei of radioactive cobalt-60. If the half-life of cobalt-60 is 5.27 yr, how many nuclei will be present after 1.00 yr?

12. To determine the volume of blood in a patient's body, a nuclear medicine technologist injected a small amount of a radioactive isotope $\left(T_{\frac{1}{2}} = 45 \text{ min} \right)$ into the patient's bloodstream. The activity of this isotope at the time of injection was 2.8×10^4 Bq. If after 3.0 h a 10.0 cm^3 sample of blood drawn from the patient had an activity of 3.0 Bq, what is the volume of blood in the patient?

Use the following information to answer the next question.

The following data about a sample of a radioactive isotope are given:

Activity ($\times 10^5$ Bq)	Time (min)
7.00	0
5.31	2.0
4.02	4.0
3.05	6.0
2.31	8.0
1.75	10.0

13. a) Draw an activity-time graph for the given sample.

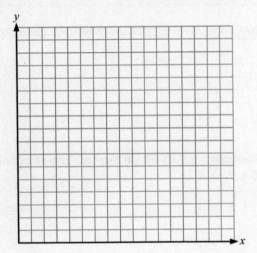

b) Using your graph, determine the half-life of the isotope.

Use the following information to answer the next question.

The following data about a sample of a radioactive isotope are given:

Number of Radioactive Nuclei Remaining ($\times 10^{17}$)	Time (h)
9.75	0
8.41	5.0
7.26	10.0
6.26	15.0
5.41	20.0
4.66	25.0
4.03	30.0

14. a) Draw a graph showing the number of radioactive nuclei remaining in the given sample versus the time of decay.

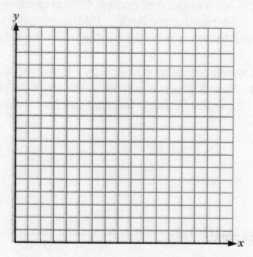

b) Using your graph, determine the half-life of the isotope.

Lesson 7 FISSION AND FUSION

ARTIFICIAL TRANSMUTATION

In 1919, Rutherford was the first person to artificially transmute an element by bombarding samples of $^{14}_{7}N$ with alpha particles. In this reaction, Rutherford produced $^{17}_{8}O$.

$$^{14}_{7}N + ^{4}_{2}\propto \rightarrow ^{17}_{8}O + ^{1}_{1}H$$

All elements with higher atomic numbers than uranium are the result of artificial transmutation.

In this transmutation, Rutherford used bombarding particles from radioactive isotopes. Today, scientists use particle accelerators to produce high-energy bombarding particles. It should be noted that no element with a higher atomic number than uranium has been found on Earth and known elements with higher atomic numbers are the result of artificial transmutation.

FISSION

In 1938, Fermi discovered nuclear fission when he bombarded uranium with a low-energy neutron. In this process, Fermi was attempting to produce element 93; however, he discovered that the uranium nucleus split in two roughly equal parts. This was the first nuclear fission reaction. Nuclear fission is different from radioactive decay. Radioactive decay is spontaneous, whereas nuclear fission is initiated by slow-moving neutrons.

Nuclear fission releases tremendous amounts of energy. However, a small amount of mass disappears. This difference in mass is the mass defect. By finding the mass defect, the amount of energy released can be calculated using Einstein's equation:

$$E = mc^2$$

where E = energy
m = mass defect
c = speed of light

Nuclear fission releases tremendous amounts of energy.

Nuclear fission involves the splitting of the nucleus.

Along with the split nucleus and energy, some neutrons are also released in nuclear fission.

$$^{235}_{92}U + ^{1}_{0}n \rightarrow ^{141}_{56}Ba + ^{92}_{36}Kr + 3^{1}_{0}n + energy$$

These released neutrons can trigger additional splitting. A chain reaction initiates in this manner.

U-235 Fission

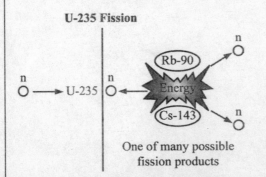

One of many possible
fission products

A nuclear fission reaction in which these neutrons are not controlled produces a nuclear bomb, such as the atomic bomb that was developed during World War II. A nuclear fission reaction in which these neutrons are controlled produces a nuclear power station.

In a nuclear fission reaction, 1.0 kg of U-235 will produce 2×10^6 times as much energy as burning (a chemical reaction) 1.0 kg of coal.

One of the major problems with using nuclear fission in power stations is the production of radioactive isotopes. These radioactive isotopes undergo radioactive decay, producing alpha, beta, and gamma radiation. This means they must be kept out of the environment forever.

FUSION

Nuclear fusion is the opposite of nuclear fission. Nuclear fusion occurs when small nuclei combine to form a large nucleus.

$${}_1^2\text{H} + {}_1^3\text{H} \rightarrow {}_2^4\text{He} + {}_0^1\text{n} + \text{energy}$$

This is one of the reactions that occur within the sun to produce solar energy. To sustain nuclear fusion, very high temperatures $\left(1 \times 10^8 \text{ K}\right)$ are required. This is because both nuclei are positive and they repel. In order to get these nuclei close enough to fuse, they must have extremely high kinetic energies.

Example

Complete the following reaction:

$${}_{92}^{235}\text{U} + {}_0^1\text{n} \rightarrow {}_{56}^{144}\text{Ba} + \underline{\quad ? \quad} + 3{}_0^1\text{n}$$

Solution

The number of protons in the reactants is 92; therefore, the number of protons in the product must be 92.

The atomic number of the unknown particle is $92 - 56 = 36$.
Element 36 is krypton (Kr).

The number of nucleons in the reactants is $235 + 1 = 236$.
Therefore, the number of nucleons in the product must be 236.
The number of nucleons of the unknown nucleus is $236 - 144 - 3 = 89$.

The unknown product is ${}_{36}^{89}\text{Kr}$.

NOTES

Example

The following atomic masses are given:

$$^{235}U = 3.9029 \times 10^{-25} \text{ kg}$$
$$n = 1.6749 \times 10^{-27} \text{ kg}$$
$$^{144}Ba = 2.3898 \times 10^{-25} \text{ kg}$$
$$^{89}Kr = 1.4765 \times 10^{-25} \text{ kg}$$

Determine the energy produced during the following reaction:

$$^{234}_{92}U + {}^{1}_{0}n \rightarrow {}^{144}_{56}Ba + {}^{89}_{36}Kr + 3{}^{1}_{0}n$$

Solution

Mass of Reactants	Mass of Products
	$^{144}Ba = 2.3898 \times 10^{-25}$ kg
$^{235}U = 3.9029 \times 10^{-25}$ kg	$^{89}Kr = 1.4765 \times 10^{-25}$ kg
$n = 1.6749 \times 10^{-27}$ kg	$3n = 5.0247 \times 10^{-27}$ kg
3.9196×10^{-25} kg	3.9165×10^{-25} kg

$$\text{mass defect} = 3.9196 \times 10^{-25} \text{ kg} - 3.9165 \times 10^{-25} \text{ kg}$$
$$= 3.102 \times 10^{-28} \text{ kg}$$

$$E = mc^2$$
$$\text{energy} = (\text{mass defect})(\text{speed of light})^2$$
$$= (3.102 \times 10^{-28} \text{ kg})(3.00 \times 10^8 \text{ m/s})^2$$
$$= 2.789 \times 10^{-11} \text{ J}$$

PRACTICE EXERCISES

Formula: $E = mc^2$

1. Complete the following fission reactions.

   a) $^{235}_{92}U + ^{1}_{0}n \rightarrow ^{90}_{38}Sr + \underline{\ ?\ } + 3^{1}_{0}n$

   b) $^{235}_{92}U + ^{1}_{0}n \rightarrow ^{107}_{43}Tc + \underline{\ ?\ } + 5^{1}_{0}n$

2. Complete the following fusion reactions.

   a) $^{6}_{3}Li + \underline{\ ?\ } \rightarrow 2^{4}_{2}He$

   b) $^{16}_{8}O + ^{2}_{1}H \rightarrow \underline{\ ?\ } + ^{4}_{2}He$

381

Use the following information to answer the next question.

> The following atomic masses are given:
> $$^{235}U = 3.9029 \times 10^{-25} \text{ kg}$$
> $$n = 1.6749 \times 10^{-27} \text{ kg}$$
> $$^{140}Xe = 2.3234 \times 10^{-25} \text{ kg}$$
> $$^{94}Sr = 1.5595 \times 10^{-25} \text{ kg}$$

3. Determine the energy produced in the following fission reaction:
$$^{235}_{92}U + {}^{1}_{0}n \rightarrow {}^{140}_{54}Xe + {}^{94}_{38}Sr + 2{}^{1}_{0}n$$

Use the following information to answer the next question.

> The following atomic masses are given:
> $$^{2}H = 3.3444 \times 10^{-27} \text{ kg}$$
> $$^{3}H = 5.0082 \times 10^{-27} \text{ kg}$$
> $$n = 1.6749 \times 10^{-27} \text{ kg}$$
> $$^{4}He = 6.6463 \times 10^{-27} \text{ kg}$$

4. Determine the energy produced in the following fusion reaction:
$$^{2}_{1}H + {}^{3}_{1}H \rightarrow {}^{4}_{2}He + {}^{1}_{0}n$$

Lesson 8 RADIATION

BIOLOGICAL EFFECTS OF RADIATION

Ultraviolet rays, X-rays, gamma rays, alpha radiation, and beta radiation are referred to as ionizing radiation. They are called ionizing radiation because they can cause the ionization of atoms and molecules.

This ionizing radiation is potentially harmful to humans because it can change the structure of molecules within living cells. This change can cause the cell to malfunction. It can even lead to the death of the cell and of the organism itself. If DNA (the genetic code) is damaged, the result may be cancer or some mutation.

The rate that tissue absorbs radiation depends on the following factors:
• Type of tissue
• Rate of exposure
• Type of radiation

Ultraviolet radiation is limited to the skin, where it can cause skin cancer. Alpha and beta particles cannot penetrate the human body to any great extent (beta particles can penetrate up to 1 cm); however, radioactive isotopes can be inhaled and ingested into the body, where they can release alpha and beta particles. Gamma radiation, like X-rays, can pass right through the body, ionizing molecules in its path.

Radiation cannot be entirely eliminated, because some of the radiation that humans are subjected to is the result of natural radiation; however, some is the result of artificially produced radiation.

APPLICATIONS OF RADIOACTIVITY

Although there are some harmful effects of radiation, radiation has a number of important applications:
• Medicine
  – Used in both the diagnosis and treatment of disease
• Industry
  – To sterilize equipment without the use of harmful chemicals or high temperatures
  – To chemically alter toxic pollutants so that they are less harmful to the environment
• Agriculture
  – To kill bacteria that cause spoilage (irradiation)
  – To kill insects
  – To mutate seeds to produce better crops
• Carbon dating
  – To determine the age of objects

CONSERVATION LAWS

Recall the following conservation laws:

- The law of conservation of energy—energy is neither created nor destroyed, but it can be converted from one form into another.
- The law of conservation of momentum—momentum is conserved in all interactions.
- The law of conservation of charge—net charge remains constant.

It should not be surprising that these fundamental laws hold true in nuclear reactions and interactions. However, it appears that energy is created, especially in fission and fusion reactions. Remember from Einstein's special theory of relativity that mass and energy are different forms of the same thing (mass and energy are equivalent). This means that matter can be converted into energy, and energy should be able to be converted into mass.

Recall that neutrinos and antineutrinos were predicted to exist before they were discovered because scientists believed in the conservation laws.

POSITRONS

Positrons, or positive electrons, also known as antielectrons, were predicted to exist by Paul Dirac in 1929 to account for the conservation laws. Carl Anderson provided clear experimental evidence of their existence in 1932, for which he received a Nobel Prize. Anderson discovered that an electron and a positron may be created when high-energy photons (gamma rays or high-energy X-rays) collide with matter.

Note that when an electron is produced, a positron must be produced in order for the law of conservation of charge to be obeyed. This process, in which a photon (energy) converts into mass (an electron and a positron), is called pair production.

$$\gamma \quad \rightarrow \quad {}^{0}_{-1}\beta \quad + \quad {}^{0}_{1}\beta$$

Gamma photon or high-energy X-ray photon   Electron   Positron

PAIR PRODUCTION

A high-energy photon collides with matter to produce an electron and a positron. The photon that is converted into the electron and positron must have a minimum of 1.02 MeV of energy $(1.64 \times 10^{-13}$ J$)$. This is because the rest mass of an electron and positron is 1.82×10^{-30} kg.

$$2(9.11 \times 10^{-31} \text{ kg}) = 1.82 \times 10^{-30} \text{ kg}$$
$$E = mc^2,$$
$$= (1.82 \times 10^{-30} \text{ kg})(3.00 \times 10^8 \text{ m/s})^2$$
$$= 1.64 \times 10^{-13} \text{ J or } 1.02 \text{ MeV}$$

With modern particle accelerators, it is possible to observe other types of pair production (such as proton-antiproton). A photon with 1 836 times the energy required to produce an electron-positron pair must be used to produce a proton-antiproton pair. This is because the mass of a proton-antiproton pair is 1 836 times larger than the mass of an electron-positron pair.

$$E = mc^2$$
$$= 2\left(1.67 \times 10^{-27} \text{ kg}\right)\left(3.00 \times 10^8 \text{ m/s}\right)^2$$
$$= 3.01 \times 10^{-10} \text{ J} \text{ or } 1.88 \text{ GeV}$$

$$\frac{3.01 \times 10^{-10} \text{ J}}{1.64 \times 10^{-13} \text{ J}} = 1836 \text{ times}$$

If pair production (energy to mass, according to $E = mc^2$) takes place, then the opposite (mass to energy, according to $E = mc^2$) should also occur. The opposite of pair production is annihilation.

ANNIHILATION

A positron is the antimatter of an electron. An antiproton is the antimatter of a proton. Just as a positron is an electron with a positive charge, an antiproton is a proton with a negative charge.

Positrons and antiprotons have only transitory existences because almost as quickly as they are produced, these particles make contact with electrons and protons. When a positron comes in contact with an electron, they annihilate each other. When an antiproton comes in contact with a proton, they also annihilate each other. This means that their mass (matter) is converted into energy (photons) according to $E = mc^2$.

In this process of annihilation, in order for momentum to be conserved, two photons must be produced.

$$_{-1}^{0}\beta \quad + \quad _{1}^{0}\beta \quad \rightarrow \quad 2\gamma$$

| Electron | Positron | Two gamma photons |

The two photons must travel in opposite directions. Remember that if the combined momentum of the electron and positron was zero before this process, the combined momentum of these two photons must also be zero after annihilation.

As in all reactions and interactions, momentum, energy, and net charge are conserved during annihilation.

Lesson 9 HIGH-ENERGY PARTICLE PHYSICS

Throughout this book, you have been taught that the atom is composed of three elementary particles: electrons, protons, and neutrons. However, you have just seen that there are also other subatomic particles, such as positrons, neutrinos, and antineutrinos. If atoms are made up of only electrons, protons, and neutrons, where did these other particles come from?

Physicists attempt to answer questions like this. In the search to understand this question, some physicists studied cosmic rays (high-energy particles from space). Cosmic rays were the first source of high-energy particles. Later, physicists built particle accelerators to create new particles by colliding fast-moving charged particles (electrons, protons, or ions) with other particles.

Cathode-ray tubes (such as the picture tube of a television) and X-ray machines accelerate electrons to high speeds, but the massive machines used by physicists to probe matter are much larger. Particle accelerators are massive machines that accelerate charged particles (electrons, protons, or ions) to high speeds through an electric field in an evacuated tube. When these particles collide with other particles at very high speeds (very high energy), the particles may break apart, producing new particles.

Using cosmic rays and particle accelerators, physicists have identified hundreds of new particles. Most of these particles are very unstable; therefore, they decay very quickly. Before studying these particles, it is important to consider particle accelerators.

PARTICLE ACCELERATORS

All particle accelerators must have the following parts:

• A source of charged particles

• A means of accelerating the charged particles

• A tube or container in which the charged particles are accelerated

There are different designs that incorporate these elements. However, particle accelerators can be classified as linear or circular accelerators.

A linear accelerator is referred to as a linac. These accelerators may be very long. For example, the linac at Stanford University is 3.2 km long.

Circular accelerators use large magnets to deflect charged particles in a circular path. The simplest and oldest circular accelerator is the cyclotron. In a cyclotron, two hollow, D-shaped containers are placed back-to-back with a gap between the containers, as shown in the following diagram:

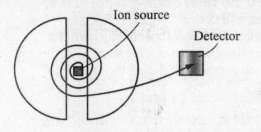

Each time the charged particle crosses the gap between the two containers, it is accelerated by a potential difference. As the charged particle accelerates, it spirals outward.

In particle accelerators, the charged particle may accelerate to relativistic speeds. If this happens, the charged particle becomes unsynchronized with the current charges; therefore, cyclotrons may be modified. These modified cyclotrons can be either synchrocyclotrons or synchrotrons.

In the synchrocyclotron, the power of the electric field in the gap between the containers gradually changes. In the synchrotron, the path of the accelerating particle is controlled by changing the magnetic field.

PARTICLE DETECTORS

When these particles reach high speeds (high energies), they collide with other particles to produce new particles. These particles are too small to be seen; therefore, a particle accelerator must be paired with a particle detector.

The bubble chamber was invented in 1952 by Donald Glaser. A bubble chamber has a sealed chamber filled with liquefied gas (usually hydrogen). The liquid is originally at a temperature just below its boiling point. When the pressure in the chamber is reduced quickly, the liquid becomes supersaturated. When a charged particle passes through this supersaturated liquid, it leaves a trail of gas bubbles. The bubble chamber is placed into a magnetic field so the charged particles are deflected.

The amount of deflection depends on the mass of the particle and its charge-to-mass ratio (q/m). The direction of the deflection depends on the nature of the charge (positive or negative). By analyzing the tracks made by the particle, physicists can tell a lot about the particle.

NOTES

The cloud chamber was invented by Charles Wilson in 1900. It is similar to the bubble chamber. It consists of a closed chamber filled with a supersaturated vapour. When the ionizing radiation passes through the vapour, it leaves a visible trail of charged particles that give the vapour something to condense on. Again, if this cloud chamber is placed in a magnetic field, the charged particles will deflect. By analyzing the tracks made, physicists can determine a lot about the ionizing particles. Neither cloud chambers nor bubble chambers are in wide use; however, the bubble chamber was very important during the early years of high-energy physics.

Particle accelerators are primarily used in research, but accelerators also have some applications in medicine and industry.

The Canadian Light Source Inc. (CLS) synchrotron, located in Saskatoon, Saskatchewan, is used to produce intense beams of light (infrared, visible, ultraviolet, and X-rays) used to study the microstructure of material. This synchrotron is used as a supermicroscope. In the CLS synchrotron, the accelerated particles are electrons. These electrons reach a speed close to the speed of light, emitting light as they change course. The information revealed from studying the light may lead to many advancements in science and technology. Applications include building more powerful computers, cleaning up pollution created by mining, developing better medication, and designing new materials for medical implants.

STANDARD MODEL

In 1932, the neutron was discovered. With this discovery, the picture of the atom seemed to be complete. The elementary particles were electrons, protons, and neutrons. However, during the 1950s, more and more elementary particles were discovered, mainly due to particle collision research using particle accelerators. With the discovery of all these additional particles, things started to become confusing.

Because scientists believe that there is order in the universe, they believed that there was some underlying order in all these elementary particles as well. In 1962, Murray Gell-Mann noticed a pattern. In order to explain this pattern, he suggested that the elementary particles were made up of smaller particles. Gell-Mann called these particles quarks. Today, the quark concept has been confirmed. The quark concept was the beginning of the standard model of elementary particles.

Fermions are responsible for matter.

Bosons are responsible for forces.

The standard model theory, which was developed in the early 1970s, describes the elementary particles and the interactions (forces) between them. It is a model that is consistent with the quantum theory and the special theory of relativity. In the standard model, there are two kinds of elementary particles: fermions and bosons. Fermions are particles that compose matter. Bosons are particles that are responsible for forces.

There are two kinds of fermions: quarks and leptons.

Quarks

Quarks have never been isolated. They exist only inside particles called hadrons. There are six types of quarks:

	Symbol	Charge
Up	u	$\dfrac{2}{3}$
Down	d	$-\dfrac{1}{3}$
Strange	s	$-\dfrac{1}{3}$
Charm	c	$\dfrac{2}{3}$
Bottom	b	$-\dfrac{1}{3}$
Top	t	$\dfrac{2}{3}$

There are also six corresponding antiquarks (remember, every elementary particle has an antiparticle). The symbols for the antiquarks are $\bar{u}, \bar{d}, \bar{s}, \bar{c}, \bar{b}$, and $\bar{t}$.

(Note that the antiquarks have opposite charges to the corresponding quarks.)

Hadrons

There are two classes of hadrons: baryons and mesons.

Baryons are hadrons that contain three quarks. The best examples, and the only stable hadrons, are protons and neutrons, which contain the following quark combinations:

- Protons $\quad u\ u\ d$
- Neutrons $\quad u\ d\ d$

Mesons are hadrons that contain one quark and one antiquark. An example of a meson is a pion, which has the following quark-antiquark combination:

- Pion $\quad u\ \bar{d}$

The charge on fermions is multiplied by the elementary charge.

Baryons contain three quarks.

Mesons contain two quarks.

Leptons:

- Electron / anti-electron
- Muon / anti-muon
- Tau / anti-tau
- Electron neutrino / anti-electron neutrino
- Muon neutrino / anti-muon neutrino
- Tau neutrino / anti-tau neutrino

Leptons

Unlike quarks, leptons can be isolated, or **found alone**. Like quarks, there are six types of leptons:

	Symbol	Charge
Electron	e	-1
Muon	μ	-1
Tau	τ	-1
Electron neutrino	υ_e	0
Muon neutrino	υ_μ	0
Tau neutrino	υ_τ	0

The electron, muon, and tau all have **negative charges**. The neutrinos have no charge and almost no mass. The only **stable lepton** is the electron.

There are also the following six corresponding **antileptons**: $\bar{e}, \bar{\mu}, \bar{\tau}, \bar{\upsilon}_e, \bar{\upsilon}_\mu$, and $\bar{\upsilon}_\tau$

The particles $\bar{e}, \bar{\mu}$, and $\bar{\tau}$ all have **positive charges, and** $\bar{\upsilon}_e, \bar{\upsilon}_\mu$, and $\bar{\upsilon}_\tau$ have no charge and are almost massless.

Bosons

Bosons are responsible for forces in nature. **Recall that** there are four fundamental forces:

- Gravitational forces
- Electromagnetic forces
- Strong nuclear forces
- Weak nuclear forces

All of these forces, with the exception of **gravitational** forces, act within the atom.

In the standard model, the fermions interact **by means** of the fundamental forces. These forces have carriers that are **other particles**.

- The force carrier for electromagnetic forces is **the photon**.
- The force carrier for the strong nuclear force is **the gluon**.
- The force carrier for the weak nuclear force is **the** W+, W°, and Z bosons.

Bosons:
- Photon
- Gluon
- W$^+$, W°, and Z bosons

These bosons have been detected, but the hypothesized force carrier of gravity (graviton) has never been detected. Thus, the graviton is not part of the standard model.

The standard model theory is not a complete theory, because it does not include the gravitational force. It leaves some unanswered questions. The goal of modern theoretical physics is to unify the description of the universe. Another theory has attempted to do this: the string theory.

String Theory

In the string theory, elementary particles are thought of as very short strings (one-dimensional objects) rather than as points. These strings can vibrate in different modes. The basic idea is that each mode of vibration corresponds to a certain type of elementary particle. Using this model, all elementary particles can be described by a string.

Both the standard model and the string theory have potential, but the search for knowledge continues. Physicists will continue to search for a theory that unifies the description of the universe.

PRACTICE QUIZ

1. Doubly charged ^{25}Mg ions are deflected by a uniform magnetic field (B = 0.725 T) in the ion separation region of a mass spectrometer. If these ions have a kinetic energy of 8.35×10^{-16} J as they enter the ion separation region, what is the radius of curvature of their path?

2. A mass spectrometer uses a potential difference of 3.50×10^3 V to accelerate doubly charged ions from rest. These ions now enter a uniform magnetic field (B = 0.725 T) perpendicularly to the field. The magnetic force acting on these ions causes them to travel in a circular path with a radius of 7.22 cm. What is the magnetic force acting on the ions?

3. Carbon dating is a process that is used to determine the age of material. Knowing that carbon-14 has a half-life of 5.73×10^3 yr and that the carbon-14 activity in living material is 0.23 Bq/g of material, what would be the expected activity of a non-living material that is 1.00×10^3 yr old?

Use the following information to answer the next question.

The following atomic masses are given:
$$^{235}U = 3.9029 \times 10^{-25} \text{ kg}$$
$$n = 1.6749 \times 10^{-27} \text{ kg}$$
$$^{142}La = 2.3563 \times 10^{-25} \text{ kg}$$
$$^{91}Br = 1.5097 \times 10^{-25} \text{ kg}$$

4. Determine the energy produced in the following fission reaction:
$$^{235}_{92}U + ^{1}_{0}n \rightarrow ^{142}_{57}La + ^{91}_{35}Br + 3^{1}_{0}n$$

Use the following information to answer the next question.

The following atomic masses are given:
$$^{16}O = 2.6560 \times 10^{-26} \text{ kg}$$
$$^{2}H = 3.3444 \times 10^{-27} \text{ kg}$$
$$^{4}He = 6.6463 \times 10^{-27} \text{ kg}$$
$$^{14}N = 2.3252 \times 10^{-26} \text{ kg}$$

5. Determine the energy produced in the following fusion reaction:
$$^{16}_{8}O + ^{2}_{1}H \rightarrow ^{14}_{7}N + ^{4}_{2}He$$

REVIEW SUMMARY

- Radioactivity
  - Isotopes
  - Nuclear forces
  - Types of radioactivity
  - Nuclear binding energy
  - Half-life
  - Fission and fusion
- High-energy particle physics
  - Particle accelerators and detectors
  - Standard model
  - String theory
- The following formulas were used in this chapter:
  - $F_m = qvB_\perp$
  - $\overline{F}_e = q\overline{E}$
  - $\overline{F}_g = m\overline{g}$
  - $F_c = \dfrac{mv^2}{r}$
  - $N = N_0 \left(\dfrac{1}{2} \right)^n$
  - $E = mc^2$

PRACTICE TEST

Use the following information to answer the next question.

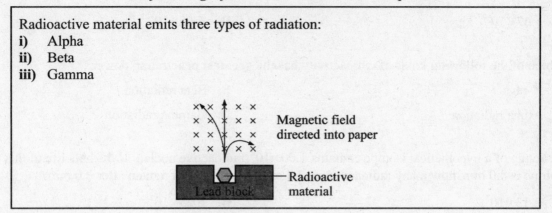

Radioactive material emits three types of radiation:
i) Alpha
ii) Beta
iii) Gamma

Magnetic field directed into paper

Lead block ── Radioactive material

1. In the given diagram, rays 1, 2, and 3 respectively are

   A. i), ii), iii)

   B. i), iii), ii)

   C. ii), i), iii)

   D. ii), iii), i)

2. Stars generate their energy **mainly** by

   A. combustion reactions

   B. chemical reactions

   C. fission reactions

   D. fusion reactions

3. Neutrinos were suggested approximately 25 years before they were detected. They were thought to exist in order to account for the conservation of

   A. charge and mass

   B. charge and energy

   C. momentum and mass

   D. energy and momentum

4. An electron and a positron combine to produce

   A. photons

   B. neutrons

   C. beta particles

   D. alpha particles

5. The mass of a positron is

   A. 0.00 kg

   B. 9.11×10^{-31} kg

   C. 1.67×10^{-27} kg

   D. 6.65×10^{-27} kg

6. Which of the following kinds of radioactivity has the **greatest** penetrating power?

   A. X-rays

   B. Beta radiation

   C. Alpha radiation

   D. Gamma radiation

7. A sample of a hypothetical isotope contains 1.00×10^4 radioactive nuclei. If the half-life of this isotope is 8.0 min, how many radioactive nuclei of this isotope will remain after 7.0 min?

   A. 3.13×10^2

   B. 6.25×10^2

   C. 1.25×10^3

   D. 5.45×10^3

8. When a positron and an electron collide, two photons of equal energy are produced. What is the energy of each photon?

   A. 0.128 MeV

   B. 0.256 MeV

   C. 0.512 MeV

   D. 1.02 MeV

9. When $_3^7 \text{Li}$ undergoes beta decay, it transmutes into

   A. $_1^3 \text{H}$

   B. $_2^3 \text{H}$

   C. $_2^7 \text{He}$

   D. $_4^7 \text{Be}$

10. When a certain nucleus underwent radioactive decay, its atomic number increased. The type of radiation emitted is

   A. beta

   B. alpha

   C. gamma

   D. positron

11. During a fusion reaction between hydrogen nuclei, there is

   A. no change in mass

   B. a small loss in mass

   C. a small gain in mass

   D. a doubling of the mass

12. Which of the following statements about a nucleus undergoing fission is **false**?

   A. The products of fission are radioactive.

   B. Neutrons are released during fission.

   C. Energy is emitted during fission.

   D. The nuclei gain some mass.

13. Which kind of radioactive decay does **not** result in a change in either the mass number or the atomic number of the nucleus?

   A. Alpha

   C. Beta-positive

   B. Gamma

   D. Beta-negative

14. A positron is the antimatter of

   A. an electron

   C. a neutron

   B. a fermion

   D. a proton

15. In the standard model, the two kinds of elementary particles are

   A. quarks and leptons

   C. fermions and quarks

   B. bosons and leptons

   D. fermions and bosons

16. *Strange* and *charm* are names of

   A. hadrons

   C. bosons

   B. leptons

   D. quarks

17. Photons and gluons are types of

   A. hadrons

   C. bosons

   B. leptons

   D. quarks

18. W^+ and W^o are force carriers of which of the following forces?

   A. Electromagnetic

   C. Weak nuclear

   B. Strong nuclear

   D. Gravitational

19. An electron is a type of

   A. hadron

   C. boson

   B. lepton

   D. quark

20. A neutron is a type of

   A. hadron

   C. boson

   B. lepton

   D. quark

21. A proton contains the quarks u, u, and d. What are the respective names of these three quarks?

   A. Up, up, down

   C. Down, down, up

   B. Top, top, bottom

   D. Bottom, bottom, top

22. $_{-1}^{0}\beta + _{1}^{0}\beta \rightarrow \gamma$

The given process is an example of

A. pair production

B. annihilation

C. fission

D. fusion

Use the following information to answer the next question.

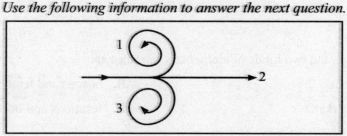

23. The particle tau is a lepton and has a charge of –1. If this particle passes through a bubble chamber in which the magnetic field is directed into this page, which of the following paths **best** describes the motion of this particle?

A. 1

B. 2

C. 3

D. 1 or 2

Student Notes and Problems

ANSWERS AND SOLUTIONS

CASTLE ROCK
RESEARCH CORP

MOMENTUM AND IMPULSE

Lesson 1—Momentum and Impulse

PRACTICE EXERCISE
ANSWERS AND SOLUTIONS

1. $\vec{p} = m\vec{v}$
$= (4.0 \text{ kg})(12.0 \text{ m/s})$
$= 48 \text{ kg} \cdot \text{m/s east}$

3. $\vec{p} = m\vec{v}$
$m = \dfrac{\vec{p}}{\vec{v}}$
$= \dfrac{36.0 \text{ kg} \cdot \text{m/s}}{8.0 \text{ m/s}}$
$= 4.5 \text{ kg}$

5. $\vec{F}_{\text{g}} = m\vec{g}$
$m = \dfrac{\vec{F}}{\vec{g}}$
$= \dfrac{6.6 \text{ N}}{9.81 \text{ m/s}^2}$
$= 0.673 \text{ kg}$
$\vec{p} = m\vec{v}$
$= (0.673 \text{ kg})(3.0 \text{ m/s})$
$= 2.0 \text{ kg} \cdot \text{m/s north}$

7. $\vec{a} = \dfrac{\vec{v}_{\text{f}} - \vec{v}_{\text{i}}}{t}$
$-9.81 \text{ m/s}^2 = \dfrac{\vec{v}_{\text{f}} - 0}{0.25 \text{ s}}$
$\vec{v}_{\text{f}} = -2.45 \text{ m/s}$
$\vec{p} = m\vec{v}$
$= (5.0 \text{ kg})(-2.45 \text{ m/s})$
$= -12 \text{ kg} \cdot \text{m/s up or } 12 \text{ kg} \cdot \text{m/s down}$

9. $\vec{J} = \vec{F}t$
$t = \dfrac{\vec{J}}{\vec{F}}$
$= \dfrac{7.00 \text{ N} \cdot \text{s}}{11.2 \text{ N}}$
$t = 0.625 \text{ s}$

11. $\vec{F}t = m\Delta\vec{v}$
$(31.6 \text{ N})t = (15.0 \text{ kg})(10.0 \text{ m/s})$
$t = 4.75 \text{ s}$

13. $\vec{J} = m\Delta\vec{v}$
$= (5.00 \text{ kg})(15.0 \text{ m/s})$
$= 75.0 \text{ kg} \cdot \text{m/s east}$

15. $\vec{p} = m\vec{v}$
$\vec{v} = \dfrac{\vec{p}}{m}$
$= \dfrac{6.0 \text{ kg} \cdot \text{m/s}}{3.0 \text{ kg}}$
$= 2.0 \text{ m/s down}$
$v_{\text{f}}^2 = v_{\text{i}}^2 + 2ad$
$(2.0 \text{ m/s})^2 = 2(-9.81 \text{ m/s}^2)d$
$d = 0.20 \text{ m}$

17. $F = m\vec{a}$
$\vec{a} = \dfrac{\vec{F}}{m}$
$= \dfrac{1.5 \times 10^5 \text{ N}}{9.5 \times 10^3 \text{ kg}}$
$= 15.8 \text{ m/s}^2$
$\vec{a} = \dfrac{\vec{v}_{\text{f}} - \vec{v}_{\text{i}}}{t}$
$15.8 \text{ m/s}^2 = \dfrac{\vec{v}_{\text{f}} - 0}{15 \text{ s}}$
$\vec{v}_{\text{f}} = 2.4 \times 10^2 \text{ m/s up}$
or
$\vec{F}t = m\Delta\vec{v}$
$(1.5 \times 10^5 \text{ N})(15 \text{ s}) = (9.5 \times 10^3 \text{ kg})\vec{v}$
$\vec{v} = 2.4 \times 10^2 \text{ m/s up}$

19. $\vec{F}t = m\Delta\vec{v}$
$(225 \text{ N})t = (1.0 \times 10^3 \text{ kg})(5.0 \text{ m/s} - 2.0 \text{ m/s})$
$t = 13 \text{ s}$

Lesson 2—Conservation of Momentum

PRACTICE EXERCISE
ANSWERS AND SOLUTIONS

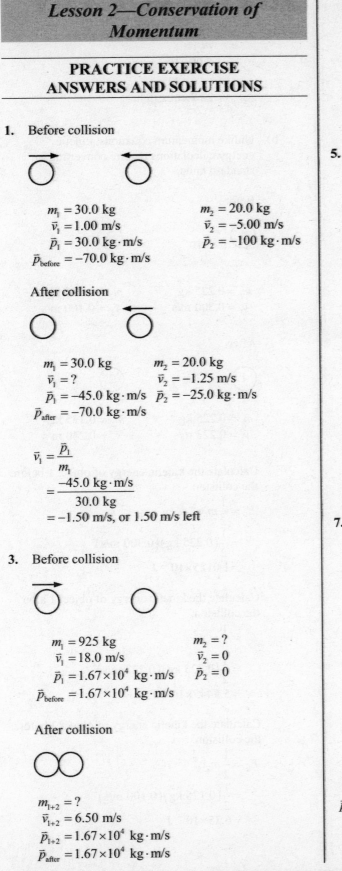

1. Before collision

$m_1 = 30.0$ kg $\qquad m_2 = 20.0$ kg
$\vec{v}_1 = 1.00$ m/s $\qquad \vec{v}_2 = -5.00$ m/s
$\vec{p}_1 = 30.0$ kg·m/s $\qquad \vec{p}_2 = -100$ kg·m/s
$\vec{P}_{\text{before}} = -70.0$ kg·m/s

After collision

$m_1 = 30.0$ kg $\qquad m_2 = 20.0$ kg
$\vec{v}_1 = ?$ $\qquad \vec{v}_2 = -1.25$ m/s
$\vec{p}_1 = -45.0$ kg·m/s $\quad \vec{p}_2 = -25.0$ kg·m/s
$\vec{P}_{\text{after}} = -70.0$ kg·m/s

$$\vec{v}_1 = \frac{\vec{p}_1}{m_1}$$
$$= \frac{-45.0 \text{ kg·m/s}}{30.0 \text{ kg}}$$
$$= -1.50 \text{ m/s, or } 1.50 \text{ m/s left}$$

3. Before collision

$m_1 = 925$ kg $\qquad m_2 = ?$
$\vec{v}_1 = 18.0$ m/s $\qquad \vec{v}_2 = 0$
$\vec{p}_1 = 1.67 \times 10^4$ kg·m/s $\quad \vec{p}_2 = 0$
$\vec{P}_{\text{before}} = 1.67 \times 10^4$ kg·m/s

After collision

$m_{1+2} = ?$
$\vec{v}_{1+2} = 6.50$ m/s
$\vec{p}_{1+2} = 1.67 \times 10^4$ kg·m/s
$\vec{P}_{\text{after}} = 1.67 \times 10^4$ kg·m/s

$$m_{1+2} = \frac{\vec{p}_{1+2}}{\vec{v}_{1+2}}$$
$$= \frac{1.67 \times 10^4 \text{ kg·m/s}}{6.50 \text{ m/s}}$$
$$= 2.56 \times 10^3 \text{ kg}$$
$$m_2 = 2.56 \times 10^3 \text{ kg} - 925 \text{ kg}$$
$$= 1.64 \times 10^3 \text{ kg}$$

5. Before collision

$m_1 = 40.0$ g $\qquad m_2 = 55.0$ g
$\vec{v}_1 = 9.00$ m/s $\qquad \vec{v}_2 = -6.00$ m/s
$\vec{p}_1 = 3.60 \times 10^2$ g·m/s $\quad \vec{p}_2 = -3.30 \times 10^2$ g·m/s

$\vec{P}_{\text{before}} = 3.0 \times 10^1$ g·m/s

After collision

$m_{1+2} = 95.0$ g $\qquad \vec{v}_{1+2} = \dfrac{\vec{P}_{1+2}}{m_{1+2}}$
$\vec{v}_{1+2} = ?$
$\vec{p}_{1+2} = ?$ $\qquad\qquad = \dfrac{3.0 \times 10^1 \text{ g·m/s}}{95.0 \text{ g}}$
$\vec{P}_{\text{after}} = 3.0 \times 10^1$ g·m/s $\qquad = 0.32$ m/s right

7. Before

$m_{1+2} = 1.13 \times 10^3$ kg
$\vec{v}_{1+2} = 0$
$\vec{p}_{1+2} = 0$
$\vec{P}_{\text{before}} = 0$

After

$m_1 = 1.1 \times 10^3$ kg $\qquad m_2 = 25$ kg
$\vec{v}_1 = ?$ $\qquad\qquad \vec{v}_2 = 325$ m/s
$\vec{p}_1 = -8.13 \times 10^3$ kg·m/s $\quad \vec{p}_2 = 8.13 \times 10^3$ kg·m/s
$\vec{P}_{\text{after}} = 0$

$$\vec{v}_1 = \frac{\vec{p}_1}{m_1}$$
$$= \frac{-8.13 \times 10^3 \text{ kg} \cdot \text{m/s}}{1.1 \times 10^3 \text{ kg}}$$
$$= -7.4 \text{ m/s, or } 7.4 \text{ m/s west}$$

9. Before

$$m_{1+2} = 7.0 \text{ kg}$$
$$\vec{v}_{1+2} = 0$$
$$\vec{p}_{1+2} = 0$$
$$\vec{P}_{\text{before}} = 0$$

After collision

$$m_1 = 5.0 \text{ kg} \qquad m_2 = 2.0 \text{ kg}$$
$$\vec{v}_1 = ? \qquad \vec{v}_2 = 10 \text{ m/s}$$
$$\vec{p}_1 = -20.0 \text{ kg} \cdot \text{m/s} \qquad \vec{p}_2 = 20.0 \text{ kg} \cdot \text{m/s}$$
$$\vec{P}_{\text{before}} = 0$$

$$\vec{v}_1 = \frac{\vec{p}_1}{m_1}$$
$$= \frac{-20.0 \text{ kg} \cdot \text{m/s}}{5.0 \text{ kg}}$$
$$= -4.0 \text{ m/s, or } 4.0 \text{ m/s left}$$

11. a) Before collision

$$m_1 = 225 \text{ g} \qquad m_2 = 125 \text{ g}$$
$$\vec{v}_1 = 30.0 \text{ cm/s} \qquad \vec{v}_2 = 10.0 \text{ cm/s}$$
$$\vec{p}_1 = 6.75 \times 10^3 \text{ g} \cdot \text{cm/s} \qquad \vec{p}_2 = 1.25 \times 10^3 \text{ g} \cdot \text{cm/s}$$
$$\vec{P}_{\text{before}} = 8.00 \times 10^3 \text{ g} \cdot \text{cm/s}$$

After collision

$$m_1 = 225 \text{ g} \qquad m_2 = 125 \text{ g}$$
$$\vec{v}_1 = ? \qquad \vec{v}_2 = 24.0 \text{ cm/s}$$
$$\vec{p}_1 = 5.00 \times 10^3 \text{ g} \cdot \text{cm/s} \qquad \vec{p}_2 = 3.00 \times 10^3 \text{ g} \cdot \text{cm/s}$$

$$\vec{P}_{\text{after}} = 8.00 \times 10^3 \text{ g} \cdot \text{cm/s}$$
$$\vec{v}_1 = \frac{\vec{p}_1}{m_1}$$
$$= \frac{5.00 \times 10^3 \text{ g} \cdot \text{cm/s}}{225 \text{ g}}$$
$$= 22.2 \text{ cm/s right}$$

b) Unlike momentum equations, kinetic energy calculations require converting to standard units.

Before

$$m_1 = 0.225 \text{ kg} \qquad m_2 = 0.125 \text{ kg}$$
$$\vec{v}_1 = 0.300 \text{ m/s} \qquad \vec{v}_2 = 0.100 \text{ m/s}$$

After

$$m_1 = 0.225 \text{ kg} \qquad m_2 = 0.125 \text{ kg}$$
$$\vec{v}_1 = 0.222 \text{ m/s} \qquad \vec{v}_2 = 0.240 \text{ m/s}$$

Calculate the kinetic energy of object 1 before the collision.
$$E_k = \frac{1}{2} m_1 v_1^2$$
$$= \frac{1}{2}(0.225 \text{ kg})(0.300 \text{ m/s})^2$$
$$= 1.0125 \times 10^{-2} \text{ J}$$

Calculate the kinetic energy of object 1 after the collision.
$$E_k = \frac{1}{2} m_1 v_1^2$$
$$= \frac{1}{2}(0.225 \text{ kg})(0.222 \text{ m/s})^2$$
$$= 5.5445 \times 10^{-3} \text{ J}$$

Calculate the kinetic energy of object 2 before the collision.
$$E_k = \frac{1}{2} m_2 v_2^2$$
$$= \frac{1}{2}(0.125 \text{ kg})(0.100 \text{ m/s})^2$$
$$= 6.25 \times 10^{-4} \text{ J}$$

Calculate the kinetic energy of object 2 after the collision.

$$E_k = \frac{1}{2}m_2 v_2^2$$
$$= \frac{1}{2}(0.125 \text{ kg})(0.240 \text{ m/s})^2$$
$$= 3.60 \times 10^{-3} \text{ J}$$

Calculate the total kinetic energy before the collision.
$$= 1.012\ 5 \times 10^{-2} \text{ J} + 6.25 \times 10^{-4} \text{ J}$$
$$= 1.075 \times 10^{-2} \text{ J}$$

Calculate the total kinetic energy after the collision.
$$= 5.544\ 5 \times 10^{-3} \text{ J} + 3.60 \times 10^{-3} \text{ J}$$
$$= 9.144\ 5 \times 10^{-3} \text{ J}$$

Calculate the mechanical (kinetic) energy lost in the collision.
$$= 1.075 \times 10^{-2} \text{ J} - 9.1445 \times 10^{-3} \text{ J}$$
$$= 1.61 \times 10^{-3} \text{ J}$$

$\therefore$ The collision is inelastic.

c) Most of the lost energy was converted into thermal energy, while some was converted into sound and other forms of energy.

Lesson 3—Two-Dimensional Interactions

PRACTICE EXERCISE ANSWERS AND SOLUTIONS

1. Before

$$m_1 = 2.0 \times 10^3 \text{ kg}$$
$$\vec{v}_1 = 35.0 \text{ km/h}$$
$$\vec{p}_1 = 7.00 \times 10^4 \text{ kg} \cdot \text{km/h}$$

$$m_2 = 1.4 \times 10^3 \text{ kg}$$
$$\vec{v}_2 = 37.0 \text{ km/h}$$
$$\vec{p}_2 = 5.18 \times 10^4 \text{ kg} \cdot \text{km/h}$$

After

$$m_{1+2} = 3.4 \times 10^3 \text{ kg}$$
$$\vec{v}_{1+2} = ?$$
$$\vec{p}_{after} = 8.71 \times 10^4 \text{ kg} \cdot \text{km/h } 36.5° \text{ W of N}$$

$$\vec{p}_2 = 5.18 \times 10^4 \text{kg} \cdot \text{km / h}$$
$$\vec{p}_2 = 7.00 \times 10^4 \text{kg} \cdot \text{km / h}$$

$$p_R = \sqrt{p_1^2 + p_2^2}$$
$$= \sqrt{(7.00 \times 10^4 \text{ kg} \cdot \text{km/h})^2 + (5.18 \times 10^4 \text{ kg} \cdot \text{km/h})^2}$$
$$= 8.71 \times 10^4 \text{ kg} \cdot \text{km/h}$$

$$\tan\theta = \frac{p_2}{p_1}$$
$$= \frac{5.18 \times 10^4 \text{ kg} \cdot \text{km/h}}{7.00 \times 10^4 \text{ kg} \cdot \text{km/h}}$$
$$= 0.740$$
$$\theta = 36.5° \text{ W of N}$$
$$\vec{v} = \frac{\vec{p}}{m}$$
$$= \frac{8.71 \times 10^4 \text{ kg} \cdot \text{km/h}}{3.4 \times 10^3 \text{ kg}}$$
$$= 26 \text{ km/h } 37° \text{ W of N}$$

3.

Before

$$m_1 = 3.0 \times 10^4 \text{ N} \qquad m_2 = 4.0 \times 10^4 \text{ N}$$
$$\vec{v}_1 = 5.0 \text{ m/s} \qquad \vec{v}_2 = 8.0 \text{ m/s}$$
$$\vec{p}_1 = 1.5 \times 10^5 \text{ N} \cdot \text{m/s} \qquad \vec{p}_2 = 3.2 \times 10^5 \text{ N} \cdot \text{m/s}$$

After collision

$$m_{1+2} = 7.0 \times 10^4 \text{ N}$$
$$\vec{v}_{1+2} = ?$$
$$\vec{p}_{after} = 3.53 \times 10^5 \text{ N} \cdot \text{m/s}$$

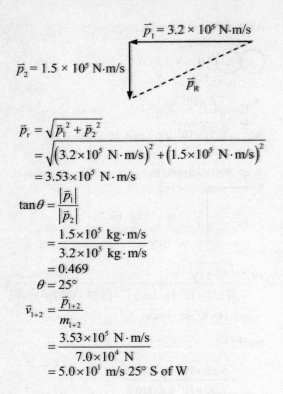

$$\vec{p}_r = \sqrt{\vec{p}_1^{\,2} + \vec{p}_2^{\,2}}$$
$$= \sqrt{\left(3.2\times10^5 \ \text{N} \cdot \text{m/s}\right)^2 + \left(1.5\times10^5 \ \text{N} \cdot \text{m/s}\right)^2}$$
$$= 3.53\times10^5 \ \text{N} \cdot \text{m/s}$$

$$\tan\theta = \frac{|\vec{p}_1|}{|\vec{p}_2|}$$
$$= \frac{1.5\times10^5 \ \text{kg} \cdot \text{m/s}}{3.2\times10^5 \ \text{kg} \cdot \text{m/s}}$$
$$= 0.469$$
$$\theta = 25°$$

$$\vec{v}_{1+2} = \frac{\vec{p}_{1+2}}{m_{1+2}}$$
$$= \frac{3.53\times10^5 \ \text{N} \cdot \text{m/s}}{7.0\times10^4 \ \text{N}}$$
$$= 5.0\times10^1 \ \text{m/s} \ 25° \ \text{S of W}$$

5. **a)** Before

$$m_1 = 15.0 \ \text{kg} \qquad m_2 = 10.0 \ \text{kg}$$
$$\vec{v}_1 = 7.0 \ \text{m/s east} \qquad \vec{v}_2 = 0$$
$$\vec{p}_1 = 105 \ \text{kg} \cdot \text{m/s east} \qquad \vec{p}_2 = 0$$

After

$$m_1 = 15.0 \ \text{kg} \qquad m_2 = 10.0 \ \text{kg}$$
$$\vec{v}_1 = 4.2 \ \text{m/s} \ 20.0° \ \text{S of E} \qquad \vec{v}_2 = ?$$
$$\vec{p}_1 = 63 \ \text{kg} \cdot \text{m/s} \ 20.0° \ \text{S of E} \qquad \vec{p}_2 = ?$$

$$\vec{p}_{\text{after}} = \vec{p}_{\text{before}}$$
$$\vec{p}_{\text{before}} = 105 \ \text{kg} \cdot \text{m/s east}$$
$$\vec{p}_{\text{after}} = 105 \ \text{kg} \cdot \text{m/s east}$$

Find the horizontal and vertical components of 63 kg·m/s 20.0° S of E

$$20.0° \ \text{S of E} = 340° \ (\text{RCS})$$

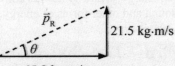

$$p_y = p\sin\theta$$
$$= (63 \ \text{kg} \cdot \text{m/s})(\sin 340°)$$
$$= -21.5 \ \text{kg} \cdot \text{m/s}$$
$$p_x = p\cos\theta$$
$$= (63 \ \text{kg} \cdot \text{m/s})(\cos 340°)$$
$$= 59.2 \ \text{kg} \cdot \text{m/s}$$

After the collision, the 10.0 kg object must have a horizontal component of
105 kg·m/s − 59.2 kg·m/s = 45.8 kg·m/s east

After the collision, the 10.0 kg object must have a vertical component of
$$0 - (-21.5 \ \text{kg} \cdot \text{m/s}) = 21.5 \ \text{kg} \cdot \text{m/s north}$$

Add 45.8 kg·m/s E and 21.5 kg·m/s N.

$$p_2 = \sqrt{p_x^{\,2} + p_y^{\,2}}$$
$$= \sqrt{(45.8 \ \text{kg} \cdot \text{m/s})^2 + (21.5 \ \text{kg} \cdot \text{m/s})^2}$$
$$= 50.6 \ \text{kg} \cdot \text{m/s}$$

$$\vec{v}_2 = \frac{\vec{p}_2}{m_2}$$
$$= \frac{50.6 \ \text{kg} \cdot \text{m/s}}{10.0 \ \text{kg}}$$
$$= 5.1 \ \text{m/s}$$

$$\tan\theta = \frac{p_y}{p_x}$$
$$= \frac{21.5 \ \text{kg} \cdot \text{m/s}}{45.8 \ \text{kg} \cdot \text{m/s}}$$
$$\theta = 25° \text{N of E}$$
$$\vec{v}_2 = 5.1 \ \text{m/s} \ 25° \ \text{N of E}$$

b) Before

①   ②

$m_1 = 15.0$ kg $m_2 = 10.0$ kg
$\vec{v}_1 = 7.0$ m/s $\vec{v}_2 = 0$

After

①   ②

$m_1 = 15.0$ kg $m_2 = 10.0$ kg
$\vec{v}_1 = 4.2$ m/s $\vec{v}_2 = 5.1$ m/s

Calculate the kinetic energy of object 1 before the collision.

$$E_k = \frac{1}{2}mv^2$$
$$= \frac{1}{2}(15.0 \text{ kg})(7.0 \text{ m/s})^2$$
$$= 3.7 \times 10^2 \text{ J}$$

Calculate the kinetic energy of object 1 after the collision.

$$E_k = \frac{1}{2}mv^2$$
$$= \frac{1}{2}(15.0 \text{ kg})(4.2 \text{ m/s})^2$$
$$= 1.3 \times 10^2 \text{ J}$$

Calculate the kinetic energy of object 2 before the collision.

$$E_k = \frac{1}{2}mv^2$$
$$= \frac{1}{2}(10.0 \text{ kg})(0)^2$$
$$= 0$$

Calculate the kinetic energy of object 2 after the collision

$$E_k = \frac{1}{2}mv^2$$
$$= \frac{1}{2}(10.0 \text{ kg})(5.1 \text{ m/s})^2$$
$$= 1.30 \times 10^2 \text{ J}$$

Calculate the total kinetic energy before the collision.

$$= 3.7 \times 10^2 \text{ J} + 0$$
$$= 3.7 \times 10^2 \text{ J}$$

Calculate the total kinetic energy after the collision.

$$= 1.3 \times 10^2 \text{ J} + 1.3 \times 10^2 \text{ J}$$
$$= 2.6 \times 10^2 \text{ J}$$

Calculate the mechanical (kinetic) energy lost in the collision.

$$= 3.7 \times 10^2 \text{ J} - 2.6 \times 10^2 \text{ J} = 1.1 \times 10^2 \text{ J}$$

$\therefore$ The collision is inelastic. Kinetic energy was not conserved.

c) Most of the lost mechanical energy was converted into thermal and sound energy.

Practice Quiz

ANSWERS AND SOLUTIONS

1. In this case, consider the acceleration due to gravity as positive in order to get a positive result for the weight.

$$\vec{p} = m\vec{v}$$
$$m = \frac{\vec{p}}{\vec{v}}$$
$$= \frac{2.0 \times 10^2 \text{ kg} \cdot \text{m/s}}{10.0 \text{ m/s}}$$
$$= 2.0 \times 10^1 \text{ kg}$$
$$\vec{F}_g = m\vec{g}$$
$$= (2.0 \times 10^1 \text{ kg})(9.81 \text{ m/s}^2)$$
$$= 2.0 \times 10^2 \text{ N}$$

3. $\vec{J} = m\Delta \vec{v}$
$$= (5.0 \times 10^{-2} \text{ kg})(30.0 \text{ m/s})$$
$$= 1.5 \text{ N} \cdot \text{s in the horizontal direction of the flight of the ball}$$

5. $E_k = \frac{1}{2}mv^2$
$$v = \sqrt{\frac{2E_k}{m}}$$
$$= \sqrt{\frac{2(9.0 \text{ J})}{0.15 \text{ kg}}}$$
$$= 11.0 \text{ m/s}$$
$$\vec{p} = m\vec{v}$$
$$= (0.15 \text{ kg})(11.0 \text{ m/s})$$
$$= 1.6 \text{ kg} \cdot \text{m/s in the direction of the object's motion}$$

7.

$\vec{v}_i$	$\vec{v}_f$	$\vec{a}$	$\vec{d}$	t
375 m/s	0		0.250 m	?

$$\vec{d} = \left(\frac{\vec{v}_f + \vec{v}_i}{2}\right)t$$

$$0.250 \text{ m} = \left(\frac{375 \text{ m/s}}{2}\right)t$$

$$t = 1.33 \times 10^{-3} \text{ s}$$

$$\vec{F}t = m\Delta\vec{v}$$

$$\vec{F} = \frac{m\Delta\vec{v}}{t}$$

$$= \frac{\left(5.00 \times 10^{-2} \text{ kg}\right)\left(375 \text{ m/s}\right)}{1.33 \times 10^{-3} \text{ s}}$$

$$= 1.41 \times 10^4 \text{ N opposite the}$$
direction of the bullet

9. $\vec{J}$ = area

$$\text{area} = \frac{1}{2}(6.0 \text{ N})(4.0 \text{ s})$$

$$= 12 \text{ N} \cdot \text{s in the direction of the}$$
acceleration

$$\vec{J} = m\Delta\vec{v}$$

$$\Delta\vec{v} = \frac{\text{Impulse}}{m}$$

$$= \frac{12 \text{ N} \cdot \text{s}}{0.75 \text{ kg}}$$

$$= 16 \text{ m/s in the direction of}$$
the acceleration

11. $\vec{F} = m\vec{a}$

$$= (2.0 \text{ kg})(3.5 \text{ m/s}^2)$$

$$= 7.0 \text{ N in the direction of the acceleration}$$

$$\vec{J} = \vec{F}t$$

$$= (7.0 \text{ N})(2.5 \text{ s})$$

$$= 18 \text{ N} \cdot \text{s in the direction of}$$
the acceleration

or

$$\vec{v} = \vec{a}t$$

$$= (3.5 \text{ m/s}^2)(2.5 \text{ s})$$

$$= 8.75 \text{ m/s in the direction of the acceleration}$$

$$\vec{p} = m\vec{v}$$

$$= (2.0 \text{ kg})(8.75 \text{ m/s})$$

$$= 18 \text{ kg} \cdot \text{m/s in the direction of the acceleration}$$

13. $\vec{p} = m\vec{v}$

$$\vec{v} = \frac{\vec{p}}{m}$$

$$= \frac{0.070 \text{ kg} \cdot \text{m/s}}{0.020 \text{ kg}}$$

$$= 3.5 \text{ m/s}$$

$$\Delta E_k + \Delta E_p = 0$$

$$\frac{1}{2}mv_f^2 - \frac{1}{2}mv_i^2 + mg\Delta h = 0$$

$$(h_f - h_i) = -\frac{v_f^2}{2g}$$

$$-h_i = -\frac{(3.5 \text{ m/s})^2}{2(9.81 \text{ m/s}^2)}$$

$$h_i = 0.62 \text{ m}$$

or

$$\vec{p} = m\vec{v}$$

$$\vec{v} = \frac{\vec{p}}{m}$$

$$= \frac{0.070 \text{ kg} \cdot \text{m/s}}{0.020 \text{ kg}}$$

$$= 3.5 \text{ m/s}$$

$$v_f^2 = v_i^2 + 2ad$$
but since v_i is 0

$$v_f^2 = 2gh \Rightarrow h = \frac{v_f^2}{2g}$$

$$h = \frac{(3.5 \text{ m/s})^2}{2(9.81 \text{ m/s}^2)}$$

$$= 0.62 \text{ m}$$

15. $\vec{J} = m\Delta\vec{v}$

$$= (0.45 \text{ kg})(10.0 \text{ m/s west} - 11.0 \text{ m/s east})$$

$$= (0.45 \text{ kg})(21.0 \text{ m/s west})$$

$$= 9.5 \text{ kg} \cdot \text{m/s west}$$

17. $\vec{p}_1 = m_1\vec{v}_1$

$$= (0.15 \text{ kg})(25 \text{ m/s})$$

$$\doteq 3.75 \text{ kg} \cdot \text{m/s north}$$

$$\vec{p}_2 = m_2\vec{v}_2$$

$$= (0.15 \text{ kg})(22 \text{ m/s})$$

$$= 3.30 \text{ kg} \cdot \text{m/s west}$$

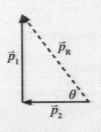

$$p_R = \sqrt{p_1^{\,2} + p_2^{\,2}}$$
$$= \sqrt{(3.75 \text{ kg} \cdot \text{m/s})^2 + (3.30 \text{ kg} \cdot \text{m/s})^2}$$
$$= 5.0 \text{ kg} \cdot \text{m/s}$$

$$\tan\theta = \frac{p_1}{p_2}$$
$$= \frac{3.75 \text{ kg} \cdot \text{m/s}}{3.30 \text{ kg} \cdot \text{m/s}}$$
$$= 1.14$$
$$\theta = 49°$$
$$\vec{p}_R = 5.0 \text{ kg} \cdot \text{m/s } 49° \text{ N of W}$$

19. Find the height of the box, *h*.

$$\sin\theta = \frac{\text{opposite}}{\text{hypotenuse}}$$
$$\sin 35.0° = \frac{h}{25.0 \text{ m}}$$
$$h = 14.3 \text{ m}$$
$$E_p = mgh$$
$$= (98.0 \text{ N})(14.3 \text{ m})$$
$$= 1.41 \times 10^3 \text{ J}$$

Find energy lost due to friction.
$$W = Fd$$
$$= (32.0 \text{ N})(25.0 \text{ m})$$
$$= 8.00 \times 10^2 \text{ J}$$

Find energy of the box at the bottom of the incline.
$$E_k = 1.41 \times 10^3 \text{ J} - 8.00 \times 10^2 \text{ J}$$
$$= 605 \text{ J}$$
$$\vec{F}_g = m\vec{g}$$
$$m = \frac{\vec{g}}{\vec{F}_g}$$
$$= \frac{98.0 \text{ N}}{9.81 \text{ m/s}^2}$$
$$= 9.99 \text{ kg}$$
$$E_k = \frac{1}{2}mv^2$$
$$v = \sqrt{\frac{2E_k}{m}}$$
$$= \sqrt{\frac{2(605 \text{ J})}{9.99 \text{ kg}}}$$
$$= 11.0 \text{ m/s}$$
$$\vec{p} = m\vec{v}$$
$$= (9.99 \text{ kg})(11.0 \text{ m/s})$$
$$= 1.10 \times 10^2 \text{ kg} \cdot \text{m/s down the ramp}$$

21. Before

$$m = 45.25 \text{ kg}$$
$$\vec{v} = 0$$
$$\vec{p} = 0$$

$$\vec{p}_{\text{before}} = 0$$

After

$m_1 = 45 \text{ kg}$	$m_2 = 0.25 \text{ kg}$
$\vec{v}_1 = ?$	$\vec{v}_2 = 9.0 \text{ m/s}$
$\vec{p}_1 = -2.25 \text{ kg} \cdot \text{m/s}$	$\vec{p}_2 = 2.25 \text{ kg} \cdot \text{m/s}$

$$\vec{p}_{\text{after}} = 0$$
$$\vec{v} = \frac{\vec{p}}{m}$$
$$= \frac{-2.25 \text{ kg} \cdot \text{m/s}}{45 \text{ kg}}$$
$$= -5.0 \times 10^{-2} \text{ m/s, or } 5.0 \times 10^{-2} \text{ m/s west}$$

23. Before

N   S
(1)   (2)

$m_1 = 6.0 \text{ g}$	$m_2 = 6.0 \text{ g}$
$\vec{v}_1 = 3.0 \text{ m/s}$	$\vec{v}_2 = -2.0 \text{ m/s}$
$\vec{p}_1 = 18.0 \text{ g} \cdot \text{m/s}$	$\vec{p}_2 = -12.0 \text{ g} \cdot \text{m/s}$

$$\vec{p}_{\text{before}} = 6.0 \text{ g} \cdot \text{m/s north}$$

After

(1)   (2)

$m_1 = 6.0 \text{ g}$	$m_2 = 6.0 \text{ g}$
$\vec{v}_1 = -1.0 \text{ m/s}$	$\vec{v}_2 = ?$
$\vec{p}_1 = -6.0 \text{ g} \cdot \text{m/s}$	$\vec{p}_2 = 12.0 \text{ g} \cdot \text{m/s}$

$\vec{P}_{\text{after}} = 6.0 \text{ g} \cdot \text{m/s north}$

$\vec{v} = \dfrac{\vec{p}}{m}$

$= \dfrac{12.0 \text{ g} \cdot \text{m/s north}}{6.0 \text{ g}}$

$= 2.0 \text{ m/s north}$

25. Before

$m = m_{\text{gun}} + m_{\text{bullet}}$

$\vec{v} = 0$

$\vec{p} = 0$

$m_{\text{gun}} = \dfrac{\vec{F}_g}{\vec{g}}$

$m_{\text{gun}} = \dfrac{25 \text{ N}}{9.81 \text{ m/s}^2} = 2.548 \text{ kg}$

After

$m_{\text{bullet}} = 6.0 \times 10^{-2} \text{ kg} \qquad m_{\text{gun}} = 2.548 \text{ kg}$

$\vec{v}_{\text{bullet}} = 325 \text{ m/s west} \qquad \vec{v}_{\text{gun}} = ?$

$\vec{p}_{\text{bullet}} = m\vec{v}$

$\qquad = 6.0 \times 10^{-2} \text{ kg} (325 \text{ m/s west})$

$\vec{p}_{\text{bullet}} = 19.5 \text{ kg m/s west}$

$\vec{p}_{\text{before}} = \vec{p}_{\text{after}}$

$\vec{p}_{\text{after}} = 0$

$\vec{p}_{\text{bullet}} + \vec{p}_{\text{gun}} = 0$

$\vec{p}_{\text{bullet}} = -\vec{p}_{\text{gun}}$

$\vec{p}_{\text{gun}} = -19.5 \text{ kg} \cdot \text{m/s west}$

$\vec{v}_{\text{gun}} = \dfrac{\vec{p}_{\text{gun}}}{m_{\text{gun}}} = \dfrac{-19.5 \text{ kg} \cdot \text{m/s west}}{2.548 \text{ kg}}$

$v_{\text{gun}} = -7.7 \text{ m/s west, or } 7.7 \text{ m/s east}$

27. a) Before

$m_1 = 3.0 \text{ kg} \qquad m_2 = 2.0 \text{ kg}$

$\vec{v}_1 = 0 \qquad\quad \vec{v}_2 = 5.0 \text{ m/s west}$

$\vec{p}_1 = 0 \qquad\quad \vec{p}_2 = 10.0 \text{ kg} \cdot \text{m/s west}$

$\vec{p}_{\text{before}} = 10.0 \text{ kg} \cdot \text{m/s west}$

After

$m = 3.0 \text{ kg} \qquad\qquad m = 2.0 \text{ kg}$

$\vec{v} = ? \qquad\qquad\qquad \vec{v} = 1.5 \text{ m/s west}$

$\vec{p} = 7.0 \text{ kg} \cdot \text{m/s west} \quad \vec{p} = 3.0 \text{ kg} \cdot \text{m/s west}$

$\vec{p}_{\text{after}} = 10.0 \text{ kg} \cdot \text{m/s west}$

$\vec{v} = \dfrac{\vec{p}}{m}$

$\quad = \dfrac{7.0 \text{ kg} \cdot \text{m/s}}{3.0 \text{ kg}}$

$\quad = 2.3 \text{ m/s west}$

b) To determine if the collision is elastic or inelastic, calculate the kinetic energies before and after the collision. If the energies are the same, the collision is elastic. If the kinetic energies after are less than before, then the collision is inelastic.

Before

$m_1 = 3.0 \text{ kg} \qquad m_2 = 2.0 \text{ kg}$

$\vec{v}_1 = 0 \qquad\quad \vec{v}_2 = 5.0 \text{ m/s west}$

After

$m_1 = 3.0 \text{ kg} \qquad\quad m_2 = 2.0 \text{ kg}$

$\vec{v}_1 = 2.3 \text{ m/s west} \qquad \vec{v}_2 = 1.5 \text{ m/s west}$

Calculate the kinetic energy of object 2 before the collision.

$E_k = \dfrac{1}{2} mv^2$

$\quad = \dfrac{1}{2} (2.0 \text{ kg})(5.0 \text{ m/s})^2$

$\quad = 25 \text{ J}$

Calculate the kinetic energy of object 2 after the collision.

$$E_k = \frac{1}{2}mv^2$$
$$= \frac{1}{2}(2.0 \text{ kg})(1.5 \text{ m/s})^2$$
$$= 2.25 \text{ J}$$

Calculate the kinetic energy of object 1 before the collision.

$$E_k = \frac{1}{2}mv^2$$
$$= \frac{1}{2}(3.0 \text{ kg})(0)$$
$$= 0$$

Calculate the kinetic energy of object 1 after the collision.

$$E_k = \frac{1}{2}mv^2$$
$$= \frac{1}{2}(3.0 \text{ kg})(2.3 \text{ m/s})^2$$
$$= 7.94 \text{ J}$$

Calculate the total kinetic energy before the collision.
$$= 25 \text{ J}$$

Calculate the total kinetic energy after the collision.
$$2.25 \text{ J} + 7.94 \text{ J} = 10.2 \text{ J}$$

Calculate the mechanical (kinetic) energy lost in the collision.
$$25 \text{ J} - 10.2 \text{ J} = 15 \text{ J}$$

Mechanical (kinetic) energy is lost, so the collision is inelastic. Most of this lost energy converted into thermal and sound energy.

29. Before collision

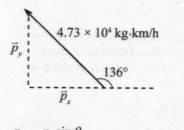

$m_1 = 775 \text{ kg}$ $m_2 = 1\,125 \text{ kg}$
$\vec{v}_1 = ?$ $\vec{v}_2 = ?$
$\vec{p}_1 = ?$ $\vec{p}_2 = ?$

After collision

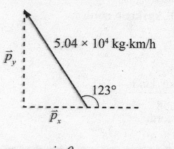

$m_1 = 775 \text{ kg}$ $m_2 = 1\,125 \text{ kg}$
$\vec{v}_1 = 65.0 \text{ km/h}$ $\vec{v} = 42.0 \text{ km/h}$
  $33.0°$ W of N $46.0°$ W of N
$\vec{p}_1 = 5.04 \times 10^4 \text{ kg} \cdot \text{km/h}$ $\vec{p}_2 = 4.73 \times 10^4 \text{ kg} \cdot \text{km/h}$
  $33.0°$ W of N $46.0°$ W of N

Find the horizontal and vertical components of $\vec{p}_1$, $5.04 \times 10^4 \text{ kg} \cdot \text{km/h}$ $33.0°$ W of N.

$$p_y = p_1 \sin \theta$$
$$= (5.04 \times 10^4 \text{ kg} \cdot \text{km/h})(\sin 123.0°)$$
$$= 4.23 \times 10^4 \text{ kg} \cdot \text{km/h}$$
$$p_x = p_1 \cos \theta$$
$$= (5.04 \times 10^4 \text{ kg} \cdot \text{km/h})(\cos 123°)$$
$$= -2.75 \times 10^4 \text{ kg} \cdot \text{km/h}$$

Find the horizontal and vertical components of $\vec{p}_2$, $4.73 \times 10^4 \text{ kg} \cdot \text{km/h}$ $46.0°$ W of N.

$$p_y = p_2 \sin \theta$$
$$= (4.73 \times 10^4 \text{ kg} \cdot \text{km/h})(\sin 136.0°)$$
$$= 3.29 \times 10^4 \text{ kg} \cdot \text{km/h}$$
$$p_x = p_2 \cos \theta$$
$$= (4.73 \times 10^4 \text{ kg} \cdot \text{km/h})(\cos 136°)$$
$$= -3.40 \times 10^4 \text{ kg} \cdot \text{km/h}$$
$$\Sigma \vec{p}_y = 4.23 \times 10^4 \text{ kg} \cdot \text{km/h} + 3.29 \times 10^4 \text{ kg} \cdot \text{km/h}$$
$$= 7.52 \times 10^4 \text{ kg} \cdot \text{km/h}$$
$$\Sigma \vec{p}_x = (-2.75 \times 10^4 \text{ kg} \cdot \text{km/h}) + (-3.40 \times 10^4 \text{ kg} \cdot \text{km/h})$$
$$= -6.15 \times 10^4 \text{ kg} \cdot \text{km/h}$$

Before collision, car 1 had only a horizontal component.
$$\therefore \vec{p}_1 = -6.15 \times 10^4 \text{ kg} \cdot \text{km/h east,}$$
$$\text{or } 6.15 \times 10^4 \text{ kg} \cdot \text{km/h west}$$

$\vec{p} = m\vec{v}$

$\vec{v} = \dfrac{\vec{p}}{m}$

$= \dfrac{6.15 \times 10^4 \text{ kg} \cdot \text{km/h west}}{775 \text{ kg}}$

$= 79.3 \text{ km/h west}$

Before collision, car 2 had only a vertical component.

$\therefore \vec{p}_2 = 7.52 \times 10^4 \text{ kg} \cdot \text{km/h north}$

$\vec{p} = m\vec{v}$

$\vec{v} = \dfrac{\vec{p}}{m}$

$= \dfrac{7.52 \times 10^4 \text{ kg} \cdot \text{km/h}}{1\,125 \text{ kg}}$

$= 66.7 \text{ km/h north}$

Practice Test

ANSWERS AND SOLUTIONS

1. When an object is lifted at a constant velocity, only its potential energy increases. To change the kinetic energy or momentum, the velocity or mass would have to change.

    A is the answer.

3. In order for an object to have kinetic energy or momentum, the object must have some velocity (v). However, an object at rest does not have a velocity.

    $\vec{p} = m\vec{v}$ and $E_k = \dfrac{1}{2}mv^2$

    D is the answer.

5. All objects have gravitational potential energy unless they are infinitely distant from their source of gravity. As well, an object that has momentum is in motion, so it must have kinetic energy (energy of movement). Force requires that an object has changing velocity. This is not the case for an object with constant momentum. Impulse requires that the momentum of an object is changing over time.

    C is the answer.

7. $\vec{p} = m\vec{v}$

    $E_k = \dfrac{1}{2}mv^2$

    $v = \sqrt{\dfrac{2E_k}{m}}$

    $p = m\sqrt{\dfrac{2E_k}{m}}$ and $m\sqrt{\dfrac{1}{m}} = \sqrt{m}$

    $p = \sqrt{2E_k m}$

    B is the answer.

9. If the object is sliding along a frictionless surface, the net force on the object will be zero. The force of gravity is balanced by the normal force from the surface. With no forces acting on the object, the velocity must remain constant. This means the kinetic energy and momentum must also be constant because both quantities are dependent on the velocity. The potential energy must also be constant because the object slides along the surface. This means its potential energy is zero.

    D is the answer.

11. Before

    $m = \left(1.30 \times 10^2 + 2.80 \times 10^3\right) \text{kg}$

    $\quad = 2.93 \times 10^3 \text{ kg}$

    $\vec{v} = 0$

    $\therefore \vec{p}_b = 0$

    After

    $m_s = 2.80 \times 10^3 \text{ kg}$ $\qquad m_E = 1.30 \times 10^2 \text{ kg}$

    $\vec{v}_s = ?$ $\qquad\qquad\qquad \vec{v}_E = 9.00 \text{ m/s}$

    $\vec{p}_s = ?$ $\qquad\qquad\qquad \vec{p}_E = 1\,170 \text{ kg} \cdot \text{m/s}$

    $\vec{p}_{before} = \vec{p}_{after}$

    $\qquad\quad = \vec{p}_s + \vec{p}_E$

    $\therefore \vec{p}_s = -\vec{p}_E = -1\,170 \text{ kg} \cdot \text{m/s}$

    $\Rightarrow \vec{v} = \dfrac{-1\,170 \text{ kg} \cdot \text{m/s}}{2.80 \times 10^3 \text{ kg}} = -0.418 \text{ m/s}$

    $\therefore \vec{v}_{total} = 9.42 \text{ m/s}$

    $\therefore t = \dfrac{\vec{d}}{\vec{v}} = \dfrac{22 \text{ m}}{9.42 \text{ m/s}} = 2.34 \text{ m/s}$

    C is the answer.

13. An elastic collision is a collision in which both kinetic energy and momentum are conserved.

C is the answer.

14. Impulse is a vector quantity. Use the negative sign to designate that when the ball returns at –2.5 m/s, it is in the opposite direction to the initial velocity.

$$\overline{\text{Impulse}} = m\Delta\vec{v}$$
$$= m(\vec{v}_f - \vec{v}_i)$$
$$= 0.25 \text{ kg}(-2.5 \text{ m/s} - 3.0 \text{ m/s})$$
$$= -1.4 \text{ N} \cdot \text{s, or } 1.4 \text{ N} \cdot \text{s}$$
$$\text{away from the wall}$$

C is the answer.

15. $\vec{p} = m\vec{v}$

$$\vec{p}_1 = (1.1 \times 10^3 \text{ kg})(25 \text{ km/h})$$
$$= 2.75 \times 10^4 \text{ kg} \cdot \text{km/h}$$
$$\vec{p}_2 = (2.3 \times 10^3 \text{ kg})(-15 \text{ km/h})$$
$$= -3.45 \times 10^4 \text{ kg} \cdot \text{km/h}$$
$$\vec{p}_{\text{net}} = \vec{p}_1 + \vec{p}_2$$
$$= (2.75 \times 10^4 \text{ kg} \cdot \text{km/h}) + (-3.45 \times 10^4 \text{ kg} \cdot \text{km/h})$$
$$= -7.00 \times 10^3 \text{ kg} \cdot \text{km/h}$$

$$\vec{v}_{\text{net}} = \frac{\vec{p}_{\text{net}}}{m_{\text{net}}}$$
$$= \frac{-7.00 \times 10^3 \text{ kg} \cdot \text{km/h}}{(1.1 \times 10^3 \text{ kg}) + (2.3 \times 10^3 \text{ kg})}$$
$$= -2.1 \text{ km/h, or } 2.1 \text{ km/h west}$$

B is the answer.

ELECTRIC FORCES AND FIELDS

Lesson 1—Electric Forces

PRACTICE EXERCISE ANSWERS AND SOLUTIONS

1. $F_g = \dfrac{Gm_1 m_2}{r^2}$

$$= \frac{\left(6.67 \times 10^{-11} \dfrac{\text{N} \cdot \text{m}^2}{\text{kg}^2}\right)(70.0 \text{ kg})(52.0 \text{ kg})}{(1.50 \text{ m})^2}$$
$$= 1.08 \times 10^{-7} \text{ N}$$

3. $F_e = \dfrac{kq_1 q_2}{r^2}$

$$= \frac{\left(8.99 \times 10^9 \dfrac{\text{N} \cdot \text{m}^2}{\text{C}^2}\right)(4.00 \times 10^{-6} \text{ C})(3.00 \times 10^{-6} \text{ C})}{(2.00 \times 10^{-2} \text{ m})^2}$$
$$= 2.70 \times 10^2 \text{ N}$$

5. $F_e = \dfrac{kq_1 q_2}{r^2}$

$$r^2 = \frac{kq_1 q_2}{F_e}$$
$$r = \sqrt{\frac{\left(8.99 \times 10^9 \dfrac{\text{N} \cdot \text{m}^2}{\text{C}^2}\right)(2.0 \times 10^{-6} \text{ C}) \times (4.0 \times 10^{-6} \text{ C})}{\left|(5.6 \times 10^{-1} \text{ N})\right|}}$$
$$= 3.6 \times 10^{-1} \text{ m}$$

7. $F_e = \dfrac{kq_1 q_2}{r^2}$

$$F_e \propto \frac{1}{r^2}$$
$$F_e \propto \frac{q_1 q_2}{r^2}$$
$$\propto \frac{(3)(3)}{(2)^2}$$
$$\propto 2.25$$
$$F_e = (4.5 \times 10^{-3} \text{ N})(2.25)$$
$$= 1.0 \times 10^{-2} \text{ N}$$

9. $F_e = \dfrac{kq_1q_2}{r^2}$

$F_e \propto \dfrac{1}{r^2}$

Distance changes by the following factor:

$\dfrac{\text{to}}{\text{from}} = \dfrac{4.04 \times 10^{-1} \text{ m}}{3.11 \times 10^{-1} \text{ m}} = 1.30$

Distance increases by a factor of 1.30.

$F_e \propto \dfrac{1}{(1.30)^2}$

$\propto 0.592$

$F_e = (5.2 \times 10^{-4} \text{ N})(0.592)$

$= 3.1 \times 10^{-4} \text{ N}$

11.

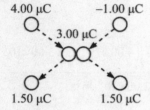

4.00 μC   −1.00 μC

3.00 μC

1.50 μC   1.50 μC

$F_2 = \dfrac{kq_1q_2}{r^2}$

$= \dfrac{\left(8.99 \times 10^9 \, \dfrac{\text{N} \cdot \text{m}^2}{\text{C}^2}\right)(1.50 \times 10^{-6} \text{ C})^2}{(2.00 \times 10^{-1} \text{ m})^2}$

$= 5.06 \times 10^{-1} \text{ N}$

13. $F \propto \dfrac{1}{r^2}$

$\dfrac{F_{CB}}{F_{AB}} \propto \dfrac{r_{AB}^{\,2}}{r_{CB}^{\,2}}$

$F_{CB} \propto \dfrac{(1.5)^2}{(4.5)^2} F_{AB} = \dfrac{1}{9} F_{AB} = 0.11\, F_{AB}$

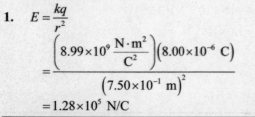

Lesson 2—Electric Fields

PRACTICE EXERCISE
ANSWERS AND SOLUTIONS

1. $E = \dfrac{kq}{r^2}$

$= \dfrac{\left(8.99 \times 10^9 \, \dfrac{\text{N} \cdot \text{m}^2}{\text{C}^2}\right)(8.00 \times 10^{-6} \text{ C})}{(7.50 \times 10^{-1} \text{ m})^2}$

$= 1.28 \times 10^5 \text{ N/C}$

3. $E = \dfrac{kq}{r^2}$

$r = \sqrt{\dfrac{kq}{E}}$

$= \sqrt{\dfrac{\left(8.99 \times 10^9 \, \dfrac{\text{N} \cdot \text{m}^2}{\text{C}^2}\right)(4.60 \times 10^{-6} \text{ C})}{2.75 \times 10^5 \text{ N/C}}}$

$= 3.88 \times 10^{-1} \text{ m}$

5. $F \propto q$

$\dfrac{\text{to}}{\text{from}} = \dfrac{1.60 \times 10^{-19} \text{ C}}{3.20 \times 10^{-19} \text{ C}}$

$= 0.500$

$F = (0.500)(0.250 \text{ N})$

$= 0.125 \text{ N}$

7. $\vec{E} = \dfrac{\vec{F}_e}{q}$

$\vec{F}_e = q\vec{E}$

$= (3.20 \times 10^{-19} \text{ C})(7.60 \times 10^4 \text{ N/C})$

$= 2.43 \times 10^{-14} \text{ N}$

$\vec{F} = m\vec{a}$

$\vec{a} = \dfrac{\vec{F}}{m}$

$= \dfrac{2.43 \times 10^{-14} \text{ N}}{6.65 \times 10^{-27} \text{ kg}}$

$= 3.66 \times 10^{12} \text{ m/s}^2$

9.

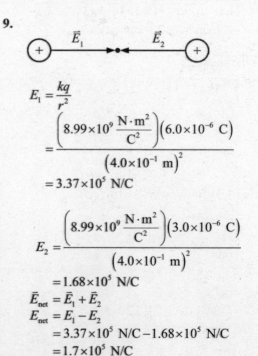

$E_1 = \dfrac{kq}{r^2}$

$= \dfrac{\left(8.99 \times 10^9 \, \dfrac{\text{N} \cdot \text{m}^2}{\text{C}^2}\right)(6.0 \times 10^{-6} \text{ C})}{(4.0 \times 10^{-1} \text{ m})^2}$

$= 3.37 \times 10^5 \text{ N/C}$

$E_2 = \dfrac{\left(8.99 \times 10^9 \, \dfrac{\text{N} \cdot \text{m}^2}{\text{C}^2}\right)(3.0 \times 10^{-6} \text{ C})}{(4.0 \times 10^{-1} \text{ m})^2}$

$= 1.68 \times 10^5 \text{ N/C}$

$\vec{E}_{net} = \vec{E}_1 + \vec{E}_2$

$E_{net} = E_1 - E_2$

$= 3.37 \times 10^5 \text{ N/C} - 1.68 \times 10^5 \text{ N/C}$

$= 1.7 \times 10^5 \text{ N/C}$

11. $\vec{F} = m\vec{a}$

$= \left(9.11 \times 10^{-31} \text{ kg}\right)\left(7.50 \times 10^{12} \text{ m/s}^2\right)$

$= 6.83 \times 10^{-18} \text{ N}$

$\vec{E} = \dfrac{\vec{F}_e}{q} = \dfrac{6.83 \times 10^{-18} \text{ N}}{1.60 \times 10^{-19} \text{ C}}$

$= 4.27 \times 10^1 \text{ N/C}$

13. $E = \dfrac{kq}{r^2} \qquad E \propto \dfrac{1}{r^2}$

$r^2 \propto \dfrac{1}{E} \qquad r \propto \sqrt{\dfrac{1}{E}}$

Field is changed by the following factor:

$\dfrac{\text{to}}{\text{from}} = \dfrac{4.20 \times 10^4 \text{ N/C}}{2.10 \times 10^4 \text{ N/C}} = 2.00$.

E changes by a factor of 2.00.

$\therefore r$ changes by a factor of $\sqrt{\dfrac{1}{2.00}} = 0.707$.

$E = \left(7.50 \times 10^{-1} \text{ m}\right)(0.707)$

$= 5.30 \times 10^{-1} \text{ m}$

Lesson 3—Electric Potential in a Uniform Electric Field

PRACTICE EXERCISE
ANSWERS AND SOLUTIONS

1. $E = \dfrac{V}{d}$

$= \dfrac{12.0 \text{ V}}{9.00 \times 10^{-2} \text{ m}}$

$= 1.33 \times 10^2 \text{ V/m}$

3. $E = \dfrac{V}{d}$

$V = Ed$

$= \left(2.0 \times 10^3 \text{ V/m}\right)\left(7.3 \times 10^{-2} \text{ m}\right)$

$= 1.5 \times 10^2 \text{ V}$

5. $V = \dfrac{\Delta E}{q}$

$\Delta E = qV$

$= \left(1.60 \times 10^{-19} \text{ C}\right)\left(7.20 \times 10^2 \text{ V}\right)$

$= 1.15 \times 10^{-16} \text{ J}$

7. **a)** Because the proton moves parallel to the plates, there is no change in the potential energy of the proton. Therfore, no work is done.

b) $E = \dfrac{V}{d}$

$= \dfrac{7.5 \times 10^1 \text{ V}}{6.0 \times 10^{-2} \text{ m}}$

$E = 1.25 \times 10^3 \text{ V/m}$

$W = qEd$

$= \left\{ \begin{array}{l} \left(1.60 \times 10^{-19} \text{ C}\right)\left(1.25 \times 10^3 \text{ V/m}\right) \\ \times \left(3.0 \times 10^{-2} \text{ m}\right) \end{array} \right\}$

$= 6.0 \times 10^{-18} \text{ J}$

9. First, find the initial energy.

$E_k = \dfrac{1}{2}mv^2$

$= \dfrac{1}{2}\left(6.65 \times 10^{-27} \text{ kg}\right)\left(7.15 \times 10^4 \text{ m/s}\right)^2$

$= 1.70 \times 10^{-17} \text{ J}$

Now, find the change in energy.

$E = \dfrac{V}{d}$

$V = Ed$

$= \left(1.70 \times 10^2 \text{ V/m}\right)\left(9.00 \times 10^{-2} \text{ m}\right)$

$= 1.53 \times 10^1 \text{ V}$

$V = \dfrac{\Delta E}{q}$

$\Delta E = qV$

$= \left(3.20 \times 10^{-19} \text{ C}\right)\left(1.53 \times 10^1 \text{ V}\right)$

$= 4.90 \times 10^{-18} \text{ J}$

Therefore, the energy of the alpha particle when it hit the plate is calculated as follows:

$4.90 \times 10^{-18} \text{ J} + 1.70 \times 10^{-17} \text{ J} = 2.19 \times 10^{-17} \text{ J}$

$E_k = \dfrac{1}{2}mv^2$

$v = \sqrt{\dfrac{2E_k}{m}}$

$= \sqrt{\dfrac{2\left(2.19 \times 10^{-17} \text{ J}\right)}{6.65 \times 10^{-27} \text{ kg}}}$

$= 8.11 \times 10^4 \text{ m/s}$

11. $E = \dfrac{V}{d}$

$E \propto \dfrac{V}{d}$

$\dfrac{\text{to}}{\text{from}} = \dfrac{5.0 \text{ cm}}{7.0 \text{ cm}} = 0.714$

Distance changes by a factor of 0.714. Therefore, the electric field will change by a factor that is calculated as follows:

$\dfrac{1}{0.714} = 1.40$

$E = \left(9.3 \times 10^2 \text{ V/m}\right)(1.40)$

$= 1.3 \times 10^3 \text{ V/m}$

13. $E_k = \dfrac{1}{2}mv^2$

$= \dfrac{1}{2}\left(9.11 \times 10^{-31} \text{ kg}\right)\left(6.00 \times 10^6 \text{ m/s}\right)^2$

$= 1.64 \times 10^{-17} \text{ J}$

$V = \dfrac{\Delta E}{q}$

$= \dfrac{1.64 \times 10^{-17} \text{ J}}{1.60 \times 10^{-19} \text{ C}}$

$= 1.02 \times 10^2 \text{ V}$

15. $E = \dfrac{F}{q}$

$= \dfrac{5.30 \times 10^{-14} \text{ N}}{3.20 \times 10^{-19} \text{ C}}$

$= 1.66 \times 10^5 \text{ N/C}$

$E = \dfrac{V}{d}$

$V = Ed$

$= \left(1.66 \times 10^5 \text{ N/C}\right)\left(7.50 \times 10^{-2} \text{ m}\right)$

$= 1.24 \times 10^4 \text{ V}$

17. a) The speed of the proton when it reaches plate Y is calculated as follows:

$\Delta E_p = qV$

$= \left(1.60 \times 10^{-19} \text{ C}\right)(60.0 \text{ V})$

$= 9.60 \times 10^{-18} \text{ J}$

$\Delta E_k = \Delta E_p = \dfrac{1}{2}mv^2$

$9.60 \times 10^{-18} \text{ J} = \dfrac{1}{2}\left(1.67 \times 10^{-27} \text{ kg}\right)v^2$

$v = \sqrt{\dfrac{2\left(9.60 \times 10^{-18} \text{ J}\right)}{1.67 \times 10^{-27} \text{ kg}}}$

$= 1.07 \times 10^5 \text{ m/s}$

b) The speed of the electron when it reaches plate X is calculated as follows:

$\Delta E_p = qV$

$= \left(1.60 \times 10^{-19} \text{ C}\right)(60.0 \text{ V})$

$= 9.60 \times 10^{-18} \text{ J}$

$\Delta E_k = \Delta E_p = mv^2$

$9.60 \times 10^{-18} \text{ J} = \dfrac{1}{2}\left(9.11 \times 10^{-31} \text{ kg}\right)v^2$

$v = \sqrt{\dfrac{2\left(9.60 \times 10^{-18} \text{ J}\right)}{9.11 \times 10^{-31} \text{ kg}}}$

$= 4.59 \times 10^6 \text{ m/s}$

19. $\Delta E = qV$

$= \left(1.60 \times 10^{-19} \text{ C}\right)\left(5.00 \times 10^3 \text{ V}\right)$

$= 8.00 \times 10^{-16} \text{ J}$

$E_k = \dfrac{1}{2}mv^2$

$v = \sqrt{\dfrac{2E_k}{m}}$

$= \sqrt{\dfrac{2\left(8.00 \times 10^{-16} \text{ J}\right)}{9.11 \times 10^{-31} \text{ kg}}}$

$= 4.19 \times 10^7 \text{ m/s}$

Practice Quiz

ANSWERS AND SOLUTIONS

1. $g = \dfrac{Gm}{r^2}$

$r = \sqrt{\dfrac{Gm}{g}}$

$= \sqrt{\dfrac{\left(6.67 \times 10^{-11} \dfrac{\text{N} \cdot \text{m}^2}{\text{kg}^2}\right)\left(5.98 \times 10^{24} \text{ kg}\right)}{6.13 \times 10^{-1} \text{ N/kg}}}$

$= 2.55 \times 10^7 \text{ m}$

The distance from surface is calculated as follows:

$= 2.55 \times 10^7 \text{ m} - 6.38 \times 10^6 \text{ m (Earth's radius)}$

$= 1.91 \times 10^7 \text{ m}$

3. $F_g = \dfrac{Gm_1m_2}{r^2}$

$= \dfrac{\left(6.67 \times 10^{-11} \dfrac{\text{N} \cdot \text{m}^2}{\text{kg}^2}\right)\left(3.40 \times 10^{27} \text{ kg}\right)(15.0 \text{ kg})}{\left(5.74 \times 10^7 \text{ m}\right)^2}$

$= 1.03 \times 10^3 \text{ N}$

5.

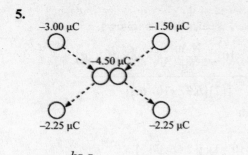

$$F_e = \frac{kq_1q_2}{r^2}$$

$$= \frac{\left(8.99\times10^9\ \frac{N\cdot m^2}{C^2}\right)\left(2.25\times10^{-6}\ C\right)^2}{\left(5.00\times10^{-1}\ m\right)^2}$$

$$= 1.82\times10^{-1}\ N$$

7. $E_1 = \frac{kq}{r^2} \qquad\qquad q = \frac{Er^2}{k}$

$$= \frac{\left(2.70\times10^4\ N/C\right)\left(1.50\ m\right)^2}{\left(8.99\times10^9\ \frac{N\cdot m^2}{C^2}\right)}$$

$$= 6.76\times10^{-6}\ C$$

$$E_2 = \frac{kq}{r^2}$$

$$= \frac{\left(8.99\times10^9\ \frac{N\cdot m^2}{C^2}\right)\left(6.76\times10^{-6}\ C\right)}{\left(7.50\times10^{-1}\right)^2}$$

$$= 1.08\times10^5\ N/C$$

or

$$E \propto \frac{1}{r^2}$$

$$\frac{to}{from} = \frac{0.75}{1.5} = 0.50$$

$$E_2 = \frac{1}{\left(0.50\right)^2}E_1 = 4\left(2.70\times10^4\ N/C\right)$$

$$E_2 = 1.08\times10^5\ N/C$$

9. $\bar{E} = \frac{\bar{F}_e}{q}$

$$= \frac{2.44\times10^{-14}\ N}{3\left(1.60\times10^{-19}\ C\right)}$$

$$= 5.08\times10^4\ N/C$$

11. $E = \frac{F_e}{q}$

$$= \frac{3.50\times10^{-13}\ N}{2.00\times10^{-16}\ C}$$

$$= 1.75\times10^3\ N/C$$

$$E = \frac{V}{d}$$

$$V = Ed$$

$$= \left(1.75\times10^3\ N/C\right)\left(5.00\times10^{-2}\ m\right)$$

$$= 8.75\times10^1\ V$$

or

$$E = \frac{F_e}{q} = \frac{V}{d} \Rightarrow V = \frac{F_e d}{q}$$

$$V = \frac{\left(3.50\times10^{-13}\ N\right)\left(5.00\times10^{-2}\ m\right)}{2.00\times10^{-16}\ C}$$

$$V = 8.75\times10^1\ V$$

13. a) $E = \frac{V}{d}$

$$= \frac{12.0\ V}{2.00\times10^{-2}\ m}$$

$$= 6.00\times10^2\ V/m$$

$$F_e = qE$$

$$= \left(3.20\times10^{-19}\ C\right)\left(6.00\times10^2\ V/m\right)$$

$$= 1.92\times10^{-16}\ N$$

or

$$E = \frac{V}{d} \text{ and } F_e = qE$$

$$\Rightarrow F_e = \frac{qV}{d} = \frac{\left(3.20\times10^{-19}\ C\right)\left(6.00\times10^2\ V\right)}{2.00\times10^{-2}\ m}$$

$$F_e = 1.92\times10^{-16}\ N$$

$$\therefore\ \bar{F}_e = 1.92\times10^{-16}\ N\ up$$

b) $\bar{F}_g = m\bar{g}$

$$= \left(6.65\times10^{-27}\ kg\right)\left(9.81\ N/kg\right)$$

$$= 6.52\times10^{-26}\ N\ down$$

c) $\bar{F}_{net} = \bar{F}_e + \bar{F}_g$

$$= 1.92\times10^{-16}\ N - 6.52\times10^{-26}\ N$$

$$= 1.92\times10^{-16}\ N\ up$$

d) $\vec{F}_{net} = m\vec{a}$

$\vec{a} = \dfrac{\vec{F}_{net}}{m}$

$= \dfrac{1.92 \times 10^{-16} \text{ N}}{6.65 \times 10^{-27} \text{ kg}}$

$= 2.89 \times 10^{10} \text{ m/s}^2 \text{ up}$

e) $F_e = F_g$

$F_e = 6.52 \times 10^{-26} \text{ N}$

$F_e = qE$

$E = \dfrac{F_e}{q}$

$= \dfrac{6.52 \times 10^{-26} \text{ N}}{3.20 \times 10^{-19} \text{ C}}$

$= 2.04 \times 10^{-7} \text{ N/C}$

$V = Ed$

$= \left(2.04 \times 10^{-7} \text{ N/C}\right)\left(2.00 \times 10^{-2} \text{ m}\right)$

$= 4.08 \times 10^{-9} \text{ V}$

or

$F_e = F_g = qE$

$E = \dfrac{V}{d}$

$\Rightarrow V = \dfrac{F_e d}{q} = \dfrac{\left(6.52 \times 10^{-26} \text{ N}\right)\left(2.00 \times 10^{-2} \text{ m}\right)}{3.20 \times 10^{-19} \text{ C}}$

$V = 4.08 \times 10^{-9} \text{ V}$

Practice Test

ANSWERS AND SOLUTIONS

1. You must calculate the acceleration due to gravity at a distance of one Earth radius above Earth's surface. To do this, you must multiply the radius of Earth by 2.

weight $= F_g = mg$

$m = \dfrac{F_g}{g}$

$= \dfrac{2.0 \text{ N}}{9.81 \text{ m/s}^2}$

$= 2.0 \times 10^{-1} \text{ kg}$

$g = \dfrac{Gm}{r^2}$

$g = \dfrac{\left(6.67 \times 10^{-11} \dfrac{\text{N} \cdot \text{m}^2}{\text{kg}^2}\right)\left(5.98 \times 10^{24} \text{ kg}\right)}{\left((2)\left(6.37 \times 10^6 \text{ m}\right)\right)^2}$

$g = 2.46 \text{ m/s}^2$

$F_g = mg$

$= \left(2.0 \times 10^{-1} \text{ kg}\right)\left(2.46 \text{ m/s}^2\right)$

$= 0.50 \text{ N}$

or

$F_g = \dfrac{Gm_1 m_2}{r^2} \Rightarrow F_g \propto \dfrac{1}{r^2}$

$\dfrac{\text{To}}{\text{From}} = \dfrac{2r_E}{1r_E} = 2$

$F_g = \left(\dfrac{1}{2^2}\right)(2.0 \text{ N}) = 0.50 \text{ N}$

A is the answer.

3. When the balls touch, the charge will distribute evenly between them.

$q_{after} = \dfrac{-3.00 \mu C + -1.00 \mu C}{2}$

$= -2.00 \mu C \text{ each}$

$F_e = \dfrac{kq_1 q_2}{r^2}$

$= \dfrac{\left(8.99 \times 10^9 \dfrac{\text{N} \cdot \text{m}}{\text{C}}\right)\left(2.00 \times 10^{-6} \text{ C}\right)^2}{\left(2.00 \times 10^{-2} \text{ m}\right)^2}$

$= 90.0 \text{ N}$

D is the answer.

5. $F_1 = \dfrac{kq_1 q_2}{r^2}$

$= \dfrac{\left(8.99 \times 10^9 \dfrac{\text{N} \cdot \text{m}^2}{\text{C}^2}\right)\left(3.00 \times 10^{-6} \text{ C}\right)^2}{\left(0.333 \text{ m}\right)^2}$

$= 7.30 \times 10^{-1} \text{ N}$

$F_2 = F_1$

$= 7.30 \times 10^{-1} \text{ N}$

$F_{net} = \sqrt{F_1^2 + F_2^2}$

$= \sqrt{\left(7.30 \times 10^{-1} \text{ N}\right)^2 + \left(7.30 \times 10^{-1} \text{ N}\right)^2}$

$= 1.03 \text{ N}$

C is the answer.

7. $F_e = \dfrac{kq_1q_2}{r^2}$

$$G_e = \dfrac{\left(8.99\times10^9 \ \dfrac{\text{N}\cdot\text{m}^2}{\text{C}^2}\right)\left(3.00\times10^{-6} \ \text{C}\right)^2}{\left(2.00\times10^{-2} \ \text{m}\right)^2}$$

$= 2.02\times10^2 \ \text{N}$

$F = ma$

$a = \dfrac{F}{m}$

$= \dfrac{2.02\times10^2 \ \text{N}}{5.00\times10^{-4} \ \text{kg}}$

$= 4.05\times10^5 \ \text{m/s}^2$

or

$F = ma$ and $F_e = \dfrac{kq_1q_2}{r^2} \Rightarrow ma = \dfrac{kq_1q_2}{r^2}$

$$\therefore a = \dfrac{kq_1q_2}{mr^2} = \dfrac{\left(8.99\times10^9 \ \dfrac{\text{N}\cdot\text{m}^2}{\text{C}^2}\right)\left(3.00\times10^{-6} \ \text{C}\right)^2}{\left(5.00\times10^{-4} \ \text{kg}\right)\left(2.00\times10^{-2} \ \text{m}\right)^2}$$

$a = 4.05\times10^5 \ \text{m/s}^2$

C is the answer.

9. The direction of an electric field is the direction that a positive test charge will move when placed into the field: from positive toward negative. An electron will be repelled from the negative, so it will accelerate in the direction opposite to the electric field.

C is the answer.

11. $E = \dfrac{kq}{r^2}$

The smaller the distance between the points, the more the potential energy will increase.

A is the answer.

13. The direction of an electric field is defined as the direction that a positive test charge will move when place in the field: from positive toward negative. In the given diagram, the electric field will be directed vertically downward.

B is the answer.

15. You want to bring a known charge near to the head of the electroscope first. This will cause the electrons to be somewhat displaced. This results in the electroscope's leaves and head having opposite charges. Since the known charge was negative, the electroscope's leaves are negative, and the head is positive. If you touch the electroscope's head, electrons will flow onto the electroscope, making the net charge on the entire electroscope negative. Since both leaves have a negative charge, they repel each other and remain spread apart.
When the plastic rod is brought near the head of the electroscope, it will cause another displacement of the electrons on the electroscope. If the plastic rod is negative, the electrons on the electroscope will be somewhat displaced toward its leaves, causing them to repel even more. If the plastic rod is positive, the opposite will happen: the leaves will not repel as much.

B is the answer.

17. When the negatively charged rubber rod is brought near the head of the electroscope, the leaves of the electroscope converge. A negatively charged rubber rod repels more electrons into the leaves. Convergence means the electroscope leaves must be more neutral. If negative charge is added and the leaves are now more neutral, then the electroscope must have been positively charged.

A is the answer.

19. The conductor is not spherical. Therefore, the distribution is not uniform. The greater the curvature, the greater the concentration of charge. Also, the excess charge will be distributed on the conductor's surface.

A is the answer.

MAGNETIC FORCES AND FIELDS

Lesson 1—Magnetic Forces and Fields

PRACTICE EXERCISE
ANSWERS AND SOLUTIONS

1. $F_m = qvB_\perp$

$B_\perp = \dfrac{F_m}{qv}$

$\quad = \dfrac{9.50 \times 10^{-14} \text{ N}}{\left(1.60 \times 10^{-19} \text{ C}\right)\left(2.10 \times 10^{5} \text{ m/s}\right)}$

$\quad = 2.83 \text{ T}$

3. $F_m = qvB_\perp$

$\quad = \left(1.60 \times 10^{-19} \text{ C}\right)\left(3.52 \times 10^{5} \text{ m/s}\right)\left(2.80 \times 10^{-1} \text{ T}\right)$

$\quad = 1.58 \times 10^{-14} \text{ N}$

$\therefore \vec{F}_m = 1.58 \times 10^{-14} \text{ N west}$

5. $F_m = qvB_\perp$

$B_\perp = \dfrac{F_m}{qv}$

$\quad = \dfrac{1.70 \times 10^{-14} \text{ N}}{\left(1.60 \times 10^{-19} \text{ C}\right)\left(1.90 \times 10^{4} \text{ m/s}\right)}$

$\quad = 5.59 \text{ T}$

$\therefore \vec{B}_\perp = 5.59 \text{ T up}$

7. The alpha particle travels parallel to the magnetic field, so there is no force.

$F_m = qvB \sin \theta$

$\quad = qvB \sin(0) = 0$

9. $\Delta E = qV$

$\quad = \left(1.60 \times 10^{-19} \text{ C}\right)\left(1.70 \times 10^{3} \text{ V}\right)$

$\quad = 2.72 \times 10^{-16} \text{ J}$

$E_k = \dfrac{1}{2}mv^2$

$v = \sqrt{\dfrac{2E_k}{m}}$

$\quad = \sqrt{\dfrac{2\left(2.72 \times 10^{-16} \text{ J}\right)}{9.11 \times 10^{-31} \text{ kg}}}$

$\quad = 2.44 \times 10^{7} \text{ m/s}$

$F_m = qvB_\perp$

$\quad = \left(1.60 \times 10^{-19} \text{ C}\right)\left(2.44 \times 10^{7} \text{ m/s}\right) \times \left(2.50 \times 10^{-1} \text{ T}\right)$

$\quad = 9.77 \times 10^{-13} \text{ N}$

or

$\Delta E = E_k \Rightarrow qV = \dfrac{1}{2}mv^2$

$\therefore v = \sqrt{\dfrac{2qV}{m}}$

$F_m = qvB_\perp$

so $F_m = qB_\perp \sqrt{\dfrac{2qV}{m}}$

$\quad = \left(1.60 \times 10^{-19} \text{ C}\right)\left(2.50 \times 10^{-1} \text{ T}\right) \times$

$\quad \sqrt{\dfrac{2\left(1.60 \times 10^{-19} \text{ C}\right)\left(1.70 \times 10^{3} \text{ V}\right)}{9.11 \times 10^{-31} \text{ kg}}}$

$\quad = 9.77 \times 10^{-13} \text{ N}$

11. $F_m = qvB_\perp$

$\quad = \left(1.60 \times 10^{-19} \text{ C}\right)\left(6.20 \times 10^{5} \text{ m/s}\right)\left(2.30 \times 10^{-1} \text{ T}\right)$

$\quad = 2.28 \times 10^{-14} \text{ N}$

$F = ma$

$a = \dfrac{F}{m}$

$\quad = \dfrac{2.28 \times 10^{-14} \text{ N}}{9.11 \times 10^{-31} \text{ kg}}$

$\quad = 2.50 \times 10^{16} \text{ m/s}^2$

or

$F_m = qvB_\perp = ma$

$\therefore a = \dfrac{qvB_\perp}{m}$

$\quad = \dfrac{\left(1.60 \times 10^{-19} \text{ C}\right)\left(6.20 \times 10^{5} \text{ m/s}\right)\left(2.30 \times 10^{-1} \text{ T}\right)}{9.11 \times 10^{-31} \text{ kg}}$

$\quad = 2.50 \times 10^{16} \text{ m/s}^2$

Practice Quiz

ANSWERS AND SOLUTIONS

1. $F_m = qvB_\perp$

$B_\perp = \dfrac{F_m}{qv}$

$\quad = \dfrac{7.30 \times 10^{-13} \text{ N}}{\left(1.60 \times 10^{-19} \text{ C}\right)\left(7.80 \times 10^{4} \text{ m/s}\right)}$

$\quad = 5.85 \times 10^{1} \text{ T}$

$\therefore \vec{B}_\perp = 5.85 \times 10^{1} \text{ T south}$

3. $F_m = qvB_\perp$

$$v = \frac{F_m}{qB_\perp}$$

$$= \frac{6.20 \times 10^{-14} \text{ N}}{(3.20 \times 10^{-19} \text{ C})(5.50 \times 10^{-1} \text{ T})}$$

$$= 3.52 \times 10^5 \text{ m/s}$$

$$E_k = \frac{1}{2}mv^2$$

$$= \frac{(6.65 \times 10^{-27} \text{ kg})(3.52 \times 10^5 \text{ m/s})^2}{2}$$

$$= 4.07 \times 10^{-16} \text{ J}$$

$$V = \frac{E}{q}$$

$$= \frac{4.07 \times 10^{-16} \text{ J}}{3.20 \times 10^{-19} \text{ C}}$$

$$= 1.29 \times 10^3 \text{ V}$$

or

given $F_m = qvB_\perp$ and $E_k = \frac{1}{2}mv^2$ we get

$$v = \frac{F_m}{qB_\perp} \Rightarrow E_k = \frac{1}{2}m\left(\frac{F_m}{qB_\perp}\right)^2$$

plugging into $V = \dfrac{\Delta E}{q} = \dfrac{m}{2q}\left(\dfrac{F_m}{qB_\perp}\right)^2$

$$V = \frac{m}{2q^3}\left(\frac{F_m}{B_\perp}\right)^2$$

$$V = \frac{(6.65 \times 10^{-27} \text{ kg})}{2(3.20 \times 10^{-19} \text{ C})^3}\left(\frac{6.20 \times 10^{-14} \text{ N}}{5.50 \times 10^{-1} \text{ T}}\right)^2$$

$$= 1.29 \times 10^3 \text{ V}$$

5. $F_m = qvB_\perp$

$$= (1.60 \times 10^{-19} \text{ C})(6.20 \times 10^5 \text{ m/s})(2.3 \times 10^{-1} \text{ T})$$

$$= 2.28 \times 10^{-14} \text{ N}$$

$$F = ma$$

$$a = \frac{F}{m}$$

$$= \frac{2.28 \times 10^{-14} \text{ N}}{9.11 \times 10^{-31} \text{ kg}}$$

$$= 2.51 \times 10^{16} \text{ m/s}^2$$

or

$$F = ma \Rightarrow a = \frac{F}{m} = \frac{qvB_\perp}{m}$$

$$= \frac{(1.60 \times 10^{-19} \text{ C})(6.20 \times 10^5 \text{ m/s})(2.30 \times 10^{-1} \text{ T})}{9.11 \times 10^{-31} \text{ kg}}$$

$$= 2.51 \times 10^{16} \text{ m/s}^2$$

7. $F_m = B_\perp Il$

$$= (2.7 \times 10^{-3} \text{ T})(2.0 \text{ A})(0.75 \text{ m})$$

$$= 4.1 \times 10^{-3} \text{ N}$$

$$\therefore \vec{F}_m = 4.1 \times 10^{-3} \text{ N west}$$

9. $F_m = B_\perp Il$

$$= (5.20 \times 10^{-4} \text{ T})(2.10 \text{ A})(0.120 \text{ m})$$

$$= 1.31 \times 10^{-4} \text{ N}$$

$$\therefore \vec{F}_m = 1.31 \times 10^{-4} \text{ N south}$$

11. **a)** Since the net force, $\vec{F}_{net}$, is greater than the gravitational force, the magnetic force, $\vec{F}_m$, is in the same direction as the gravitational force, $\vec{F}_g$, which is down.

b)

Magnetic Force (N) $\vec{F}_m = \vec{F}_{net} - \vec{F}_g$	Magnetic Field Strength (T) $B_\perp = \dfrac{F_m}{Il}$
$= 0.779 - 0.748$ $= 0.031$ N	$= \dfrac{0.031 \text{ N}}{(5.0 \text{ A})(1.0 \times 10^{-2} \text{ m})}$ $= 0.62$ T
$= 0.812 - 0.748$ $= 0.064$ N	$= \dfrac{0.064 \text{ N}}{(5.0 \text{ A})(2.0 \times 10^{-2} \text{ m})}$ $= 0.64$ T
$= 0.838 - 0.748$ $= 0.080$ N	$= \dfrac{0.090 \text{ N}}{(5.0 \text{ A})(3.0 \times 10^{-2} \text{ m})}$ $= 0.60$ T
$= 0.869 - 0.748$ $= 0.121$ N	$= \dfrac{0.121 \text{ N}}{(5.0 \text{ A})(4 \times 10^{-2} \text{ m})}$ $= 0.61$ T
$= 0.935 - 0.748$ $= 0.187$ N	$= \dfrac{0.187 \text{ N}}{(5.0 \text{ A})(6.0 \times 10^{-2} \text{ m})}$ $= 0.60$ T
$= 0.998 - 0.748$ $= 0.250$ N	$= \dfrac{0.250 \text{ N}}{(5.0 \text{ A})(8.0 \times 10^{-2} \text{ m})}$ $= 0.63$ T

c)

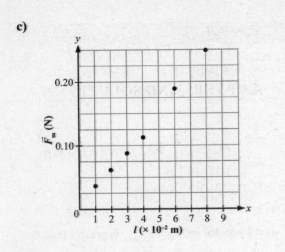

d) $F_m \propto I$

Practice Test

ANSWERS AND SOLUTIONS

1. Conventional flow uses the right-hand rule and will flow from point **A** to point **B** through point **G**. The magnetic field induced within the solenoid repels the magnet.

    C is the answer.

3. Lenz's law is an example of the conservation of energy.

    C is the answer.

5. There is no force when current travels parallel through magnetic fields.

    D is the answer.

7. Use the first left-hand rule for negative charges moving in a conductor. With your thumb pointing north, the fingers of your left hand curl around and point to the west when directly above the conductor.

    C is the answer.

9. Faraday noticed the galvanometer fluctuates when the switch is being opened or closed; however, it will not move while the switch is open or closed.

    C is the answer.

11. An ampere is defined in terms of forces between current-carrying conductors.

    C is the answer.

13. A motor converts electric energy to mechanical energy.

    A is the answer.

15. Deflection is caused by the force: the larger the magnetic force, the larger the deflection. The force is affected by charge, velocity, and the magnetic field as described by the equation
    $F_m = qvB_\perp$.

    It is not affected by the mass of the particles. Therefore, to increase the force, at least one of these elements needs to be increased.

    B is the answer.

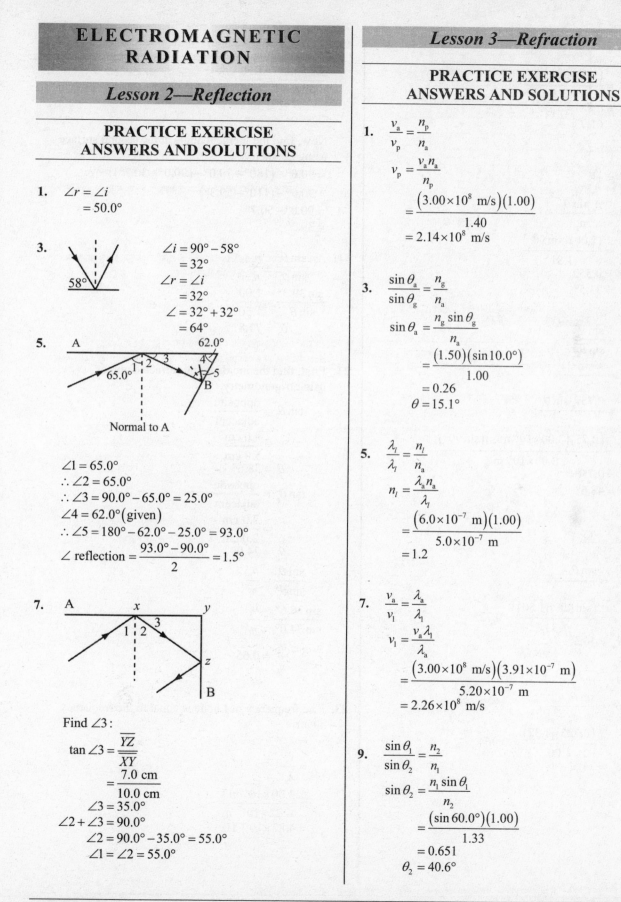

ELECTROMAGNETIC RADIATION

Lesson 2—Reflection

PRACTICE EXERCISE
ANSWERS AND SOLUTIONS

1. $\angle r = \angle i$
    $= 50.0°$

3. $\angle i = 90° - 58°$
    $= 32°$
    $\angle r = \angle i$
    $= 32°$
    $\angle = 32° + 32°$
    $= 64°$

    $58°$

5. A $62.0°$

    $65.0°$

    B

    Normal to A

    $\angle 1 = 65.0°$
    $\therefore \angle 2 = 65.0°$
    $\therefore \angle 3 = 90.0° - 65.0° = 25.0°$
    $\angle 4 = 62.0° (\text{given})$
    $\therefore \angle 5 = 180° - 62.0° - 25.0° = 93.0°$
    $\angle \text{ reflection} = \dfrac{93.0° - 90.0°}{2} = 1.5°$

7. A x y

    z

    B

    Find $\angle 3$:

    $\tan \angle 3 = \dfrac{\overline{YZ}}{\overline{XY}}$

    $= \dfrac{7.0 \text{ cm}}{10.0 \text{ cm}}$

    $\angle 3 = 35.0°$
    $\angle 2 + \angle 3 = 90.0°$
    $\angle 2 = 90.0° - 35.0° = 55.0°$
    $\angle 1 = \angle 2 = 55.0°$

Lesson 3—Refraction

PRACTICE EXERCISE
ANSWERS AND SOLUTIONS

1. $\dfrac{v_a}{v_p} = \dfrac{n_p}{n_a}$

    $v_p = \dfrac{v_a n_a}{n_p}$

    $= \dfrac{\left(3.00 \times 10^8 \text{ m/s}\right)(1.00)}{1.40}$

    $= 2.14 \times 10^8 \text{ m/s}$

3. $\dfrac{\sin \theta_a}{\sin \theta_g} = \dfrac{n_g}{n_a}$

    $\sin \theta_a = \dfrac{n_g \sin \theta_g}{n_a}$

    $= \dfrac{(1.50)(\sin 10.0°)}{1.00}$

    $= 0.26$
    $\theta = 15.1°$

5. $\dfrac{\lambda_l}{\lambda_l} = \dfrac{n_l}{n_a}$

    $n_l = \dfrac{\lambda_a n_a}{\lambda_l}$

    $= \dfrac{\left(6.0 \times 10^{-7} \text{ m}\right)(1.00)}{5.0 \times 10^{-7} \text{ m}}$

    $= 1.2$

7. $\dfrac{v_a}{v_l} = \dfrac{\lambda_a}{\lambda_l}$

    $v_l = \dfrac{v_a \lambda_l}{\lambda_a}$

    $= \dfrac{\left(3.00 \times 10^8 \text{ m/s}\right)\left(3.91 \times 10^{-7} \text{ m}\right)}{5.20 \times 10^{-7} \text{ m}}$

    $= 2.26 \times 10^8 \text{ m/s}$

9. $\dfrac{\sin \theta_1}{\sin \theta_2} = \dfrac{n_2}{n_1}$

    $\sin \theta_2 = \dfrac{n_1 \sin \theta_1}{n_2}$

    $= \dfrac{(\sin 60.0°)(1.00)}{1.33}$

    $= 0.651$
    $\theta_2 = 40.6°$

11. $\dfrac{\sin\theta_1}{\sin\theta_a} = \dfrac{n_a}{n_1}$

$\sin\theta_1 = \dfrac{(1.33)(\sin 90°)}{1.51}$

$= 0.881$

$\theta_1 = 61.7°$

13. $\dfrac{\sin\theta_s}{\sin\theta_a} = \dfrac{n_a}{n_s}$

$\sin\theta_s = \dfrac{n_a \sin\theta_a}{n_s}$

$= \dfrac{(1.00)(\sin 90°)}{1.81}$

$= 0.552$

$= 33.5°$

15. $\dfrac{v_1}{v_a} = \dfrac{\sin\theta_1}{\sin\theta_a}$

$\sin\theta_1 = \dfrac{v_1 \sin\theta_a}{v_a}$

$= \dfrac{0.75 v_a \sin\theta_a}{v_a}$

$= \dfrac{(0.75)(3.00\times10^8 \text{ m/s})(\sin 90°)}{3.00\times10^8 \text{ m/s}}$

$= 0.750$

$\theta = 48.6°$

17. $\dfrac{\sin\theta_g}{\sin\theta_w} = \dfrac{n_w}{n_g}$

$\sin\theta_w = \dfrac{\sin\theta_g n_g}{n_w}$

$= \dfrac{(\sin 40°)(1.50)}{1.33} = 0.725$

$\theta_w = 46.5°$

$\dfrac{\sin\theta_w}{\sin\theta_a} = \dfrac{n_a}{n_w}$

$\sin\theta_a = \dfrac{\sin\theta_w n_w}{n_a}$

$= \dfrac{(0.725)(1.33)}{1.00} = 0.964$

$\theta_a = 74.6°$

19. $\dfrac{\sin\theta_a}{\sin\theta_1} = \dfrac{n_1}{n_a}$

$\dfrac{\sin 50.0°}{\sin\theta_1} = \dfrac{1.50}{1.00}$

$\theta_1 = 30.7°$

Now, find the incident angle at the second surface using geometry.

$= 90.0° - \left(180° - 70.0° - (90.0° - 30.7°)\right)$

$= 90.0° - \left(110° - 59.3°\right)$

$= 90.0° - 50.7°$

$= 39.3°$

$\dfrac{\sin\theta_1}{\sin\theta_a} = \dfrac{n_a}{n_1}$

$\dfrac{\sin 39.3°}{\sin\theta_a} = \dfrac{1.00}{1.50}$

$\theta_a = 71.8°$

21. First, find the incident and refracted angles using trigonometry.

$\tan\theta_1 = \dfrac{\text{opposite}}{\text{adjacent}}$

$= \dfrac{4.0 \text{ cm}}{5.0 \text{ cm}}$

$\theta_1 = 38.6°$

$\tan\theta_p = \dfrac{\text{opposite}}{\text{adjacent}}$

$= \dfrac{7.0 \text{ cm}}{2.0 \text{ cm}}$

$\theta_p = 74.0°$

$\dfrac{\sin\theta_1}{\sin\theta_p} = \dfrac{n_p}{n_1}$

$\dfrac{\sin 38.6°}{\sin 74.0°} = \dfrac{n_p}{n_1}$

$\dfrac{n_p}{n_1} = 0.65$

23. The frequency in Lucite is equal to the frequency in air.

$v_a = \lambda_a f$

$f = \dfrac{v_a}{\lambda_a}$

$= \dfrac{3.00\times10^8 \text{ m/s}}{6.22\times10^{-7} \text{ m}}$

$= 4.82\times10^{14} \text{ Hz}$

25. $\dfrac{v_a}{v_w} = \dfrac{n_w}{n_a} \Rightarrow v_w = \dfrac{n_a v_a}{n_w}$

$\therefore v_w = \dfrac{3.00 \times 10^8 \text{ m/s}}{1.33}$

$\quad = 2.26 \times 10^8 \text{ m/s}$

$v = \dfrac{d}{t} \Rightarrow t = \dfrac{d}{v}$

$t = \dfrac{1.00 \times 10^2 \text{ m}}{2.26 \times 10^8 \text{ m/s}}$

$\quad = 4.43 \times 10^{-7} \text{ s}$

Calculate the distance travelled in air.

$d_a = v_a t$

$\quad = \left(3.00 \times 10^8 \text{ m/s}\right)\left(4.43 \times 10^{-7} \text{ s}\right)$

$\quad = 133 \text{ m}$

Lesson 4—Reflection from Curved Mirrors

PRACTICE EXERCISE ANSWERS AND SOLUTIONS

1. a) Real, inverted, and the same size

b) Real, inverted, and larger

c) Virtual, upright, and smaller

d) Real, inverted, and smaller

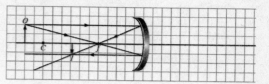

e) No image is produced.

f) Virtual, upright, and smaller

g) Virtual, upright, and larger

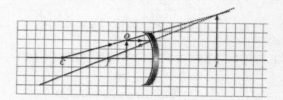

3. $\dfrac{h_i}{h_o} = -\dfrac{d_i}{d_o} \Rightarrow d_i = -\dfrac{h_i d_o}{h_o}$

$d_i = -\dfrac{(1.0 \text{ cm})(6.0 \text{ cm})}{(3.0 \text{ cm})} = -2.0 \text{ cm}$

$\dfrac{1}{f} = \dfrac{1}{d_o} + \dfrac{1}{d_i} = \dfrac{1}{6.0 \text{ cm}} + \dfrac{1}{(-2.0 \text{ cm})} = -\dfrac{2}{6 \text{ cm}}$

$f = -3.0 \text{ cm}$

Because the object was placed outside the focal point and still created a virtual image, the mirror must be a convex mirror.

5. $\dfrac{1}{f} = \dfrac{1}{d_o} + \dfrac{1}{d_i} \Rightarrow \dfrac{1}{d_o} = \dfrac{1}{f} - \dfrac{1}{d_i}$

$\dfrac{1}{d_o} = \dfrac{1}{-5.0 \text{ cm}} - \dfrac{1}{-3.0 \text{ cm}} = \dfrac{2}{15 \text{ cm}}$

$d_o = 7.5 \text{ cm}$

7. $M = \dfrac{d_i}{d_o} \Rightarrow d_i = Md_o = 2.5(5.0\ \text{cm}) = 12.5\ \text{cm}$

$\dfrac{1}{f} = \dfrac{1}{d_o} + \dfrac{1}{d_i} = \dfrac{1}{5.0\ \text{cm}} + \dfrac{1}{12.5\ \text{cm}} = \dfrac{7}{25.0\ \text{cm}}$

$f = 3.6\ \text{cm} \Rightarrow O = 7.1\ \text{cm}$

9. $\dfrac{h_i}{h_o} = -\dfrac{d_i}{d_o} \Rightarrow d_o = -\dfrac{h_o d_i}{h_i} = -\dfrac{3.0\ \text{cm}(-2.5\ \text{cm})}{2.0\ \text{cm}}$

$d_o = 3.75\ \text{cm}$

$\dfrac{1}{f} = \dfrac{1}{d_o} + \dfrac{1}{d_i} = \dfrac{1}{3.75\ \text{cm}} + \dfrac{1}{-2.5\ \text{cm}} = \dfrac{-2}{15\ \text{cm}}$

$f = \dfrac{-15\ \text{cm}}{2} = -7.5\ \text{cm}$, convex

A negative focal length indicates a virtual focal point. Therefore, the mirror is convex.

11. When a concave mirror produces a smaller image, the image is always inverted. This means the value of the magnification will be $-\dfrac{1}{2}$.

$M = -\dfrac{d_i}{d_o}$

$-\dfrac{1}{2} = -\dfrac{d_i}{d_o}$

$\Rightarrow d_o = 2d_i$

$\dfrac{1}{f} = \dfrac{1}{d_o} + \dfrac{1}{d_i} = \dfrac{1}{2d_i} + \dfrac{2}{2d_i} = \dfrac{3}{2d_i}$

$\dfrac{1}{5.0\ \text{cm}} = \dfrac{3}{2d_i}$

$\Rightarrow d_i = \dfrac{3(5.0\ \text{cm})}{2} = 7.5\ \text{cm}$

$\therefore\ d_o = 2d_i = 15.0\ \text{cm}$

Lesson 5—Lenses

PRACTICE EXERCISE
ANSWERS AND SOLUTIONS

1. a) Real, inverted, and larger

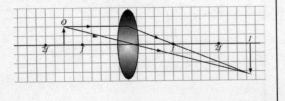

b) Real, inverted, and same size

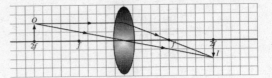

c) Virtual, upright, and smaller

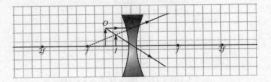

d) Real, inverted, and smaller

e) Virtual, upright, and larger

f) No image is produced.

g) Virtual, upright, and smaller

3. a) $\dfrac{1}{f} = \dfrac{1}{d_o} + \dfrac{1}{d_i} \Rightarrow \dfrac{1}{d_i} = \dfrac{1}{f} - \dfrac{1}{d_o}$

The focus is virtual, so it is negative.

$\dfrac{1}{d_i} = \dfrac{1}{-4.5\ \text{cm}} - \dfrac{1}{4.5\ \text{cm}} = -\dfrac{2}{4.5\ \text{cm}}$

$d_i = -2.3\ \text{cm}$

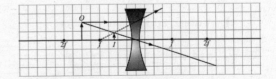

b) $\dfrac{h_i}{h_o} = -\dfrac{d_i}{d_o} \Rightarrow h_i = -\dfrac{d_i h_o}{d_o}$

$$h_i = -\dfrac{(-2.3 \text{ cm})(5.0 \text{ cm})}{4.5 \text{ cm}} = 2.5 \text{ cm}$$

c) Virtual, upright, and smaller

5. A virtual image is always upright; that is, h is positive.

$\dfrac{h_i}{h_o} = -\dfrac{d_i}{d_o} \Rightarrow d_i = -\dfrac{h_i d_o}{h_o}$

$d_i = -\dfrac{(4.0 \text{ cm})(5.0 \text{ cm})}{2.0 \text{ cm}} = -10 \text{ cm}$

$\dfrac{1}{f} = \dfrac{1}{d_o} + \dfrac{1}{d_i} = \dfrac{1}{5.0 \text{ cm}} + \dfrac{1}{-10 \text{ cm}} = \dfrac{1}{10 \text{ cm}}$

$f = 10 \text{ cm}$, convex

A positive focal length indicates a real focal length; therefore, the lens is convex.

7. $\dfrac{1}{f} = \dfrac{1}{d_o} + \dfrac{1}{d_i} \Rightarrow \dfrac{1}{d_o} = \dfrac{1}{f} - \dfrac{1}{d_i}$

$\dfrac{1}{d_o} = \dfrac{1}{-6.0 \text{ cm}} - \dfrac{1}{-2.5 \text{ cm}} = \dfrac{1}{0.23 \text{ cm}}$

$d_o = 4.3 \text{ cm}$

9. The image produced by the convex lens is real and larger than the object. Therefore, the image will be inverted. This means the value of the magnification will be -2.0.

$M = -\dfrac{d_i}{d_o} \Rightarrow d_i = -Md_o$

$d_i = -(-2.0)(7.0 \text{ cm}) = 14 \text{ cm}$

$\dfrac{1}{f} = \dfrac{1}{d_o} + \dfrac{1}{d_i} = \dfrac{1}{7.0 \text{ cm}} + \dfrac{1}{14 \text{ cm}} = \dfrac{3}{14 \text{ cm}}$

$f = 4.7 \text{ cm}$

11. $\dfrac{h_i}{h_o} = -\dfrac{d_i}{d_o} \Rightarrow d_i = -\dfrac{h_i d_o}{h_o}$

$d_i = -\dfrac{(6.0 \text{ cm})(7.0 \text{ cm})}{3.0 \text{ cm}} = -14 \text{ cm}$

$\dfrac{1}{f} = \dfrac{1}{d_o} + \dfrac{1}{d_i} = \dfrac{1}{7.0 \text{ cm}} + \dfrac{1}{(-14 \text{ cm})} = \dfrac{1}{14 \text{ cm}}$

$f = 14 \text{ cm}$

13. If you study the ray diagrams, you can reason that you have a convex lens because the virtual image is farther from the lens than the virtual focal point $(d_i > f)$.

$\dfrac{1}{f} = \dfrac{1}{d_o} + \dfrac{1}{d_i} \Rightarrow \dfrac{1}{d_o} = \dfrac{1}{f} - \dfrac{1}{d_i}$

$\dfrac{1}{d_o} = \dfrac{1}{4.0 \text{ cm}} - \dfrac{1}{-6.0 \text{ cm}} = \dfrac{5}{12 \text{ cm}}$

$d_o = 2.4 \text{ cm}$

$M = -\dfrac{d_i}{d_o} = -\dfrac{-6.0 \text{ cm}}{2.4 \text{ cm}} = 2.5$

15. $\dfrac{1}{f} = \dfrac{1}{d_o} + \dfrac{1}{d_i} \Rightarrow \dfrac{1}{d_i} = \dfrac{1}{f} - \dfrac{1}{d_o}$

$\dfrac{h_i}{h_o} = -\dfrac{d_i}{d_o} \Rightarrow h_i = -\dfrac{d_i h_o}{d_o}$

Calculate the information for the objective lens:

$\dfrac{1}{d_i} = \dfrac{1}{f} - \dfrac{1}{d_o} = \dfrac{1}{1.6 \text{ cm}} - \dfrac{1}{2.0 \text{ cm}} = \dfrac{1}{8} \text{ cm}^{-1}$

$d_i = 8.0 \text{ cm}$

$h_i = -\dfrac{d_i h_o}{d_o} = -\dfrac{(8.0 \text{ cm})(1.5 \text{ cm})}{2.0 \text{ cm}}$

$h_i = -6.0 \text{ cm}$

The image distance from the objective lens is 8 cm, and the distance to the eye piece is 10 cm. Therefore, the distance of the object from the eye piece (which is the image resulting from the objective lens) is as follows:

$d_o = 10 \text{ cm} - 8.0 \text{ cm} = 2.0 \text{ cm}$

Calculate the information for the eyepiece:

$\dfrac{1}{d_i} = \dfrac{1}{f} - \dfrac{1}{d_o} = \dfrac{1}{3.0 \text{ cm}} - \dfrac{1}{2.0 \text{ cm}} = -\dfrac{1}{6} \text{ cm}^{-1}$

$d_i = -6.0 \text{ cm}$

$h_i = -\dfrac{d_i h_o}{d_o} = -\dfrac{(6.0 \text{ cm})(-6.0 \text{ cm})}{2.0 \text{ cm}}$

$h_i = 18 \text{ cm}$

The total magnification is calculated as follows:

$M = \dfrac{h_i}{h_o} = \dfrac{18 \text{ cm}}{1.5 \text{ cm}} = 12$

Lesson 6—The Wave Nature of Light

PRACTICE EXERCISE
ANSWERS AND SOLUTIONS

1. $\lambda = \dfrac{d\sin\theta}{n} \Rightarrow \sin\theta = \dfrac{n\lambda}{d}$

$\sin\theta = \dfrac{(1)(4.10\times10^{-7}\text{ m})}{6.00\times10^{-6}\text{ m}}$

$= 6.83\times10^{-2}$

$\theta = 3.92°$

3. $\lambda = \dfrac{d\sin\theta}{n} \Rightarrow d = \dfrac{n\lambda}{\sin\theta}$

$d = \dfrac{(1.5)(5.30\times10^{-7}\text{ m})}{\sin16.0°}$

$= 2.88\times10^{-6}\text{ m}$

$\dfrac{x}{1\text{ m}} = \dfrac{1\text{ line}}{2.88\times10^{-6}\text{ m}}$

$x = 3.47\times10^{5}\text{ lines/m}$

5. $d = \dfrac{1}{5.00\times10^{4}\text{ lines/m}} = 2.00\times10^{-5}\text{ m}$

$\lambda = \dfrac{dx}{nl}$

$= \dfrac{(2.00\times10^{-5}\text{ m})(3.11\times10^{-2}\text{ m})}{(1)(1.5\text{ m})}$

$= 4.15\times10^{-7}\text{ m}$

7. $d = \dfrac{1}{5.00\times10^{5}\text{ lines/m}} = 2.00\times10^{-6}\text{ m}$

$\lambda = \dfrac{d\sin\theta}{n} \Rightarrow n = \dfrac{d\sin\theta}{\lambda}$

$n = \dfrac{(2.00\times10^{-6}\text{ m})\sin\theta}{(5.80\times10^{-7}\text{ m})}$

$n = 3.45\sin\theta$

The maximum value of $\sin\theta$ is 1, so the maximum value of n is 3.45; however, n must be a whole number, so the number of orders of maxima that can be observed is 3.

9. $\lambda = \dfrac{c}{f} = \dfrac{3.00\times10^{8}\text{ m/s}}{6.50\times10^{14}\text{ Hz}} = 4.62\times10^{-7}\text{ m}$

$d = \dfrac{1}{4.00\times10^{4}\text{ lines/m}} = 2.50\times10^{-5}\text{ m}$

$\lambda = \dfrac{dx}{nl} \Rightarrow x = \dfrac{\lambda nl}{d}$

$x = \dfrac{(4.62\times10^{-7}\text{ m})(1)(1.10\text{ m})}{2.50\times10^{-5}\text{ m}}$

$x = 2.03\times10^{-2}\text{ m}$

11. $\lambda = \dfrac{dx}{nl} = \dfrac{(3.0\times10^{-5}\text{ m})(1.7\times10^{-2}\text{ m})}{(1)(1.00\text{ m})}$

$\lambda = 5.1\times10^{-7}\text{ m}$

$f = \dfrac{c}{\lambda} = \dfrac{3.0\times10^{8}\text{ m/s}}{5.1\times10^{-7}\text{ m}}$

$f = 5.9\times10^{14}\text{ Hz}$

13. $d = \dfrac{1}{9.30\times10^{4}\text{ lines/m}} = 1.08\times10^{-5}\text{ m}$

$\lambda = \dfrac{dx}{nl} \Rightarrow x = \dfrac{\lambda nl}{d}$

$x = \dfrac{(5.61\times10^{-7}\text{ m})(1)(1.50\text{ m})}{1.08\times10^{-5}\text{ m}} = 7.80\times10^{-2}\text{ m}$

15. $\lambda = \dfrac{dx}{nl} \Rightarrow x = \dfrac{\lambda nl}{d} = \dfrac{\left(\dfrac{c}{f}\right)nl}{d} = \dfrac{cnl}{fd}$

so, if $f' = \dfrac{4}{5}f$, then $x' = \dfrac{5}{4}x$, since $x \propto \dfrac{1}{f}$.

$\therefore x' = \dfrac{5}{4}(5.22\times10^{-2}\text{ m}) = 6.53\times10^{-2}\text{ m}$

Lesson 8—Speed of Light

PRACTICE EXERCISE
ANSWERS AND SOLUTIONS

1. $t = \dfrac{d}{v} = \dfrac{1.49\times10^{11}\text{ m}}{3.00\times10^{8}\text{ m/s}}$

$t = 4.97\times10^{2}\text{ s}$

3. The time for $\frac{1}{8}$ of a revolution is given by the following equation:

$$\frac{5.40\times10^2 \text{ rev}}{1 \text{ s}} = \frac{\frac{1}{8} \text{ rev}}{t}$$

$$t = \frac{\frac{1}{8} \text{ rev}\cdot\text{s}}{5.40\times10^2 \text{ rev}} = 2.31\times10^{-4} \text{ s}$$

$$d = vt = (3.00\times10^8 \text{ m/s})(2.31\times10^{-4} \text{ s})$$

$$d = 6.94\times10^4 \text{ m}$$

5. $$t = \frac{d}{v} = \frac{2(3.00\times10^4 \text{ m})}{3.00\times10^8 \text{ m/s}}$$

$$t = 2.0\times10^{-4} \text{ s}$$

$$\frac{\frac{1}{8} \text{ rev}}{2.0\times10^{-4} \text{ s}} = \frac{R}{1 \text{ s}}$$

$$R = 6.25\times10^2 \text{ revolution/s}$$

7. $$\frac{4.88\times10^4 \text{ rev}}{60 \text{ s}} = \frac{\frac{1}{6} \text{ rev}}{t}$$

$$t = \frac{10 \text{ rev}\cdot\text{s}}{4.88\times10^4 \text{ rev}} = 2.05\times10^{-4} \text{ s}$$

$$v = \frac{d}{t} = \frac{6.0\times10^4 \text{ m}}{2.05\times10^{-4} \text{ s}}$$

$$v = 2.93\times10^8 \text{ m/s}$$

9. $$d = 2r_E = 2(1.49\times10^{11} \text{ m})$$

$$d = 2.98\times10^{11} \text{ m}$$

$$t = \frac{d}{v} = \frac{2.98\times10^{11} \text{ m}}{3.00\times10^8 \text{ m/s}}$$

$$t = 9.93\times10^2 \text{ s}$$

11. $$d = vt = (3.0\times10^8 \text{ m/s})(1.5\times10^4 \text{ s})$$

$$d = 4.5\times10^{12} \text{ m}$$

Since this is the total distance the light travelled, the distance to the object is calculated as follows:

$$d_o = \frac{d}{2} = \frac{4.5\times10^{12} \text{ m}}{2} = 2.3\times10^{12} \text{ m}$$

Lesson 10—Wave-Particle Duality

PRACTICE EXERCISE
ANSWERS AND SOLUTIONS

1. $$E = hf$$
$$= (6.63\times10^{-34} \text{ J}\cdot\text{s})(0.100 \text{ Hz})$$
$$= 6.63\times10^{-35} \text{ J}$$

3. $$E = hf$$
$$= (6.63\times10^{-34} \text{ J}\cdot\text{s})(4.74\times10^{14} \text{ Hz})$$
$$= 3.14\times10^{-19} \text{ J}$$

5. $$E = \frac{hc}{\lambda}$$
$$\lambda = \frac{hc}{E}$$
$$= \frac{(6.63\times10^{-34} \text{ J}\cdot\text{s})(3.00\times10^8 \text{ m/s})}{1.5(1.60\times10^{-19} \text{ J})}$$
$$= 8.29\times10^{-7} \text{ m}$$

7. $$v = \lambda f$$
$$f = \frac{v}{\lambda}$$
$$= \frac{3.00\times10^8 \text{ m/s}}{5.5\times10^{-7} \text{ m}}$$
$$= 5.45\times10^{14} \text{ Hz}$$

$$E = hf$$
$$= (6.63\times10^{-34} \text{ J}\cdot\text{s})(5.45\times10^{14} \text{ Hz})$$
$$= 3.61\times10^{-19} \text{ J/photon}$$

$$P = \frac{E}{t}$$
$$E_{\text{Total}} = Pt$$
$$= (40.0 \text{ J/s})(1.00 \text{ s})$$
$$= 40.0 \text{ J}$$

Only 5.0% of the energy is converted to light.
$$40.0 \text{ J}\times5.0\% = 2.0 \text{ J}$$

$$\#\text{photons} = \frac{E_{\text{Total}}}{E \text{ per photon}}$$
$$= \frac{2.0 \text{ J}}{3.61\times10^{-19} \text{ J/photon}}$$
$$= 5.5\times10^{18} \text{ photons}$$

9. $v = \lambda f$

$$f = \frac{v}{\lambda}$$
$$= \frac{3.0 \times 10^8 \text{ m/s}}{625 \times 10^{-9} \text{ m}}$$
$$= 4.8 \times 10^{14} \text{ Hz}$$

$$E = hf$$
$$= \left(6.63 \times 10^{-34} \text{ J} \cdot \text{s}\right)\left(4.8 \times 10^{14} \text{ Hz}\right)$$
$$= 3.2 \times 10^{-19} \text{ J/photon}$$

$$\# \text{photons} = \frac{E_{\text{Total}}}{E \text{ per photon}}$$

$$E_{\text{Total}} = \left(\# \text{photons}\right)\left(E \text{ per photon}\right)$$
$$= \left(2.0 \times 10^{19} \text{ photons}\right) \times \left(3.2 \times 10^{-19} \text{ J/photon}\right)$$
$$= 6.4 \text{ J}$$

$$P = \frac{E}{t}$$
$$= \frac{6.4 \text{ J}}{1.0 \text{ s}}$$
$$= 6.4 \text{ W}$$

Lesson 11—Photoelectric Effect

PRACTICE EXERCISE
ANSWERS AND SOLUTIONS

1. $E = hf$
$$= \left(6.63 \times 10^{-34} \text{ J} \cdot \text{s}\right)\left(4.50 \times 10^{14} \text{ Hz}\right)$$
$$= 2.98 \times 10^{-19} \text{ J}$$

3. $E_{\text{kmax}} = \dfrac{hc}{\lambda} - W$
$$= \frac{\left(6.63 \times 10^{-34} \text{ J} \cdot \text{s}\right)\left(3.00 \times 10^8 \text{ m/s}\right)}{5.30 \times 10^{-7} \text{ m}}$$
$$- \left(1.7 \text{ eV}\right)\left(1.60 \times 10^{-19} \text{ J/eV}\right)$$
$$= 1.03 \times 10^{-19} \text{ J}$$

5. $E = \dfrac{hc}{\lambda}$
$$= \frac{\left(6.63 \times 10^{-34} \text{ J} \cdot \text{s}\right)\left(3.00 \times 10^8 \text{ m/s}\right)}{4.66 \times 10^{-7} \text{ m}}$$
$$= 4.27 \times 10^{-19} \text{ J}$$

7. $W = hf_0$
$$f_0 = \frac{W}{h}$$
$$= \frac{\left(2.75 \text{ eV}\right)\left(1.60 \times 10^{-19} \text{ J/eV}\right)}{6.63 \times 10^{-34} \text{ J} \cdot \text{s}}$$
$$= 6.64 \times 10^{14} \text{ Hz}$$

9. $E_{\text{kmax}} = \dfrac{hc}{\lambda} - W$

$$W = \frac{hc}{\lambda} - E_{\text{kmax}}$$
$$= \frac{\left(6.63 \times 10^{-34} \text{ J} \cdot \text{s}\right)\left(3.00 \times 10^8 \text{ m/s}\right)}{4.10 \times 10^{-7} \text{ m}}$$
$$- \left(1.2 \text{ eV}\right)\left(1.6 \times 10^{-19} \text{ J/eV}\right)$$
$$= 2.93 \times 10^{-19} \text{ J}$$

11. $E_{\text{k}} = \dfrac{1}{2}mv^2$
$$= \frac{1}{2}\left(9.11 \times 10^{-31} \text{ kg}\right)\left(4.20 \times 10^5 \text{ m/s}\right)^2$$
$$= 8.04 \times 10^{-20} \text{ J}$$

$$E_{\text{kmax}} = \frac{hc}{\lambda} - W$$

$$\frac{hc}{\lambda} = E_{\text{kmax}} + W$$
$$= 8.04 \times 10^{-20} \text{ J}$$
$$+ \left(2.55 \text{ eV}\right)\left(1.60 \times 10^{-19} \text{ J/eV}\right)$$
$$= 4.88 \times 10^{-19} \text{ J}$$

$$\lambda = \frac{hc}{4.88 \times 10^{-19} \text{ J}}$$
$$= 4.07 \times 10^{-7} \text{ m}$$

13. $E_{\text{kmax}} = qV_{\text{stop}}$
$$V_{\text{stop}} = \frac{E_{\text{kmax}}}{q}$$
$$= \frac{5.40 \times 10^{-19} \text{ J}}{1.60 \times 10^{-19} \text{ C}}$$
$$= 3.38 \text{ V}$$

15. The shorter the light's wavelength, the greater its energy. Therefore, use only the shortest wavelength in this problem.

$$E_{\text{kmax}} = \frac{hc}{\lambda} - W$$
$$= \frac{\left(6.63 \times 10^{-34} \text{ J} \cdot \text{s}\right)\left(3.00 \times 10^8 \text{ m/s}\right)}{4.0 \times 10^{-7} \text{ m}}$$
$$- \left(2.3 \text{ eV}\right)\left(1.60 \times 10^{-19} \text{ J/eV}\right)$$
$$= 1.3 \times 10^{-19} \text{ J}$$

17. $E_{kmax} = qV_{stop}$
$$= \left(1.60\times10^{-19} \text{ C}\right)\left(2.00 \text{ V}\right)$$
$$= 3.20\times10^{-19} \text{ J}$$

$$E_k = \frac{1}{2}mv^2$$

$$v = \sqrt{\frac{2E_k}{m}}$$

$$= \sqrt{\frac{2\left(3.20\times10^{-19} \text{ J}\right)}{9.11\times10^{-31} \text{ kg}}}$$

$$= 8.38\times10^5 \text{ m/s}$$

19. a)

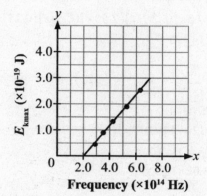

Frequency (×10^{14} Hz)

Frequency (×10^{14} Hz)	E_{kmax} (×10$^{×19}$ J)
6.2	2.56
5.3	1.92
4.2	1.31
3.5	0.90
2.9	0.45

b) i) From the graph, it can be seen that the threshold frequency is 2.0×10^{14} Hz. One can determine the error of this reading by first calculating the threshold frequency.

$$E_{k_{max}} = hf - hf_0$$

$$\Rightarrow f_0 = f - \frac{E_{k_{max}}}{h}$$

$$f_0 = 5.3\times10^{14} - \frac{2.00\times10^{-19}}{6.63\times10^{-34}}$$

$$f_0 = 2.28\times10^{14}$$

Now, find the percentage error between the value determined from the graph and

the calculated value.

$$\text{error} = \left|\frac{2.00\times10^{14} - 2.28\times10^{14}}{2.28\times10^{14}}\right|\times100\%$$

$$\text{error} = 12\%$$

ii) $\text{slope} = \frac{\text{rise}}{\text{run}} = \frac{y_2 - y_1}{x_2 - x_1}$

$$= \frac{\left(2.3 - 0.2\right)\times10^{-19} \text{ J}}{\left(5.8 - 2.4\right)\times10^{14} \text{ Hz}}$$

$$= 6.18\times10^{-34} \text{ J}\cdot\text{s}$$

Find the percentage error between the value found from the slope of the graph and the known value for Planck's constant.

$$\text{error} = \left|\frac{6.18\times10^{-34} - 6.63\times10^{-34}}{6.63\times10^{-34}}\right|\times100\%$$

$$\text{error} = 6.8\%$$

21. a)

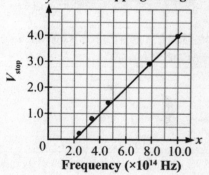

Frequency of Radiation versus Stopping Voltage

Frequency (×10^{14} Hz)

b) i) 2.0×10^{14} Hz

ii) $\text{slope} = \frac{\text{rise}}{\text{run}} = \frac{y_2 - y_1}{x_2 - x_1}$

$$= \frac{\left(3.9 - 0\right)\text{V}}{\left(9.5 - 2\right)\times10^{14} \text{ Hz}}$$

$$= 5.20\times10^{-15} \text{ V}\cdot\text{s}$$

$$h = q(\text{slope})$$

$$= \left(1.60\times10^{-19} \text{ C}\right)\left(5.20\times10^{-15} \text{ V}\cdot\text{s}\right)$$

$$= 8.32\times10^{-34} \text{ J}\cdot\text{s}$$

Lesson 12—Compton Effect

PRACTICE EXERCISE
ANSWERS AND SOLUTIONS

1. $p = \dfrac{hf}{c}$

$= \dfrac{\left(6.63 \times 10^{-34} \text{ J} \cdot \text{s}\right)\left(9.65 \times 10^{14} \text{ Hz}\right)}{3.00 \times 10^8 \text{ m/s}}$

$= 2.13 \times 10^{-27} \text{ kg} \cdot \text{m/s}$

3. $\lambda = \dfrac{h}{p}$

$= \dfrac{6.63 \times 10^{-34} \text{ J} \cdot \text{s}}{7.8 \times 10^{-25} \text{ kg} \cdot \text{m/s}}$

$= 8.5 \times 10^{-10} \text{ m}$

5. The speed of a photon (light) is constant at 3.00×10^8 m/s.

7. $\bar{p} = m\bar{v}$

$= \left(9.11 \times 10^{-31} \text{ kg}\right)(0.110)\left(3.00 \times 10^8 \text{ m/s}\right)$

$= 3.01 \times 10^{-23} \text{ kg} \cdot \text{m/s}$

or

$\lambda = \dfrac{h}{mv}$

$= \dfrac{6.63 \times 10^{-34} \text{ J} \cdot \text{s}}{\left(9.11 \times 10^{-31} \text{ kg}\right)(0.110)\left(3.00 \times 10^8 \text{ m/s}\right)}$

$= 2.20 \times 10^{-11} \text{ m}$

$p = \dfrac{h}{\lambda}$

$= \dfrac{6.63 \times 10^{-34} \text{ Js}}{2.20 \times 10^{-11} \text{ m}}$

$= 3.01 \times 10^{-23} \text{ kg} \cdot \text{m/s}$

9. a) $p = \dfrac{h}{\lambda}$

$= \dfrac{6.63 \times 10^{-34} \text{ J} \cdot \text{s}}{415 \times 10^{-9} \text{ m}}$

$= 1.60 \times 10^{-27} \text{ kg} \cdot \text{m/s}$

b) $E_{kmax} = hf - W$

$= \left(6.63 \times 10^{-34} \text{ J} \cdot \text{s}\right)\left(\dfrac{3.00 \times 10^8 \text{ m/s}}{415 \times 10^{-9} \text{ m}}\right)$

$\qquad - 3.50 \times 10^{-19} \text{ J}$

$= 1.29 \times 10^{-19} \text{ J}$

$E_k = \dfrac{1}{2}mv^2$

$v = \sqrt{\dfrac{2E_k}{m}}$

$= \sqrt{\dfrac{2\left(1.29 \times 10^{-19} \text{ J}\right)}{9.11 \times 10^{-31} \text{ kg}}}$

$= 5.33 \times 10^5 \text{ m/s}$

$\bar{p} = m\bar{v}$

$= \left(9.11 \times 10^{-31} \text{ kg}\right)\left(5.33 \times 10^5 \text{ m/s}\right)$

$= 4.85 \times 10^{-25} \text{ kg} \cdot \text{m/s}$

11. $E = hf(0.25)$

$= \left(6.63 \times 10^{-34} \text{ J} \cdot \text{s}\right)\left(2.50 \times 10^{16} \text{ Hz}\right)(0.25)$

$= 4.14 \times 10^{-18} \text{ J}$

$E_k = \dfrac{1}{2}mv^2$

$v = \sqrt{\dfrac{2E_k}{m}}$

$= \sqrt{\dfrac{2\left(4.14 \times 10^{-18} \text{ J}\right)}{9.11 \times 10^{-31} \text{ kg}}}$

$= 3.02 \times 10^6 \text{ m/s}$

13. $\Delta\lambda = \dfrac{h}{mc}(1 - \cos\theta)$

$= \dfrac{6.63 \times 10^{-34} \text{ J} \cdot \text{s}}{\left(9.11 \times 10^{-31} \text{ kg}\right)\left(3.00 \times 10^8 \text{ m/s}\right)}(1 - \cos 45.0°)$

$= 7.11 \times 10^{-13} \text{ m}$

$\Delta\lambda = \lambda' - \lambda$

$\lambda' = \Delta\lambda + \lambda$

$= 7.11 \times 10^{-13} \text{ m} + 8.22 \times 10^{-12} \text{ m}$

$= 8.93 \times 10^{12} \text{ m}$

$E = \dfrac{hc}{\lambda} = \dfrac{\left(6.63 \times 10^{-34} \text{ J} \cdot \text{s}\right)\left(3.00 \times 10^8 \text{ m/s}\right)}{8.93 \times 10^{-12} \text{ m}}$

$= 2.23 \times 10^{-14} \text{ J or } 1.39 \times 10^5 \text{ eV}$

15. $E = \dfrac{hc}{\lambda}$

$\lambda = \dfrac{hc}{E} = \dfrac{\left(6.63 \times 10^{-34} \text{ J} \cdot \text{s}\right)\left(3.00 \times 10^8 \text{ m/s}\right)}{\left(15.0 \times 10^3 \text{ eV}\right)\left(1.60 \times 10^{-19} \text{ J/eV}\right)}$

$= 8.29 \times 10^{-11} \text{ m}$

$$\lambda' = \frac{hc}{E'} = \frac{\left(6.63 \times 10^{-34} \text{ J} \cdot \text{s}\right)\left(3.00 \times 10^{8} \text{ m/s}\right)}{\left(14.8 \times 10^{3} \text{ eV}\right)\left(1.60 \times 10^{-19} \text{ J/eV}\right)}$$

$$= 8.40 \times 10^{-11} \text{ m}$$

$$\Delta\lambda = \lambda' - \lambda$$

$$= 8.40 \times 10^{-11} \text{ m} - 8.29 \times 10^{-11} \text{ m}$$

$$= 1.1 \times 10^{-12} \text{ m}$$

$$\Delta\lambda = \frac{h}{mc}(1 - \cos\theta)$$

$$1.1 \times 10^{-12} \text{ m} = \frac{\left(6.63 \times 10^{-34} \text{ J} \cdot \text{s}\right)}{\left(9.11 \times 10^{-31} \text{ kg}\right)\left(3.00 \times 10^{8} \text{ m/s}\right)}$$
$$(1 - \cos\theta)$$

$$\frac{1.1 \times 10^{-12} \text{ m}}{2.426 \times 10^{-12} \text{ m}} = 1 - \cos\theta$$

$$\cos\theta = 1 - 0.46$$

$$\cos\theta = 0.54$$

$$\theta = 57°$$

Practice Quiz

ANSWERS AND SOLUTIONS

1.

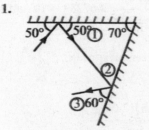

Reflection off plane mirror is the same as the incident angle.

Determine this angle by using the angle of reflection, the angle at the corner formed by mirrors, and the fact that all triangle angles add to 180°.

The reflected angle is 60°.

3. a) Real, inverted, and smaller

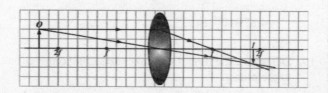

b) Virtual, upright, and smaller

5. Find the refractive index of the liquid.

$$\frac{n_1}{n_2} = \frac{v_2}{v_1}$$

$$n_1 = \frac{v_2 n_2}{v_1}$$

$$n_1 = \frac{3.00 \times 10^{8} \text{ m/s}(1.00)}{2.66 \times 10^{8} \text{ m/s}}$$

Calculate the critical angle.

$$\frac{\sin\theta_1}{\sin\theta_2} = \frac{n_2}{n_1} \qquad \sin\theta_2 = \sin 90° = 1$$

$$\sin\theta_1 = \frac{n_2}{n_1}$$

$$\theta_1 = \sin^{-1}\left(\frac{n_2}{n_1}\right)$$

$$\theta_1 = \sin^{-1}\left(\frac{1.00}{1.1278}\right) = \sin^{-1}(0.8868) = 62.5°$$

7. Calculate θ_r of the glass-water boundary.

$$\frac{\sin\theta_i}{\sin\theta_r} = \frac{n_r}{n_i}$$

$$\sin\theta_r = \frac{\sin\theta_i \cdot n_i}{n_r} = \frac{\sin 55° \cdot 1.50}{1.33} = 0.9239$$

$$\theta_r = 67.5°$$

Calculate θ_r of the water-air boundary.

$$\theta_i = 67.5° \qquad n_i = 1.33$$
$$\theta_r = ? \qquad n_r = 1.00$$

$$\frac{\sin\theta_i}{\sin\theta_r} = \frac{n_r}{n_i}$$

$$\sin\theta_r = \frac{\sin\theta_i \cdot n_i}{n_r} = \frac{\sin 67.5°(1.33)}{1.00} = 1.2287$$

$$\sin\theta_r = 1.2287$$

Since this value is greater than 1, 67.5° is greater than the critical angle between water and air. The light ray will be internally reflected.

9. Determine the velocity of light in the clear plastic block.

$$v_r = ? \quad v_i = 3.00 \times 10^8 \text{ m/s}$$
$$\theta = 70.0° \quad \theta_r = 50.0°$$
$$\frac{\sin \theta_i}{\sin \theta_r} = \frac{v_i}{v_r}$$
$$v_r = v_i \cdot \frac{\sin \theta_r}{\sin \theta_i}$$
$$v_r = \frac{3.00 \times 10^8 \text{ m/s} \cdot \sin 50.0°}{\sin 70.0°}$$
$$= 2.4456 \times 10^8 \text{ m/s}$$

Find the distance that the light travels through the plastic block.

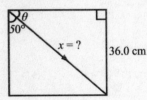

$$\theta = 40.0°$$
$$\sin 40.0° = \frac{36.0 \text{ cm}}{x}$$
$$0.64279 = \frac{36.0 \text{ cm}}{x}$$
$$x = \frac{36.0 \text{ cm}}{0.64279} = 56.0 \text{ cm}$$

Calculate the time it takes for the light to travel through the plastic.

$$t = \frac{d}{v} = \frac{0.560 \text{ m}}{2.4456 \times 10^8 \text{ m/s}} = 2.29 \times 10^{-9} \text{ s}$$

11. a)

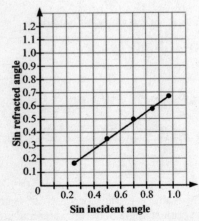

b) $$\frac{\sin \theta_i}{\sin \theta_r} = \frac{n_r}{n_i} \quad n_i = 1.00$$
$$\frac{\sin \theta_i}{\sin \theta_r} = n_r$$
$$\frac{\text{run}}{\text{rise}} = \frac{\sin \theta_i}{\sin \theta_r} = \frac{0.85 - 0.35}{0.60 - 0.25} = 1.43$$

13. Find the frequency.
$$f = \frac{c}{\lambda} = \frac{3.00 \times 10^8 \text{ m/s}}{5.40 \times 10^{-10} \text{ m}} = 5.556 \times 10^{17} \text{ Hz}$$

$$T = \frac{1}{f}$$
$$T = 1.8 \times 10^{-18} \text{ s}$$

15. $$d = \frac{1}{5.00 \times 10^5 \text{ lines/m}}$$
$$= 2.00 \times 10^{-6} \text{ m/line} \quad n = 1 \quad l = 2.00 \text{ m} \quad x = ?$$
$$f = 1.50 \left(4.28 \times 10^{14} \text{ Hz} \right)$$

Find the wavelength.
$$\lambda = \frac{c}{f} = \frac{3.00 \times 10^8 \text{ m/s}}{1.5 \left(4.28 \times 10^{14} \text{ Hz} \right)} = 4.672897 \times 10^{-7} \text{ m}$$

Solve for distance between maxima (x).
$$x = \frac{n\lambda l}{d}$$
$$= \frac{1 \left(4.672897 \times 10^{-7} \text{ m} \right) (2.00 \text{ m})}{2.00 \times 10^{-6} \text{ m}}$$
$$= 0.47 \text{ m}$$

17. $$\theta = 32.0°$$
$$d = \frac{1}{1.10 \times 10^6 \text{ lines/m}} = 9.09 \times 10^{-6} \text{ m}$$
$$n = 1$$

Calculate λ.
$$\lambda = \frac{d \sin \theta}{n}$$
$$= \frac{9.09 \times 10^{-6} \text{ m} (\sin 32.0°)}{1}$$
$$= 4.82 \times 10^{-6} \text{ m}$$

19. Determine the time it will take the signal to travel to the planet.
$$t = \frac{d}{v} = \frac{6.60 \times 10^{12} \text{ m}}{3.00 \times 10^8 \text{ m/s}} = 22\ 000 \text{ s}$$

Since the signal must travel there and back, the time must be doubled.

$22\ 000\ \text{s} \times 2 = 4.40 \times 10^4\ \text{s}$

21. a) Determine λ.

$$\lambda = \frac{c}{f} = \frac{3.00 \times 10^8\ \text{m/s}}{1.00 \times 10^9\ \text{Hz}} = 0.300\ \text{m}$$

b) A strong signal would occur because of constructive interference, and a weak signal would be caused by destructive interference.

Constructive interference should occur if both signals reach the receiver in phase. The greatest destructive interference will happen if the signals reach the receiver out of phase by $\frac{1}{2}\lambda$.

$$\frac{1.20\ \text{m}}{0.30\ \text{m}} = 4$$

Generator 1's signal reaches the receiver with 4 whole wavelengths.

$$\frac{0.750\ \text{m}}{0.30\ \text{m}} = 2.5$$

Generator 2's signal reaches the receiver with 2.5 wavelengths.

The waves are out of phase by $\frac{1}{2}\lambda$, so destructive interference will occur, and the signal will be weak.

23. $E = \dfrac{hc}{\lambda}$

$$= \frac{\left(6.63 \times 10^{-34}\ \text{J}\cdot\text{s}\right)\left(3.00 \times 10^8\ \text{m/s}\right)}{6.33 \times 10^{-7}\ \text{m}}$$

$$= 3.14 \times 10^{-19}\ \text{J/photon}$$

$P = \dfrac{\Delta E}{t}$

$\Delta E = Pt$

$$= \left(2.0\ \text{W}\right)\left(1.0\ \text{s}\right)$$

$$= 2.0\ \text{J}$$

$$\#\ \text{photons} = \frac{2.0\ \text{J}}{3.14 \times 10^{-19}\ \text{J/photon}}$$

$$= 6.4 \times 10^{18}\ \text{photons}$$

25. $E_{\text{kmax}} = qV_{\text{stop}}$

$V_{\text{stop}} = \dfrac{E_{\text{kmax}}}{q}$

$$= \frac{\left(11.0\ \text{eV}\right)\left(1.60 \times 10^{-19}\ \text{J/eV}\right)}{1.60 \times 10^{-19}\ \text{C}}$$

$$= 11.0\ \text{V}$$

27. $E_{\text{kmax}} = \dfrac{hc}{\lambda} - W$

$$= \frac{\left(6.63 \times 10^{-34}\ \text{J}\cdot\text{s}\right)\left(3.00 \times 10^8\ \text{m/s}\right)}{6.25 \times 10^{-7}\ \text{m}}$$
$$- \left(1.40\ \text{eV}\right)\left(1.60 \times 10^{-19}\ \text{J/eV}\right)$$

$$= 9.42 \times 10^{-20}\ \text{J}$$

$E_{\text{k}} = \dfrac{1}{2}m\bar{v}^2$

$\bar{v} = \sqrt{\dfrac{2E_{\text{k}}}{m}}$

$$= \sqrt{\frac{2\left(9.42 \times 10^{-20}\ \text{J}\right)}{9.11 \times 10^{-31}\ \text{kg}}}$$

$$= 4.55 \times 10^5\ \text{m/s}$$

29. $p = \dfrac{hf}{c}$

$f = \dfrac{pc}{h}$

$$= \frac{\left(7.60 \times 10^{-29}\ \text{kg}\cdot\text{m/s}\right)\left(3.00 \times 10^8\ \text{m/s}\right)}{6.63 \times 10^{-34}\ \text{J}\cdot\text{s}}$$

$$= 3.44 \times 10^{13}\ \text{Hz}$$

31. $E = hf$

$f = \dfrac{E}{h}$

$$= \frac{\left(7.00\ \text{eV}\right)\left(1.60 \times 10^{-19}\ \text{J/eV}\right)}{6.63 \times 10^{-34}\ \text{J}\cdot\text{s}}$$

$$= 1.69 \times 10^{15}\ \text{Hz}$$

$p = \dfrac{hf}{c}$

$$= \frac{\left(6.63 \times 10^{-34}\ \text{J}\cdot\text{s}\right)\left(1.69 \times 10^{15}\ \text{Hz}\right)}{3.00 \times 10^8\ \text{m/s}}$$

$$= 3.73 \times 10^{-27}\ \text{kg}\cdot\text{m/s}$$

or

$p = \dfrac{E}{c}$

$$= \frac{\left(7.00\right)\left(1.60 \times 10^{-19}\ \text{J}\right)}{3.00 \times 10^8\ \text{m/s}}$$

$$= 3.73 \times 10^{-27}\ \text{kg}\cdot\text{m/s}$$

33. $p = \dfrac{h}{\lambda}$

$\qquad = \dfrac{6.63 \times 10^{-34} \text{ J} \cdot \text{s}}{486 \times 10^{-9} \text{ m}}$

$\qquad = 1.36 \times 10^{-27} \text{ kg} \cdot \text{m/s}$

$\vec{p} = m\vec{v} \Rightarrow \vec{v} = \dfrac{\vec{p}}{m}$

$\qquad = \dfrac{1.36 \times 10^{-27} \text{ kg} \cdot \text{m/s}}{1.67 \times 10^{-27} \text{ kg}}$

$\qquad = 0.817 \text{ m/s}$

Practice Test

ANSWERS AND SOLUTIONS

1. Mechanical waves can be polarized (if they are transverse), interfere with one another, and demonstrate the Doppler effect. Only electromagnetic waves can travel through a vacuum.

C is the answer.

3. Longer wavelengths are diffracted to a larger degree than shorter wavelengths. This causes a more spread-out diffraction pattern.

D is the answer.

5. A diffraction grating with more slits produces sharper and more defined maxima due to the constructive interference at the maxima and destructive interference in between maxima. There is no change in position.

C is the answer.

7. Microwaves are about 1 mm long, visible blue light is about 450 nm long, and X-rays are only about 1 nm in length.

D is the answer.

9. A light ray passing from a lower to a higher refractive index will be bent toward the normal. The ray labelled A is reflected past the normal, which is not possible.

B is the answer.

11. The light from the fish is refracted away from the normal as it passes from water to air. This makes it look like the fish is higher than it actually is.

A is the answer.

13.

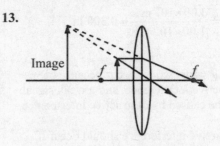

When an object is placed inside the focal point of a convex lens, the image is virtual and larger than the object.

B is the answer.

15. An incident ray parallel to the principal axis will be refracted through the focal point by a convex lens. It will travel along path Z.

D is the answer.

17. For a convex lens, an object at point $2f$ is always reproduced at real size.

C is the answer.

19. A plane mirror is capable of producing virtual images only.

A is the answer.

21. The maximum kinetic energy of the ejected electrons can be found by determining the stopping voltage.

$E_{k_{max}} = qV_{stop}$

C is the answer.

23. Increasing the intensity of the light will increase the current.

A is the answer.

25. If the energy of the photon is equal to the work function, then the energy of the emitted electron is zero. This is the situation at the threshold frequency (x-intercept).

$$W = hf_0$$

D is the answer.

27. slope $= \dfrac{\text{rise}}{\text{run}} = \dfrac{\text{energy}}{\text{frequency}}$

$$E = hf$$
$$h = \frac{E}{f}$$

B is the answer.

29. $p = \dfrac{h}{\lambda}$

$$p \propto \frac{1}{\lambda}$$

B is the answer.

31. Below the threshold frequency, no electrons are emitted. For all frequencies above this minimum, there is a linear relationship between V_{stop} and frequency.

A is the answer.

33. Max Planck developed the quantum hypothesis to explain the unusual results from graphing blackbody radiation.

B is the answer.

ATOMIC PHYSICS: ATOMIC STRUCTURE

Lesson 2—Cathode Rays, Thomson's Experiment

PRACTICE EXERCISE ANSWERS AND SOLUTIONS

1. $F_m = F_c$

$$qvB_\perp = \frac{mv^2}{r}$$
$$v = \frac{qB_\perp r}{m}$$
$$= \frac{\left(3.20 \times 10^{-19}\ \text{C}\right)\left(4.22 \times 10^{-1}\ \text{T}\right) \times \left(1.50 \times 10^{-3}\ \text{m}\right)}{6.65 \times 10^{-27}\ \text{kg}}$$
$$= 3.05 \times 10^4\ \text{m/s}$$

3. $F_m = F_c$

$$qvB_\perp = \frac{mv^2}{r}$$
$$\frac{q}{m} = \frac{v}{B_\perp r}$$
$$= \frac{3.60 \times 10^5\ \text{m/s}}{\left(6.10 \times 10^{-1}\ \text{T}\right)\left(7.40 \times 10^{-2}\ \text{m}\right)}$$
$$= 7.98 \times 10^6\ \text{C/kg}$$

5. $F_e = F_m$
$$qE = qvB_\perp$$
$$v = \frac{E}{B_\perp} = \frac{2.10 \times 10^5\ \text{N/C}}{6.50 \times 10^{-1}\ \text{T}}$$
$$= 3.23 \times 10^5\ \text{m/s}$$

7. $V = \dfrac{\Delta E}{q}$

$$\Delta E = qV$$
$$= \left(1.60 \times 10^{-19}\ \text{C}\right)\left(2.50 \times 10^3\ \text{V}\right)$$
$$= 4.00 \times 10^{-16}\ \text{J}$$
$$E_k = \frac{1}{2}mv^2$$
$$v = \sqrt{\frac{2E_k}{m}}$$
$$= \sqrt{\frac{2\left(4.00 \times 10^{-16}\ \text{J}\right)}{9.11 \times 10^{-31}\ \text{kg}}}$$
$$= 2.96 \times 10^7\ \text{m/s}$$

9. $V = \dfrac{\Delta E}{q}$

$\Delta E = qV$

$= \left(1.60 \times 10^{-19}\ \text{C}\right)\left(1.40 \times 10^{3}\ \text{V}\right)$

$= 2.24 \times 10^{-16}\ \text{J}$

$E_k = \dfrac{1}{2}mv^2$

$v = \sqrt{\dfrac{2E_k}{m}}$

$= \sqrt{\dfrac{2\left(2.24 \times 10^{-16}\ \text{J}\right)}{9.11 \times 10^{-31}\ \text{kg}}}$

$= 2.23 \times 10^{7}\ \text{m/s}$

$F_m = F_c$

$qvB_\perp = \dfrac{mv^2}{r}$

$r = \dfrac{mv}{qB_\perp}$

$= \dfrac{\left(9.11 \times 10^{-31}\ \text{kg}\right)\left(2.23 \times 10^{7}\ \text{m/s}\right)}{\left(1.60 \times 10^{-19}\ \text{C}\right)\left(2.20 \times 10^{-2}\ \text{T}\right)}$

$= 5.74 \times 10^{-3}\ \text{m}$

11. $F_m = F_c$

$qvB_\perp = \dfrac{mv^2}{r}$

$|q| = \dfrac{mv}{B_\perp r}$

$|q| = \dfrac{\left(8.4 \times 10^{-27}\ \text{kg}\right)\left(5.6 \times 10^{5}\ \text{m/s}\right)}{\left(2.8 \times 10^{-1}\ \text{T}\right)\left(3.5 \times 10^{-2}\ \text{m}\right)}$

$|q| = 4.8 \times 10^{-19}\ \text{C}$

$\therefore\ q = -4.8 \times 10^{-19}\ \text{C}$

The charge is assigned a negative sign because the question indicates that it is a negative value. However, this cannot be determined based on the equation used, because neither the velocity nor the magnetic field was assigned a direction, which would have helped determine the negative nature of the charge.

$\text{total \# e}^- = \dfrac{\text{total charge}}{\text{charge e}^-}$

$= \dfrac{-4.8 \times 10^{-19}\ \text{C}}{-1.6 \times 10^{-19}\ \text{C}}$

$= 3\ \text{e}^-$

13. $F_m = F_c$

$qvB_\perp = \dfrac{mv^2}{r}$

$v = \dfrac{qB_\perp r}{m}$

$= \dfrac{\left(1.60 \times 10^{-19}\ \text{C}\right)\left(0.75\ \text{T}\right)\left(0.30\ \text{m}\right)}{1.67 \times 10^{-27}\ \text{kg}}$

$= 2.16 \times 10^{7}\ \text{m/s}$

$\vec{p} = m\vec{v}$

$= \left(1.67 \times 10^{-27}\ \text{kg}\right)\left(2.16 \times 10^{7}\ \text{m/s}\right)$

$= 3.6 \times 10^{-20}\ \text{kg} \cdot \text{m/s}$

15. $F_m = F_c$

$qvB_\perp = \dfrac{mv^2}{r}$

$v = \dfrac{qB_\perp r}{m}$

$= \left(1.10 \times 10^{4}\ \text{C/kg}\right)\left(9.10 \times 10^{-1}\ \text{T}\right)\left(0.240\ \text{m}\right)$

$= 2.4 \times 10^{3}\ \text{m/s}$

$C = 2\pi r$

$= 2\pi\left(0.240\ \text{m}\right)$

$= 1.51\ \text{m}$

$v = \dfrac{d}{t}$

$t = \dfrac{d}{v}$

$= \dfrac{1.51\ \text{m}}{2.40 \times 10^{3}\ \text{m/s}}$

$= 6.28 \times 10^{-4}\ \text{s}$

Lesson 3—Millikan's Oil Drop Experiment

PRACTICE EXERCISE ANSWERS AND SOLUTIONS

1. $F_e = F_g$

$qE = F_g$

$q = \dfrac{F_g}{E}$

$= \dfrac{3.84 \times 10^{-15}\ \text{N}}{1.20 \times 10^{4}\ \text{N/C}}$

$= 3.20 \times 10^{-19}\ \text{C}$

3. $F_e = F_g$

$qE = mg$

$q = \dfrac{mg}{E}$

$= \dfrac{(7.20 \times 10^{-16} \text{ kg})(9.81 \text{ N/kg})}{2.20 \times 10^{4} \text{ V/m}}$

$= 3.21 \times 10^{-19} \text{ C}$

5. a)

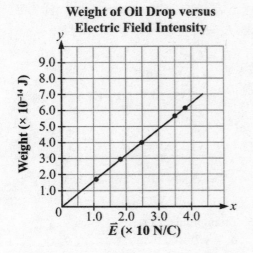

Weight of Oil Drop versus Electric Field Intensity

b) $\text{slope} = \dfrac{\text{rise}}{\text{run}} = \dfrac{y_2 - y_1}{x_2 - x_1}$

$= \dfrac{(6.1 - 0) \times 10^{-14} \text{ N}}{(3.8 - 0) \times 10^{5} \text{ N/C}}$

$= 1.6 \times 10^{-19} \text{ C}$

7. $E = \dfrac{V}{d}$

$= \dfrac{4.6 \times 10^{3} \text{ V}}{4.0 \times 10^{-2} \text{ m}}$

$= 1.15 \times 10^{5} \text{ V/m}$

$v = \dfrac{4}{3}\pi r^2$

$= \dfrac{4}{3}\pi (1.2 \times 10^{-6} \text{ m})^3$

$= 7.24 \times 10^{-18} \text{ m}^3$

$\rho = \dfrac{m}{V}$

$m = \rho V$

$= (7.8 \times 10^2 \text{ kg/m}^3)(7.24 \times 10^{-18} \text{ m}^3)$

$= 5.64 \times 10^{-15} \text{ kg}$

$F_e = F_g$

$qE = mg$

$q = \dfrac{mg}{E}$

$= \dfrac{(5.64 \times 10^{-15} \text{ kg})(9.81 \text{ N/kg})}{1.15 \times 10^{5} \text{ V/m}}$

$= 4.8 \times 10^{-19} \text{ C}$

9. $E = \dfrac{V}{d}$

$= \dfrac{175 \text{ V}}{3.20 \times 10^{-2} \text{ m}}$

$= 5.47 \times 10^{3} \text{ V/m}$

$F_{net} = F_e + F_g$

$F_e = F_{net} - F_g$

$qE = ma - mg$

$q = \dfrac{m(a - g)}{E}$

$= \dfrac{(6.20 \times 10^{-16} \text{ kg})(14.0 \text{ N/kg} - 9.81 \text{ N/kg})}{5.47 \times 10^{3} \text{ V/m}}$

$= 4.75 \times 10^{-19} \text{ C}$

Lesson 4—Atomic Models

PRACTICE EXERCISE
ANSWERS AND SOLUTIONS

1. $r_n = r_1 n^2$

$r_3 = (5.29 \times 10^{-11} \text{ m})(3)^2$

$= 4.76 \times 10^{-10} \text{ m}$

3. $\dfrac{1}{\lambda} = R_{\mathrm{H}}\left(\dfrac{1}{n_1^{\,2}} - \dfrac{1}{n_u^{\,2}}\right)$

$= \left(1.10 \times 10^7\,\mathrm{m^{-1}}\right)\left(\dfrac{1}{3^2} - \dfrac{1}{4^2}\right)$

$= 5.35 \times 10^5\,\mathrm{m^{-1}}$

$\lambda = 1.87 \times 10^{-6}\,\mathrm{m}$

5. $\dfrac{1}{\lambda} = R_{\mathrm{H}}\left(\dfrac{1}{n_1^{\,2}} - \dfrac{1}{n_u^{\,2}}\right)$

$= \left(1.10 \times 10^7\,\mathrm{m^{-1}}\right)\left(\dfrac{1}{2^2} - \dfrac{1}{6^2}\right)$

$\lambda = 4.09 \times 10^{-7}\,\mathrm{m}$

$c = \lambda f$

$f = \dfrac{c}{\lambda}$

$= \dfrac{3.00 \times 10^8\,\mathrm{m/s}}{4.09 \times 10^{-7}\,\mathrm{m}}$

$= 7.33 \times 10^{14}\,\mathrm{Hz}$

7. $c = \lambda f$

$\lambda = \dfrac{c}{f}$

$= \dfrac{3.00 \times 10^8\,\mathrm{m/s}}{3.09 \times 10^{15}\,\mathrm{Hz}}$

$= 9.71 \times 10^{-8}\,\mathrm{m}$

$\dfrac{1}{\lambda} = R_{\mathrm{H}}\left(\dfrac{1}{n_1^{\,2}} - \dfrac{1}{n_u^{\,2}}\right)$

$\Rightarrow \dfrac{1}{n_u^{\,2}} = \dfrac{1}{n_1^{\,2}} - \dfrac{1}{R_{\mathrm{H}}\lambda}$

$= \dfrac{1}{1^2} - \dfrac{1}{\left(1.10 \times 10^7\,\mathrm{m^{-1}}\right)\left(9.71 \times 10^{-8}\,\mathrm{m}\right)}$

$\dfrac{1}{n_u^{\,2}} = 6.38 \times 10^{-2}$

$\dfrac{1}{6.38 \times 10^{-2}} = 15.68$

$\sqrt{15.68} = 3.96$

$n_u = 4$

$\therefore$ Transition is from 1 to 4.

9. $r_n = r_1 n^2$

$n = \sqrt{\dfrac{r_n}{r_1}}$

$= \sqrt{\dfrac{1.90 \times 10^{-9}\,\mathrm{m}}{5.29 \times 10^{-11}\,\mathrm{m}}}$

$= 6$

11. Transition is from ∞ to 4.

$\dfrac{1}{\lambda} = R_{\mathrm{H}}\left(\dfrac{1}{n_1^{\,2}} - \dfrac{1}{n_u^{\,2}}\right)$

$= \left(1.10 \times 10^2\,\mathrm{m^{-1}}\right)\left(\dfrac{1}{4^2} - \dfrac{1}{\infty^2}\right)$

$\left(\text{note:}\dfrac{1}{\infty} = 0\right)$

$\lambda = 1.45 \times 10^{-6}\,\mathrm{m}$

13. $E_n = \dfrac{E_1}{n^2}$

$E_1 = E_n n^2$

$= \left(-1.50 \times 10^{-18}\,\mathrm{J}\right)(3)^2$

$= -1.35 \times 10^{-17}\,\mathrm{J}$ or -84.4 eV

$E_2 = \dfrac{E_1}{n^2}$

$= \dfrac{-1.35 \times 10^{-17}\,\mathrm{J}}{2^2}$

$= -3.38 \times 10^{-18}\,\mathrm{J}$ or -21.1 eV

15. From problem 14,

$r_3 = 4.76 \times 10^{-10}\,\mathrm{m}$

$C = 2\pi r$

$= 2\pi\left(4.76 \times 10^{-10}\,\mathrm{m}\right)$

$= 2.99 \times 10^{-9}\,\mathrm{m}$

$E_3 = \dfrac{E_1}{n^2}$

$= \dfrac{-2.18 \times 10^{-18}\,\mathrm{J}}{3^2}$

$= -2.42 \times 10^{-19}\,\mathrm{J}$ or -1.51 eV

$E_k = \dfrac{1}{2}mv^2$

$v = \sqrt{\dfrac{2E_k}{m}}$

$= \sqrt{\dfrac{2\left(2.42 \times 10^{-19}\,\mathrm{J}\right)}{9.11 \times 10^{-31}\,\mathrm{kg}}}$

$= 7.29 \times 10^5\,\mathrm{m/s}$

$v = \dfrac{d}{t}$

$t = \dfrac{d}{v}$

$= \dfrac{2.99 \times 10^{-9}\,\mathrm{m}}{7.29 \times 10^5\,\mathrm{m/s}}$

$= 4.10 \times 10^{-15}\,\mathrm{s}$

17. $r_4 = r_1 n^2$

$= \left(5.29 \times 10^{-11}\,\mathrm{m}\right)(4)^2$

$= 8.46 \times 10^{-10}\,\mathrm{m}$

$$F_e = \frac{kq_1q_2}{r^2}$$

$$= \frac{\left(8.99\times10^9 \, \frac{N\cdot m^2}{C^2}\right)\left(1.60\times10^{-19} \, C\right)\left(1.60\times10^{-19} \, C\right)}{\left(8.46\times10^{-10} \, m\right)^2}$$

$$= 3.22\times10^{-10} \, N$$

19. $$\lambda = \frac{d\sin\theta}{n}$$

$$= \frac{\left(5.00\times10^{-6} \, m\right)\left(\sin 4.97°\right)}{1}$$

$$= 4.33\times10^{-7} \, m$$

$$\frac{1}{\lambda} = R_H\left(\frac{1}{n_1^2} - \frac{1}{n_u^2}\right)$$

$$\frac{1}{4.33\times10^{-7} \, m} = \left(1.10\times10^7 \, m^{-1}\right)\left(\frac{1}{2^2} - \frac{1}{n_u^2}\right)$$

$$0.210 = 0.250 - \frac{1}{n_u^2}$$

$$\frac{1}{n_u^2} = 0.250 - 0.210$$

$$= 0.040$$

$$n_u = 5$$

Transition is from **5 to 2**.

Lesson 5—de Broglie

PRACTICE EXERCISE
ANSWERS AND SOLUTIONS

1. $$\lambda = \frac{h}{mv}$$

$$= \frac{6.63\times10^{-34} \, J\cdot s}{\left(9.11\times10^{-31} \, kg\right)\left(2.25\times10^7 \, m/s\right)}$$

$$= 3.23\times10^{-11} \, m$$

3. $$\lambda = \frac{h}{mv}$$

$$= \frac{6.63\times10^{-34} \, J\bullet s}{\left(9.11\times10^{-31} \, kg\right)\left(9.20\times10^5 \, m/s\right)}$$

$$= 7.91\times10^{-10} \, m$$

$$v = \lambda f$$

$$f = \frac{v}{\lambda}$$

$$= \frac{9.20\times10^5 \, m/s}{7.91\times10^{-10} \, m}$$

$$= 1.16\times10^{15} \, Hz$$

5. $$\Delta E = qV$$

$$= \left(1.60\times10^{19} \, C\right)\left(1.00\times10^3 \, J\right)$$

$$= 1.60\times10^{-16} \, J$$

$$E_k = \frac{1}{2}mv^2$$

$$v = \sqrt{\frac{2E_k}{m}}$$

$$= \sqrt{\frac{2\left(1.60\times10^{-16} \, J\right)}{9.11\times10^{-31} \, kg}}$$

$$= 1.87\times10^7 \, m/s$$

$$\lambda = \frac{h}{mv}$$

$$= \frac{6.63\times10^{-34} \, J\cdot s}{\left(9.11\times10^{-31} \, kg\right)\left(1.87\times10^7 \, m/s\right)}$$

$$= 3.88\times10^{-11} \, m$$

7. $$\lambda = \frac{h}{mv}$$

$$= \frac{6.63\times10^{-34} \, J\cdot s}{\left(6.65\times10^{-27} \, kg\right)\left(1.46\times10^{-15} \, m\right)}$$

$$= 4.83\times10^7 \, m/s$$

$$E_k = \frac{1}{2}mv^2$$

$$= \frac{1}{2}\left(6.65\times10^{-27} \, kg\right)\left(4.83\times10^7 \, m/s\right)^2$$

$$= 1.55\times10^{-11} \, J$$

9. $$\lambda = \frac{h}{mv}$$

$$v = \frac{h}{m\lambda}$$

$$= \frac{6.63\times10^{-34} \, J\cdot s}{\left(9.11\times10^{-31} \, kg\right)\left(2.75\times10^{-11} \, m\right)}$$

$$= 2.65\times10^7 \, m/s$$

$$E_k = \frac{1}{2}mv^2$$

$$= \frac{1}{2}\left(9.11\times10^{-31} \, kg\right)\left(2.65\times10^7 \, m/s\right)^2$$

$$= 3.19\times10^{-16} \, J$$

$$\Delta E = qV$$

$$V = \frac{\Delta E}{q}$$

$$= \frac{3.19\times10^{-16} \, J}{1.60\times10^{-19} \, C}$$

$$= 1.99\times10^3 \, V$$

11. $\dfrac{1 \text{ eV}}{1.60 \times 10^{-19} \text{ J}} = \dfrac{1.00 \times 10^{6} \text{ eV}}{x}$

$x = 1.60 \times 10^{-13} \text{ J}$

$E_k = \dfrac{1}{2}mv^2$

$v = \sqrt{\dfrac{2E_k}{m}}$

$\quad = \sqrt{\dfrac{2(1.60 \times 10^{-16} \text{ J})}{9.11 \times 10^{-31} \text{ kg}}}$

$\quad = 1.87 \times 10^{7} \text{ m/s}$

$\lambda = \dfrac{h}{mv}$

$\quad = \dfrac{6.63 \times 10^{-34} \text{ J} \cdot \text{s}}{(9.11 \times 10^{-31} \text{ kg})(1.87 \times 10^{7} \text{ m/s})}$

$\quad = 3.88 \times 10^{-11} \text{ m}$

$\lambda = \dfrac{h}{mv}$

$v = \dfrac{h}{m\lambda}$

$\quad = \dfrac{6.63 \times 10^{-34} \text{ J} \cdot \text{s}}{(1.67 \times 10^{-27} \text{ kg})(3.88 \times 10^{-11} \text{ m})}$

$\quad = 1.02 \times 10^{4} \text{ m/s}$

$E_k = \dfrac{1}{2}mv^2$

$\quad = \dfrac{1}{2}(1.67 \times 10^{-27} \text{ kg})(1.02 \times 10^{4} \text{ m/s})^2$

$\quad = 8.73 \times 10^{-20} \text{ J}$

Lesson 6—Standing Waves (Electrons)

PRACTICE EXERCISE
ANSWERS AND SOLUTIONS

1. $E_3 = \dfrac{E_1}{n^2}$

$\quad = \dfrac{-2.18 \times 10^{-18} \text{ J}}{3^2}$

$\quad = -2.42 \times 10^{-19} \text{ J}$

$E_k = \dfrac{1}{2}mv^2$

$v = \sqrt{\dfrac{2(2.42 \times 10^{-19} \text{ J})}{9.11 \times 10^{-31} \text{ kg}}}$

$\quad = 7.29 \times 10^{5} \text{ m/s}$

$\lambda = \dfrac{h}{mv}$

$\quad = \dfrac{6.63 \times 10^{-34} \text{ J} \cdot \text{s}}{(9.11 \times 10^{-31} \text{ kg})(7.29 \times 10^{5} \text{ m/s})}$

$\quad = 9.98 \times 10^{-10} \text{ m}$

3. $n\lambda = 2\pi r_n$

$r_3 = \dfrac{n\lambda}{2\pi}$

$\quad = \dfrac{3(7.30 \times 10^{-9} \text{ m})}{2\pi}$

$r_3 = 3.48 \times 10^{-9} \text{ m}$

$r_n = r_1 n^2 \Rightarrow r_1 = \dfrac{r_3}{n^2}$

$r_1 = \dfrac{3.48 \times 10^{-9} \text{ m}}{3^2}$

$\quad = 3.87 \times 10^{-10} \text{ m}$

5. $E_n = \dfrac{E_1}{n^2}$

$\quad = \dfrac{-2.18 \times 10^{-18} \text{ J}}{4^2}$

$\quad = -1.36 \times 10^{-19} \text{ J}$

$E_k = \dfrac{1}{2}mv^2 \Rightarrow v = \sqrt{\dfrac{2E_k}{m}}$

$v = \sqrt{\dfrac{2(1.36 \times 10^{-19} \text{ J})}{9.11 \times 10^{-31} \text{ kg}}}$

$\quad = 5.47 \times 10^{5} \text{ m/s m/s}$

$\lambda = \dfrac{h}{mv}$

$\quad = \dfrac{6.63 \times 10^{-34} \text{ J} \cdot \text{s}}{(9.11 \times 10^{-31} \text{ kg})(5.47 \times 10^{5} \text{ m/s})}$

$\quad = 1.33 \times 10^{-9} \text{ m}$

$v = \lambda f \Rightarrow f = \dfrac{v}{\lambda}$

$\quad = \dfrac{5.47 \times 10^{5} \text{ m/s}}{1.33 \times 10^{-9} \text{ m}}$

$\quad = 4.12 \times 10^{14} \text{ Hz}$

Practice Quiz

ANSWERS AND SOLUTIONS

1. $F_e = F_m$

$qE = qvB_\perp$

$v = \dfrac{E}{B_\perp}$

$\quad = \dfrac{1.94 \times 10^{4} \text{ N/C}}{1.75 \times 10^{-2} \text{ T}}$

$\quad = 1.11 \times 10^{6} \text{ m/s}$

$E_k = \dfrac{1}{2}mv^2$

$\quad = \dfrac{1}{2}(6.65 \times 10^{-27} \text{ kg})(1.11 \times 10^{6} \text{ m/s})^2$

$\quad = 4.09 \times 10^{-15} \text{ J}$

3. $E = \dfrac{V}{d}$

$\quad = \dfrac{6.50 \text{ V}}{2.00 \times 10^{-2} \text{ m}}$

$\quad = 3.25 \times 10^2 \text{ V/m}$

$F_e = qE$

$\quad = \left(1.60 \times 10^{-19} \text{ C}\right)\left(3.25 \times 10^2 \text{ V/m}\right)$

$\quad = 5.20 \times 10^{-17} \text{ N}$

$\vec{F} = m\vec{a}$

$\vec{a} = \dfrac{\vec{F}}{m}$

$\quad = \dfrac{5.20 \times 10^{-17} \text{ N}}{9.11 \times 10^{-31} \text{ kg}}$

$\quad = 5.71 \times 10^{13} \text{ m/s}^2$

5. $F_c = F_m$

$\dfrac{mv^2}{r} = qvB_\perp$

$r = \dfrac{mv}{qB_\perp}$

$r \propto \dfrac{m}{q}$

Mass:

$\dfrac{Y^+}{X^{2+}} = \dfrac{3.34 \times 10^{-27} \text{ kg}}{8.35 \times 10^{-27} \text{ kg}}$

$\quad = 0.400$

Charge:

$\dfrac{Y^+}{X^{2+}} = \dfrac{1}{2}$

$\quad = 0.500$

$r \propto \dfrac{0.400}{0.500}$

$r = \left(0.400 \text{ m}\right)\left(\dfrac{0.400}{0.500}\right)$

$\quad = 0.320 \text{ m}$

7. $F_{net} = F_e - F_g$

$F_e = F_g + F_{net}$

$qE = mg + ma$

$q = \dfrac{m(g + a)}{E}$

$\quad = \dfrac{\left(3.60 \times 10^{-16} \text{ kg}\right)\left(9.81 \text{ m/s}^2 + 1.60 \text{ m/s}^2\right)}{5.13 \times 10^3 \text{ V/m}}$

$\quad = 8.01 \times 10^{-19} \text{ C}$

9. $r_n = r_1 n^2$

$r_1 = \dfrac{r_5}{5^2}$

$\quad = \dfrac{9.20 \times 10^{-10} \text{ m}}{5^2}$

$r_1 = 3.68 \times 10^{-11} \text{ m}$

$r_3 = r_1 n^2$

$\quad = \left(3.68 \times 10^{-11} \text{ m}\right)(3)^2$

$\quad = 3.31 \times 10^{-10} \text{ m}$

11. $E_n = \dfrac{E_1}{n^2}$

$E_5 = \dfrac{-13.6 \text{ eV}}{5^2}$

$\quad = -0.544 \text{ eV}$

$E_2 = \dfrac{-13.6 \text{ eV}}{2^2}$

$\quad = -3.40 \text{ eV}$

$\dfrac{E_5}{E_2} = \dfrac{-0.544 \text{ eV}}{-3.40 \text{ eV}} = \dfrac{4}{25}$

$\quad = 0.160$

13. $\dfrac{1}{\lambda} = R_n \left(\dfrac{1}{n_e^2} - \dfrac{1}{n_u^2}\right) \qquad \lambda = 1.87 \times 10^{-6} \text{ m}$

$\quad = 1.1 \times 10^7 \text{ /m} \left(\dfrac{1}{3^2} - \dfrac{1}{4^2}\right) \qquad c = \lambda f$

$\quad = 5.35 \times 10^5 \text{ /m} \qquad\qquad\quad f = \dfrac{c}{\lambda}$

$\qquad\qquad\qquad\qquad\qquad\qquad\quad = \dfrac{3.00 \times 10^8 \text{ m/s}}{1.87 \times 10^{-6} \text{ m}}$

$\qquad\qquad\qquad\qquad\qquad\qquad\quad = 1.60 \times 10^{14} \text{ Hz}$

15. $\lambda = \dfrac{dx}{nl}$

$\quad = \dfrac{\left(\dfrac{1}{2.20 \times 10^5 \text{ m}^{-1}}\right)\left(7.00 \times 10^{-2} \text{ m}\right)}{(1)\left(7.50 \times 10^{-1} \text{ m}\right)}$

$\quad = 4.24 \times 10^{-7} \text{ m}$

$E = \dfrac{hc}{\lambda}$

$\quad = \dfrac{\left(6.63 \times 10^{-34} \text{ J·s}\right)\left(3.00 \times 10^8 \text{ m/s}\right)}{4.24 \times 10^{-7} \text{ m}}$

$\quad = 4.69 \times 10^{-19} \text{ J}$

17. $\lambda = \dfrac{h}{mv}$

$v = \dfrac{h}{m\lambda}$

$= \dfrac{6.63\times10^{-34}\text{ J}\cdot\text{s}}{\left(9.11\times10^{-31}\text{ kg}\right)\left(4.22\times10^{-11}\text{ m}\right)}$

$= 1.72\times10^{7}\text{ m/s}$

19. $\lambda = \dfrac{h}{mv}$

$= \dfrac{6.63\times10^{-34}\text{ J}\cdot\text{s}}{\left(6.65\times10^{-27}\text{ kg}\right)\left(2.00\times10^{7}\text{ m/s}\right)}$

$= 4.98\times10^{-15}\text{ m}$

21. $E_n = \dfrac{E_1}{n^2}$

$E_2 = \dfrac{\left(-18.1\text{ eV}\right)\left(1.60\times10^{-19}\text{ J/eV}\right)}{2^2}$

$= -7.24\times10^{-19}\text{ J}$

$E_k = \dfrac{1}{2}mv^2$

$v = \sqrt{\dfrac{2E_k}{m}}$

$= \sqrt{\dfrac{2\left(7.24\times10^{-19}\text{ J}\right)}{9.11\times10^{-31}\text{ kg}}}$

$= 1.26\times10^{6}\text{ m/s}$

$\lambda = \dfrac{h}{mv}$

$= \dfrac{6.63\times10^{-34}\text{ J}\cdot\text{s}}{\left(9.11\times10^{-31}\text{ kg}\right)\left(1.26\times10^{6}\text{ m/s}\right)}$

$= 5.77\times10^{-10}\text{ m}$

23. $\lambda = \dfrac{dx}{nl}$

$= \dfrac{\left(1.10\times10^{-10}\text{ m}\right)\left(7.30\times10^{-2}\text{ m}\right)}{(1)\left(2.50\times10^{-1}\text{ m}\right)}$

$= 3.21\times10^{-11}\text{ m}$

$v = \dfrac{h}{m\lambda}$

$= \dfrac{6.63\times10^{-34}\text{ J}\cdot\text{s}}{\left(9.11\times10^{-31}\text{ kg}\right)\left(3.21\times10^{-11}\text{ m}\right)}$

$= 2.26\times10^{7}\text{ m/s}$

$E_k = \dfrac{1}{2}mv^2$

$= \dfrac{1}{2}\left(9.11\times10^{-31}\text{ kg}\right)\left(2.26\times10^{7}\text{ m/s}\right)^2$

$= 2.34\times10^{-16}\text{ J}$

25. $\lambda = \dfrac{h}{mv}$

$v = \dfrac{h}{m\lambda}$

$= \dfrac{6.63\times10^{-34}\text{ J}\cdot\text{s}}{\left(4.85\times10^{-11}\text{ m}\right)\left(9.11\times10^{-31}\text{ kg}\right)}$

$= 1.50\times10^{7}\text{ m/s}$

$E_k = \dfrac{1}{2}mv^2$

$= \dfrac{1}{2}\left(9.11\times10^{-31}\text{ kg}\right)\left(1.50\times10^{7}\text{ m/s}\right)^2$

$= 1.03\times10^{-16}\text{ J}$

$V = \dfrac{\Delta E}{q}$

$= \dfrac{1.03\times10^{-16}\text{ J}}{1.60\times10^{-19}\text{ C}}$

$= 6.41\times10^{2}\text{ V}$

27. $\lambda = \dfrac{h}{mv}$

$= \dfrac{6.63\times10^{-34}\text{ J}\cdot\text{s}}{\left(9.11\times10^{-31}\text{ kg}\right)\left(5.5\times10^{7}\text{ m/s}\right)}$

$= 1.32\times10^{-11}\text{ m}$

$\lambda = \dfrac{d\sin\theta}{n} \Rightarrow d = \dfrac{n\lambda}{\sin\theta}$

$d = \dfrac{(1.5)\left(1.32\times10^{-11}\text{ m}\right)}{\sin 5.0°}$

$= 2.3\times10^{-10}\text{ m}$

29. $E_{kmax} = hf - W$

$= \left(6.63\times10^{-34}\text{ J}\cdot\text{s}\right)\left(6.67\times10^{14}\text{ Hz}\right)$

$\quad -\left(2.50\text{ eV}\right)\left(1.60\times10^{-19}\text{ J/eV}\right)$

$= 4.22\times10^{-20}\text{ J}$

$E_k = \dfrac{1}{2}mv^2 \Rightarrow v = \sqrt{\dfrac{2E_k}{m}}$

$v = \sqrt{\dfrac{2\left(4.22\times10^{-20}\text{ J}\right)}{9.11\times10^{-31}\text{ kg}}}$

$= 3.04\times10^{5}\text{ m/s}$

$F_c = F_m$

$\dfrac{mv^2}{r} = qvB_\perp \Rightarrow r = \dfrac{mv}{qB_\perp}$

$r = \dfrac{\left(9.11\times10^{-31}\text{ kg}\right)\left(3.04\times10^{5}\text{ m/s}\right)}{\left(1.60\times10^{-19}\text{ C}\right)\left(3.11\times10^{-5}\text{ T}\right)}$

$= 5.57\times10^{-2}\text{ m}$

Castle Rock Research, the creator of **The KEY** and the **SNAP Workbook**, has developed a new online study tool: **SOLARO**.

SOLARO - Student Oriented Learning, Assessment, and Reporting Online - is a grades 3-12 learning resource for math, science, and English language arts accessible both online and on mobile devices. **SOLARO** provides age-appropriate, curriculum-aligned lessons, activities, exercises, and quizzes with detailed solutions. Content, in the form of text, graphics, and multimedia is available 24 hours a day in a well-organized and highly engaging system.

SOLARO was designed by educators to respond to the needs of the three major stakeholders in education: students, parents, and teachers.

FOR TEACHERS

SOLARO's teacher interface makes it easy to manage a full suite of classes and students. The user-friendly system allows teachers to add classes and to populate them with students with just a click of the mouse.

Teachers can easily view all their course content, as well as the specific curriculum standards linked to each lesson. Educators can be confident that relevant content is covered in detail, as most curriculum standards have multiple lessons attached to them. Teachers can also use the playlist feature to add in their own customized content, including documents, media, and web links.

Properties of Air

Add an Assignment

Title	Standards	Lesson	Practice
Air Takes Up Space	SC6.1.5.1 i	View Lesson	View sample questions
Air Has Mass	SC6.1.5.1 i	View Lesson	View sample questions
Air Is A Fluid	SC6.1.5.2 i	View Lesson	View sample questions
Air Exerts Pressure	SC6.1.5.1 i	View Lesson	View sample questions
Air Can Be Compressed	SC6.1.5.2 i	View Lesson	View sample questions
Air Is Made Up of Many Gases	SC6.1.5.8 i	View Lesson	View sample questions

Forces of Flight

Add an Assignment

With the assignment generator feature in **SOLARO,** teachers can assemble customized assignments with problems selected from an extensive database of educator-reviewed questions automatically sorted by subject, topic, and lesson. Teachers manage student access to any given assignment, controlling the time available for completing each assignment. These assignments may be provided to students digitally or in print.

Questions for Assignment: Math 30-1 Test

You can review each question, responses and solution. You can replace questions with others by selecting "Replace Question" and choosing a new one from the list that will be provided. When you are satisfied, go on to the next step to save the assignment.

1   2   3   4   5

Search By Lesson

Exponents, Logarithms and Geometric Series

Exponents

Logarithms

Geometric Sequences and Series

Identify Geometric Sequences

Generating Geometric Sequences

Search Results:

Question Type:Multiple-Choice
The price of a particular computer decreased by 10% each year. If the price of the computer after 2 years was $1620, then what was its original price?

select

Question Type:Multiple-Choice
A geometric sequence is given.
200, 200(1.05), 200(1.05)2, 200(1.05)3, ...
Which of the following situations could represent the yearly exponential growth shown in the sequence?

select

Question Type:Multiple-Choice
The value of a vehicle depreciates at a rate of 25% per year. If the initial

select

Immediate scoring and reporting enables teachers to track performance and helps them to determine if further instruction or remediation may be needed at the individual or class level. Class results can be anonymously displayed on a whiteboard for class-wide review.

Student Name	Percent	Q1	Q2	Q3	Q4	Q5
Item Scores	65% Average	83% Correct	33% Correct	75% Correct	17% Correct	67% Correct
☺	100%	D ✔	C ✔	C ✔	C ✔	4 ✔
☺	100%	D ✔	C ✔	C ✔	C ✔	4 ✔
☺	80%	D ✔	C ✔	C ✔	A ✗	4 ✔
☺	80%	D ✔	C ✔	C ✔	A ✗	4 ✔
☺	80%	D ✔	C ✔	C ✔	A ✗	4 ✔
☺	60%	D ✔	C ✔	C ✔	D ✗	3 ✗

Teachers can view progress reports for every student, detailing the student's achievements by date completed, lessons viewed, practice quizzes taken, and assessment results. The assessment results link individual questions to the related curriculum standards, showing the student's areas strength and weakness in great detail. The tools in **SOLARO** benefit teachers by reducing much of the time usually spent in planning, preparing, grading, and reporting.

SOLARO provides a secure and guided online environment for students as they study, work through exercises, and take assessments. The home screen encourages good study habits by providing a customizable, ordered to-do list and an overview of previously completed assessments and quizzes.

My Classes	To Do

To Do

Math 30 Pure Assignment – "Logarithms"
New Assignment from Ms. Witzman
May 17 | Start Assignment

English Language Arts 6 "Using Pronouns" Lesson
You started the lesson but did not complete the practice questions.
May 07 | Finish Lesson | Ignore

English Language Arts 6 "Verb Forms and Types" Lesson
You started the lesson but did not complete the practice questions.
May 07 | Finish Lesson | Ignore

Completed

Mathematics 6 Practice Quiz – "Integers"
May 10 | Review Quiz — Done! (100%)

Mathematics 20–1 Practice Quiz – "Rational Expressions"
May 07 | Review Quiz — Done! (17%)

Physics 30 Practice Quiz – "The Electrical Nature of the Atom"
April 02 | Review Quiz — Done! (0%)

Mathematics 20–1 Practice Quiz – "Trigonometric Ratios"
October 25 | Review Quiz — Done! (33%)

While viewing an individual lesson, students can easily create notes and flashcards for future studying. Notes and flashcards are linked to the original lesson and assembled under a separate tab, sorted by subject. Peer tutoring is also built into the lessons by a monitored discussion board shared by all **SOLARO** users.

● Lesson Completed ● ⚠ Note was created successfully.

Trees can be categorized into two types: coniferous or deciduous.
Coniferous trees have needle-shaped leaves and are cone-bearing. Most coniferous trees remain green all year long, so these are referred to as evergreens. Evergreens lose their needles gradually over the year rather than all at once in autumn. Much less moisture is lost from a needle leaf than through a broad leaf. There are various shapes of coniferous trees.
Deciduous trees shed their leaves before the cold or dry season. Before this happens, the leaves often turn orange, red, or yellow. New leaves appear in spring. Most deciduous trees have wide-shaped leaves and are often called broadleaf trees. There are many different varieties and sizes of deciduous trees.
When you begin to examine the characteristics of specific plants, you will start to see even more similarities and differences. For example, this chart compares the characteristics of a coniferous and a deciduous tree.

Characteristics of a Coniferous Tree and a Deciduous Tree

Coniferous Tree	Deciduous Tree
Has small, needle-like leaves	Has large, flat, broad leaves
Needles shed year round	Shed leaves in the fall; new leaves sprout in the spring
Needles remain green year round	Leaves change colour in the fall before the tree sheds them
Reproduce from seeds in cones	Reproduce from seeds inside fruit
Can grow in cold and drier climates, like on mountains or the edge of deserts	Grow best in areas where the weather is warm and moist for at least part of the year

Students are awarded stars for each lesson they review or every assessment they complete. As students accumulate stars, they can use them to purchase rewards to build a personalized avatar. This provides incentive by providing a fun, interactive, motivational reward for participation and success.

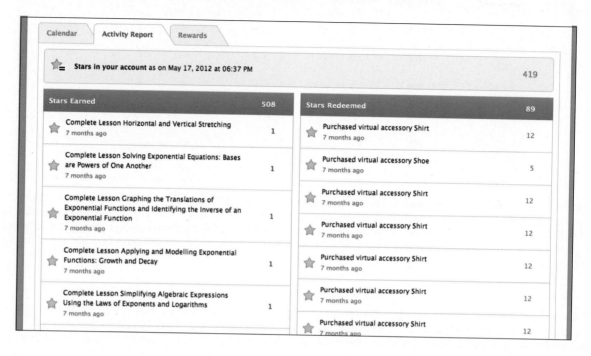

All progress is saved instantly so students can access pick up their mobile devices and continue where they left off on their home computers.

The **SOLARO** parent interface allows parents to monitor the individual progress for each of their children, and it provides detailed reports for each child's account. These easy to read reports show how many activities have been completed, when they were reported, the progress of the student through their courses, the level of achievement on tests and assignments, and deficiencies that may need to be addressed. Parents can configure reports to automatically send to their mobile devices.

ANSWERS AND SOLUTIONS

1. $\dfrac{1}{\lambda} = R_H \left(\dfrac{1}{n_l^2} - \dfrac{1}{n_u^2} \right)$

    $= \left(1.10 \times 10^7 \,/\text{m} \right) \left(\dfrac{1}{(1)^2} - \dfrac{1}{(3)^2} \right)$

    $= \left(1.10 \times 10^7 \,/\text{m} \right) \left(\dfrac{8}{9} \right)$

    $= 9.78 \times 10^6 \,/\text{m}$

    so $\lambda = \dfrac{1}{9.78 \times 10^6 \,/\text{m}} = 1.02 \times 10^{-7} \text{ m}$

    C is the answer.

3. The energy of an electron in an atom is quantized. The allowed energy levels are not evenly spaced. Electrons can move within an orbit without gaining or losing energy.

    B is the answer.

5. The deflection of electrons by a magnetic field can be explained by classical physics.

    D is the answer.

7. An alpha particle has twice the charge of a proton. It is the same as two protons and two neutrons, or the nucleus of a helium atom $\left(\text{He}^{2+} \right)$.

    B is the answer.

9. Millikan used the charge-to-mass ratio to calculate the mass of the electron by balancing the electric and gravitational forces.

    $F_e = F_g \qquad qE = mg \qquad q = \dfrac{mg}{E}$

    B is the answer.

11. EMR travels at a speed of 3.00×10^8 m/s. Cathode rays are electrons (matter), not EMR.

    C is the answer.

13. One of the weaknesses of the Bohr model of the atom was that it could not explain why orbiting electrons did not emit EMR (orbiting electrons maintain their energy).

    B is the answer.

15. Increasing the deflection means that the radius is smaller. Decreasing the mass of the particles will increase the deflection.

    A is the answer.

17. According to classical physics, the atom should not exist, because accelerating electrons, or electrons travelling in a circular orbit, should emit energy, causing the atom to collapse.

    B is the answer.

19. Bright-line spectra are produced when the light from an excited gas passes through a diffraction grating or through a prism. A neon sign uses excited neon gas to produce light.

    B is the answer.

21. The mass and charge of an electron is known.

    $E_k = \dfrac{1}{2} mv^2 \qquad$ energy

    $\vec{p} = m\vec{v} \qquad$ momentum

    $\lambda = \dfrac{h}{mv} \qquad$ wavelength

    D is the answer.

ATOMIC PHYSICS: ATOMIC NUCLEUS AND ELEMENTARY PARTICLES

Lesson 2—Isotopes

PRACTICE EXERCISE ANSWERS AND SOLUTIONS

1. **a)** Since there are 8 protons, there are $16 - 8 = 8$ neutrons.

    b) Since there are 17 protons, there are $35 - 17 = 18$ neutrons.

    c) Since there are 92 protons, there are $234 - 92 = 142$ neutrons.

    d) Since there are 90 protons, there are $234 - 90 = 144$ neutrons.

    e) Since there are 6 protons, there are $14 - 6 = 8$ neutrons.

    f) Since there is 1 proton, there are 0 neutrons.

3. **a)** 6 protons, $14 - 6 = 8$ neutrons

    b) 38 protons, $90 - 38 = 52$ neutrons

    c) 92 protons, $238 - 92 = 146$ neutrons

Lesson 3—Mass Spectrometry

PRACTICE EXERCISE ANSWERS AND SOLUTIONS

1. $$F_e = F_m$$
    $$qE = qvB_\perp$$
    $$E = vB_\perp$$
    $$= \left(3.50 \times 10^7 \text{ m/s}\right)\left(0.500 \text{ T}\right)$$
    $$= 1.75 \times 10^7 \text{ N/C}$$

3. $$F_m = F_e$$
    $$qvB_\perp = qE$$
    $$v = \frac{E}{B_\perp}$$
    $$= \frac{7.00 \times 10^3 \text{ V/m}}{2.50 \times 10^{-1} \text{ T}}$$
    $$= 2.80 \times 10^4 \text{ m/s}$$
    $$F_m = F_c$$
    $$qvB_\perp = \frac{mv^2}{r}$$
    $$m = \frac{qB_\perp r}{v}$$
    $$m = \frac{\left(1.60 \times 10^{-19} \text{ C}\right)\left(2.50 \times 10^{-1} \text{ T}\right)\left(8.12 \times 10^{-3} \text{ m}\right)}{2.80 \times 10^4 \text{ m/s}}$$
    $$= 1.16 \times 10^{-26} \text{ kg}$$

5. $$F_e = F_m$$
    $$qE = qvB_\perp$$
    $$v = \frac{E}{B_\perp}$$
    $$= \frac{4.60 \times 10^5 \text{ V/m}}{0.850 \text{ T}}$$
    $$= 5.41 \times 10^5 \text{ m/s}$$

    Mass:
    $$^{24}\text{Mg} = (24)\left(1.67 \times 10^{-27} \text{ kg}\right)$$
    $$= 4.01 \times 10^{-26} \text{ kg}$$
    $$^{25}\text{Mg} = (25)\left(1.67 \times 10^{-27} \text{ kg}\right)$$
    $$= 4.18 \times 10^{-26} \text{ kg}$$
    $$F_m = F_c$$
    $$qvB_\perp = \frac{mv^2}{r}$$
    $$r = \frac{mv}{qB_\perp}$$

    Radius:
    $$r = \frac{mv}{qB_\perp}$$
    $$r_{^{24}\text{Mg}} = \frac{\left(4.01 \times 10^{-26} \text{ kg}\right)\left(5.41 \times 10^5 \text{ m/s}\right)}{\left(1.60 \times 10^{-19} \text{ C}\right)\left(0.250 \text{ T}\right)}$$
    $$= 0.542 \text{ m}$$
    $$r_{^{25}\text{Mg}} = \frac{\left(4.18 \times 10^{-26} \text{ kg}\right)\left(5.41 \times 10^5 \text{ m/s}\right)}{\left(1.60 \times 10^{-19} \text{ C}\right)\left(0.250 \text{ T}\right)}$$
    $$= 0.565 \text{ m}$$
    $$d = 2\left(0.565 \text{ m} - 0.542 \text{ m}\right)$$
    $$= 4.52 \times 10^{-2} \text{ m}$$

7. $F_m = F_c$

$$qvB_\perp = \frac{mv^2}{r}$$

$$r = \frac{mv}{qB_\perp}$$

$$= \frac{(14)(1.67\times10^{-27}\ \text{kg})(1.00\times10^6\ \text{m/s})}{(1.60\times10^{-19}\ \text{C})(0.900\ \text{T})}$$

$$= 1.62\times10^{-1}\ \text{m}$$

9. $F_m = F_c$

$$qvB_\perp = \frac{mv^2}{r}$$

$$B_\perp = \frac{mv}{qr}$$

$$= \frac{(3.44\times10^{-25}\ \text{kg})(5.00\times10^4\ \text{m/s})}{(3.20\times10^{-19}\ \text{C})(19.6\times10^{-2}\ \text{m})}$$

$$= 2.74\times10^{-1}\ \text{T}$$

11. **Ion Accelerator**

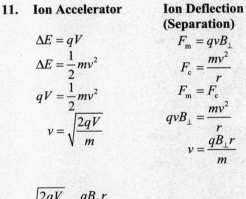

$$\Delta E = qV$$
$$\Delta E = \frac{1}{2}mv^2$$
$$qV = \frac{1}{2}mv^2$$
$$v = \sqrt{\frac{2qV}{m}}$$

Ion Deflection (Separation)

$$F_m = qvB_\perp$$
$$F_c = \frac{mv^2}{r}$$
$$F_m = F_c$$
$$qvB_\perp = \frac{mv^2}{r}$$
$$v = \frac{qB_\perp r}{m}$$

$$\sqrt{\frac{2qV}{m}} = \frac{qB_\perp r}{m}$$

$$\frac{2qV}{m} = \frac{q^2 B_\perp{}^2 r^2}{m^2}$$

$$m = \frac{qB_\perp{}^2 r^2}{2V}$$

$$= \frac{(1.60\times10^{-19}\ \text{C})(7.20\ \text{T})^2 (0.140\ \text{m})^2}{2(2.86\times10^6\ \text{V})}$$

$$= 2.84\times10^{-26}\ \text{kg}$$

Lesson 4—Radioactive Decay

PRACTICE EXERCISE
ANSWERS AND SOLUTIONS

1. a) $^{226}_{88}\text{Ra}$

b) $^{4}_{2}\alpha$

c) $^{212}_{83}\text{Bi}$

d) $^{0}_{-1}\beta$

e) $^{0}_{1}\beta$

f) $^{46}_{23}\text{V}$

3. **c and d**

5. $^{238}_{92}\text{U} \rightarrow\ ^{234}_{90}\text{Th} +\ ^{4}_{2}\alpha$

7. $^{51}_{24}\text{Cr} \rightarrow\ ^{51}_{23}\text{V} +\ ^{0}_{1}\beta$

Lesson 5—Mass Defect and Nuclear Binding Energy

PRACTICE EXERCISE
ANSWERS AND SOLUTIONS

1. a) 4 protons $= 4(1.672\ 6\times10^{-27}\ \text{kg})$
    $$= 6.690\ 4\times10^{-27}\ \text{kg}$$

    3 neutrons $= 3(1.674\ 9\times10^{-27}\ \text{kg})$
    $$= 5.024\ 7\times10^{-27}\ \text{kg}$$

    $6.6904\times10^{-27}\ \text{kg} + 5.0247\times10^{-27}\ \text{kg}$
    $= 1.1715\times10^{-26}\ \text{kg}$

    mass defect
    $= (1.1715\times10^{-26} - 1.1652\times10^{-26})\ \text{kg}$
    $= 6.31\times10^{-29}\ \text{kg}$

    b) $E = mc^2$
    $$= (6.31\times10^{-29}\ \text{kg})(3.00\times10^8\ \text{m/s})^2$$
    $$= 5.68\times10^{-12}\ \text{J}$$

    c) $\dfrac{5.68\times10^{-12}\ \text{J}}{7} = 8.11\times10^{-13}\ \text{J}$

3. 5 protons $= 5\left(1.672\,6\times10^{-27}\text{ kg}\right)$

$$= 8.363\,0\times10^{-27}\text{ kg}$$

6 neutrons $= 6\left(1.674\,9\times10^{-27}\text{ kg}\right)$

$$= 1.004\,9\times10^{-26}\text{ kg}$$

$8.363\times10^{-27}\text{ kg} + 1.0049\times10^{-26}\text{ kg}$

$= 1.8412\times10^{-26}\text{ kg}$

mass of nucleus

$= \left(1.8412\times10^{-26} - 1.3184\times10^{-28}\right)\text{kg}$

$= 1.828\times10^{-26}\text{ kg}$

Lesson 6—Half-Life

PRACTICE EXERCISE
ANSWERS AND SOLUTIONS

1. $n = \dfrac{\text{time}}{T_{\frac{1}{2}}}$

$$= \dfrac{1.00\text{ y}}{28.5\text{ y}}$$

$$= 0.0351$$

$N = N_0\left(\dfrac{1}{2}\right)^n$

$$= \left(2.00\text{ g}\right)\left(\dfrac{1}{2}\right)^{0.0351}$$

$$= 1.95\text{ g}$$

3. $n = \dfrac{\text{time}}{T_{\frac{1}{2}}}$

$$= \dfrac{9.5\text{ y}}{2.7\text{ y}}$$

$$= 3.52$$

$N = N_0\left(\dfrac{1}{2}\right)^n$

$\dfrac{N}{N_0} = \left(\dfrac{1}{2}\right)^{3.52}$

$$= 0.087$$

The sample would be 8.7% of the original sample.

5. 16 days

$n = \dfrac{\text{time}}{T_{\frac{1}{2}}}$

$$= \dfrac{16\text{ d}}{16\text{ d}}$$

$$= 1$$

$N = N_0\left(\dfrac{1}{2}\right)^n$

$$= \left(1.8\times10^3\text{ Bq}\right)\left(\dfrac{1}{2}\right)^1$$

$$= 9.0\times10^2\text{ Bq}$$

24 days

$n = \dfrac{\text{time}}{T_{\frac{1}{2}}}$

$$= \dfrac{24.0\text{ d}}{16\text{ d}} = 1.5$$

$N = N_0\left(\dfrac{1}{2}\right)^n$

$$= \left(1.8\times10^3\text{ Bq}\right)\left(\dfrac{1}{2}\right)^{1.5} = 6.4\times10^2\text{ Bq}$$

60 days

$n = \dfrac{\text{time}}{T_{\frac{1}{2}}}$

$$= \dfrac{60.0\text{ d}}{16\text{ d}}$$

$$= 3.75$$

$N = N_0\left(\dfrac{1}{2}\right)^n$

$$= \left(1.8\times10^3\text{ Bq}\right)\left(\dfrac{1}{2}\right)^{3.75}$$

$$= 1.3\times10^2\text{ Bq}$$

7. $n = \dfrac{\text{time}}{T_{\frac{1}{2}}}$

$$= \dfrac{27.0\text{ d}}{138\text{ d}} = 0.196$$

$N = N_0\left(\dfrac{1}{2}\right)^n$

$$= \left(52.5\text{ g}\right)\left(\dfrac{1}{2}\right)^{0.196} = 45.8\text{ g}$$

9. $N = N_0 \left(\dfrac{1}{2}\right)^n$

$= \left(8.50 \times 10^{-3} \text{ g}\right)\left(\dfrac{1}{2}\right)^3$

$= 1.06 \times 10^{-3}$ g

11. $n = \dfrac{\text{time}}{T_{\frac{1}{2}}}$

$= \dfrac{1.00 \text{ y}}{5.27 \text{ y}} = 0.190$

$N = N_0 \left(\dfrac{1}{2}\right)^n$

$= \left(2.00 \times 10^{18}\right)\left(\dfrac{1}{2}\right)^{0.190} = 1.75 \times 10^{18}$ nuclei

13. a)

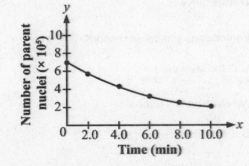

b) The half-life is approximately 5.0 min.

Lesson 7—Fission and Fusion

PRACTICE EXERCISE
ANSWERS AND SOLUTIONS

1. a) $^{143}_{54}\text{Xe}$

   b) $^{124}_{49}\text{In}$

3.

Mass of reactants	Mass of products
	$^{140}\text{Xe} = 2.3234 \times 10^{-25}$ kg
$^{235}\text{U} = 3.9029 \times 10^{-25}$ kg	$^{94}\text{Sr} = 1.5595 \times 10^{-25}$ kg
$n = 1.6749 \times 10^{-27}$ kg	$2n = 3.3498 \times 10^{-27}$ kg
$3.919\,6 \times 10^{-25}$ kg	$3.916\,4 \times 10^{-25}$ kg

mass defect

$= \left(3.9196 \times 10^{-25} - 3.9164 \times 10^{-25}\right)$ kg

$= 3.2020 \times 10^{-28}$ kg

$E = mc^2$

$= \left(3.2020 \times 10^{-28} \text{ kg}\right)\left(3.00 \times 10^8 \text{ m/s}\right)^2$

$= 2.8818 \times 10^{-11}$ J

Practice Quiz

ANSWERS AND SOLUTIONS

1. $E_k = \dfrac{1}{2}mv^2$

$v = \sqrt{\dfrac{2E_k}{m}}$

$= \sqrt{\dfrac{2\left(8.35 \times 10^{-16} \text{ J}\right)}{25\left(1.67 \times 10^{-27} \text{ kg}\right)}}$

$= 2.00 \times 10^5$ m/s

$F_m = F_c^{'}$

$qvB_\perp = \dfrac{mv^2}{r}$

$r = \dfrac{mv}{qB_\perp}$

$= \dfrac{25\left(1.67 \times 10^{-27} \text{ kg}\right)\left(2.00 \times 10^5 \text{ m/s}\right)}{\left(3.20 \times 10^{-19} \text{ C}\right)\left(0.725 \text{ T}\right)}$

$= 3.60 \times 10^{-2}$ m

3. $n = \dfrac{\text{time}}{T_{\frac{1}{2}}}$ $\qquad N = N_0 \left(\dfrac{1}{2}\right)^n$

$= \dfrac{1.00 \times 10^3 \text{ y}}{5.73 \times 10^3 \text{ y}}$ $\qquad = \left(0.23 \text{ Bq/g}\right)\left(\dfrac{1}{2}\right)^{0.174}$

$= 0.174$ $\qquad = 0.20$ Bq/g

5.

Mass of reactants	Mass of products
$^{16}\text{O} = 2.6560 \times 10^{-26}$ kg	$^{14}\text{N} = 2.3252 \times 10^{-26}$ kg
$^{2}\text{H} = 3.3444 \times 10^{-27}$ kg	$^{4}\text{He} = 6.6463 \times 10^{-27}$ kg
$2.990\,4 \times 10^{-26}$ kg	$2.989\,8 \times 10^{-26}$ kg

mass defect

$= \left(2.9904 \times 10^{-26} - 2.9898 \times 10^{-26}\right)$ kg

$= 6.10 \times 10^{-30}$ kg

$E = mc^2$

$= \left(6.10 \times 10^{-30} \text{ kg}\right)\left(3.00 \times 10^8 \text{ m/s}\right)^2$

$= 5.49 \times 10^{-13}$ J

Practice Test

ANSWERS AND SOLUTIONS

1. i) Alpha particles are positive, so use the right-hand rule. Your right fingers will point into the page, and your thumb will point along path 2. Your palm will face to the left, so the particle bends along the path shown by path 1. This is the alpha particle.

    ii) Beta particles are negative, so use the left-hand rule. Your left fingers will point into the page, and your thumb will point along path 2. Your palm will face to the right, so the particle bends along the path shown by path 3. This is the beta particle.

    iii) Gamma rays are EMR and have no charge. They will not be deflected. The particle that follows path 2 is the gamma particle.

    Thus, rays 1, 2, and 3 represent **i)**, **iii)**, and **ii)** respectively.

    B is the answer.

3. Neutrinos are emitted along with beta particles. They were predicted to exist in order to account for the conservation of energy and momentum.

    D is the answer.

5. The mass of a positron is equal to the mass of an electron, 9.11×10^{-31} kg.

    B is the answer.

7. $n = \dfrac{\text{time}}{T_{\frac{1}{2}}}$

    $n = \dfrac{7.0 \text{ min}}{8.0 \text{ min}}$
    $= 0.875$

    $N = N_0 \left(\dfrac{1}{2}\right)^n$

    $= \left(1.00 \times 10^4\right)\left(\dfrac{1}{2}\right)^{0.875}$

    $= 5.45 \times 10^3$

    D is the answer.

9. $^{7}_{3}\text{Li} \rightarrow \,^{0}_{-1}\beta + \,^{7}_{4}\text{Be}$

    D is the answer.

11. Fusion reactions produce energy by converting some mass into energy $\left(E = mc^2\right)$.

    B is the answer.

13. Gamma rays are photons. They have no mass. Therefore, gamma radiation does not change the mass or atomic number of the nucleus.

    B is the answer.

15. The standard model allows for two kinds of elementary particles: fermions and bosons. Quarks and leptons are types of fermions.

    D is the answer.

17. Photons and gluons are bosons.

    C is the answer.

19. An electron is a lepton.

    B is the answer.

21. A proton contains up, up, and down quarks.

    A is the answer.

23. Use the left-hand rule for a negative particle moving in a perpendicular magnetic field. Your left fingers will point into the page, and your thumb will point to the right. As a result, your palm will face the bottom of the page. Therefore, path 3 best describes the path that the tau particle will travel.

    C is the answer.

Student Notes and Problems

APPENDICES

CASTLE ROCK
RESEARCH CORP

PHYSICS DATA TABLES

Equations Used in This Book

KINEMATICS

$$\vec{v}_{\text{ave}} = \frac{\vec{d}}{t}$$

$$\vec{a} = \frac{\vec{v}_{\text{f}} - \vec{v}_{\text{i}}}{t}$$

$$\vec{d} = \left(\frac{\vec{v}_{\text{f}} + \vec{v}_{\text{i}}}{2} \right) t$$

$$\vec{d} = \vec{v}_{\text{i}}t + \frac{1}{2}\vec{a}t^2$$

MOMENTUM AND ENERGY

$$\vec{p} = m\vec{v} \qquad \qquad \vec{F}t = m\Delta\vec{v}$$

$$W = Fd$$

$$E_{\text{k}} = \frac{1}{2}mv^2$$

$$E_{\text{p}} = mgh \ (\text{gravitational})$$

$$P = \frac{W}{t} \ \text{or} \ P = \frac{\Delta E}{t}$$

FORCES AND FIELDS

$$\vec{F}_{\text{net}} = m\vec{a} \qquad F_{\text{e}} = \frac{kq_1q_2}{r^2} \qquad V = \frac{kq}{r}$$

$$\vec{F}_{\text{g}} = m\vec{g}$$

$$\vec{E} = \frac{\vec{F}_{\text{e}}}{q} \qquad I = \frac{q}{t}$$

$$F_{\text{c}} = \frac{mv^2}{r}$$

$$E = \frac{V}{d} \qquad F_{\text{m}} = B_{\perp}Il$$

$$F_{\text{g}} = \frac{Gm_1m_2}{r^2}$$

$$F_{\text{m}} = qvB_{\perp}$$

$$g = \frac{Gm}{r^2} \qquad \vec{E} = \frac{kq}{r^2}$$

$$\Delta V = \frac{\Delta E}{q}$$

ELECTROMAGNETIC RADIATION

$$v = \lambda f \text{ or } c = \lambda f \qquad\qquad \frac{\sin \theta_1}{\sin \theta_2} = \frac{v_1}{v_2} = \frac{\lambda_1}{\lambda_2} = \frac{n_2}{n_1}$$

$$f = \frac{1}{T} \qquad\qquad \lambda = d \sin \theta$$

$$M = \frac{h_i}{h_0} = -\frac{d_i}{d_0} \qquad\qquad \lambda = \frac{dx}{nl}$$

$$\frac{1}{f} = \frac{1}{d_o} + \frac{1}{d_i}$$

ATOMIC PHYSICS

$$E_{k\,max} = hf - W \qquad p = \frac{hf}{c} \qquad \lambda = \frac{h}{mv}$$

$$W = hf_0$$

$$E = mc^2 \qquad N = N_0 \left(\frac{1}{2}\right)^n$$

$$E_{k\,max} = qV_{Stop}$$

$$E_n = \frac{E_1}{n^2}$$

$$E = hf \qquad \Delta\lambda = \frac{h}{mc}(1 - \cos\theta)$$

$$E = \frac{hc}{\lambda} \qquad r_n = r_1 n^2$$

$$p = \frac{h}{\lambda} \qquad \frac{1}{\lambda} = R_H \left(\frac{1}{n_1^2} - \frac{1}{n_u^2}\right)$$

TRIGONOMETRY

$$\sin\theta = \frac{\text{opposite}}{\text{hypotenuse}} \qquad\qquad c^2 = a^2 + b^2$$

$$c^2 = a^2 + b^2 - 2ab\cos c$$

$$\cos\theta = \frac{\text{adjacent}}{\text{hypotenuse}}$$

$$\tan\theta = \frac{\text{opposite}}{\text{adjacent}}$$

Constants Used in This Book

Acceleration due to gravity near Earth	$g = 9.81 \text{ m/s}^2$
Gravitational field near Earth	$g = 9.81 \text{ N/kg}$
Gravitational constant	$G = 6.67 \times 10^{-11} \dfrac{\text{N} \cdot \text{m}^2}{\text{kg}^2}$
Index of refraction (air)	$n = 1.00$
Speed of light (air or vacuum)	$c = 3.00 \times 10^8 \text{ m/s}$
Coulomb's constant	$k = 8.99 \times 10^9 \dfrac{\text{N} \cdot \text{m}^2}{\text{C}^2}$
Permeability of free space	$\mu_0 = 4\pi \times 10^{-7} \dfrac{T \cdot m}{A}$
Elementary charge	$e = 1.60 \times 10^{-19} \text{ C}$
Electron volt	$1 \text{ eV} = 1.60 \times 10^{-19} \text{ J}$
Hydrogen atom (Bohr model)	
1st orbit radius	$r_1 = 5.29 \times 10^{-11} \text{ m}$
1st orbit energy	$E_1 = 2.18 \times 10^{-18} \text{ J} \left(13.6 \text{ eV}\right)$
Planck's constant	$h = 6.63 \times 10^{-34} \text{ J} \cdot \text{s}$
Rydberg's constant for hydrogen	$R_H = 1.10 \times 10^7 /\text{m}$

Particles	Rest Mass	Charge
alpha particle	$6.65 \times 10^{-27} \text{ kg}$	$3.20 \times 10^{-19} \text{ C}$
electron	$9.11 \times 10^{-31} \text{ kg}$	$-1.60 \times 10^{-19} \text{ C}$
neutron	$1.67 \times 10^{-27} \text{ kg}$	0
proton	$1.67 \times 10^{-27} \text{ kg}$	$1.60 \times 10^{-19} \text{ C}$

Prefixes

Name	Symbol	Multiplier	Name	Symbol	Multiplier
mega	M	10^6	milli	m	10^{-3}
kilo	k	10^3	micro	μ	10^{-6}
centi	c	10^{-2}	nano	n	10^{-9}

Periodic Table of Elements

KEY

28	
Ni	← Symbol of Element
58.71	
nickel	← Name

Atomic Number →
Atomic Mass →

LEGEND

METALS

NON-METALS

METALLOIDS

1																	2
H 1.01 hydrogen																	**He** 4.00 helium
3 **Li** 6.94 lithium	4 **Be** 9.01 beryllium											5 **B** 10.81 boron	6 **C** 12.01 carbon	7 **N** 14.01 nitrogen	8 **O** 16.00 oxygen	9 **F** 19.00 fluorine	10 **NE** 20.17 neon
11 **Na** 22.99 sodium	12 **Mg** 24.31 magnesium											13 **Al** 26.98 aluminum	14 **Si** 28.09 silicon	15 **P** 30.97 phosphorus	16 **S** 32.06 sulfur	17 **Cl** 35.45 chlorine	18 **Ar** 39.95 argon
19 **K** 39.10 potassium	20 **Ca** 40.08 calcium	21 **Sc** 44.96 scandium	22 **Ti** 47.90 titanium	23 **V** 50.94 vanadium	24 **Cr** 52.00 chromium	25 **Mn** 54.94 manganese	26 **Fe** 55.85 Iron	27 **Co** 58.93 cobalt	28 **Ni** 58.71 nickel	29 **Cu** 63.55 copper	30 **Zn** 65.38 zinc	31 **Ga** 69.72 gallium	32 **Ge** 72.59 germanium	33 **As** 74.92 arsenic	34 **Se** 78.96 selenium	35 **Br** 79.90 bromine	36 **Kr** 83.80 krypton
37 **Rb** 85.47 rubidium	38 **Sr** 87.62 strontium	39 **Y** 88.91 yttrium	40 **Zr** 91.22 zirconium	41 **Nb** 92.91 niobium	42 **Mo** 95.94 molybdenum	43 **Tc** 98.91 technetium	44 **Ru** 101.07 ruthenium	45 **Rh** 102.91 rhodium	46 **Pd** 106.40 palladium	47 **Ag** 107.87 silver	48 **Cd** 112.41 cadmium	49 **In** 114.82 indium	50 **Sn** 118.69 tin	51 **Sb** 121.75 antimony	52 **Te** 127 tellurium	53 **I** 126.90 iodine	54 **Xe** 131.30 xenon
55 **Cs** 132.91 cesium	56 **Ba** 137.33 barium	57 **La** 138.91 lanthanum	72 **Hf** 178.49 hafnium	73 **Ta** 180.95 tantalum	74 **W** 183.85 tungsten	75 **Re** 186.21 rhenium	76 **Os** 190.20 osmium	77 **Ir** 192.22 iridium	78 **Pt** 195.09 platinum	79 **Au** 196.97 gold	80 **Hg** 200.59 mercury	81 **Tl** 204.37 thallium	82 **Pb** 207.19 lead	83 **Bi** 208.98 bismuth	84 **Po** (209) polonium	85 **At** (210) astatine	86 **Rn** (222) radon
87 **Fr** (223) francium	88 **Ra** 226.03 radium	89 **Ac** (227) actinium	104 **Rf** (266) rutherfordium	105 **Db** (262) dubnium	106 **Sg** (263) seaborgium	107 **Bh** (262) bohrium	108 **Hs** (265) hassium	109 **Mt** (266) meitnerium	110 **Ds** (269) darmstadtium	111 **Rg** (280) roentgenium							

58 **Ce** 140.12 cerium	59 **Pr** 140.91 praseodymium	60 **Nd** 144.24 neodymium	61 **Pm** (145) promethium	62 **Sm** 150.35 samarium	63 **Eu** 151.96 europium	64 **Gd** 157.25 gadolinium	65 **Tb** 158.93 Terbium	66 **Dy** 162.50 dysprosium	67 **Ho** 164.93 holmium	68 **Er** 167.26 erbium	69 **Tm** 168.93 thulium	70 **Yb** 173.04 ytterbium	71 **Lu** 174.97 lutetium
90 **Th** 232.04 thorium	91 **Pa** 231.04 protactinium	92 **U** 238.03 uranium	93 **Np** 237.05 neptunium	94 **Pu** (244) plutonium	95 **Am** (243) americium	96 **Cm** (247) curium	97 **Bk** (247) berkelium	98 **Cf** (242) californium	99 **Es** (252) einsteinium	100 **Fm** (257) fermium	101 **Md** (258) mendelevium	102 **No** (259) nobilium	103 **Lr** (260) lawrencium

Protractor for Activity #9 and #10

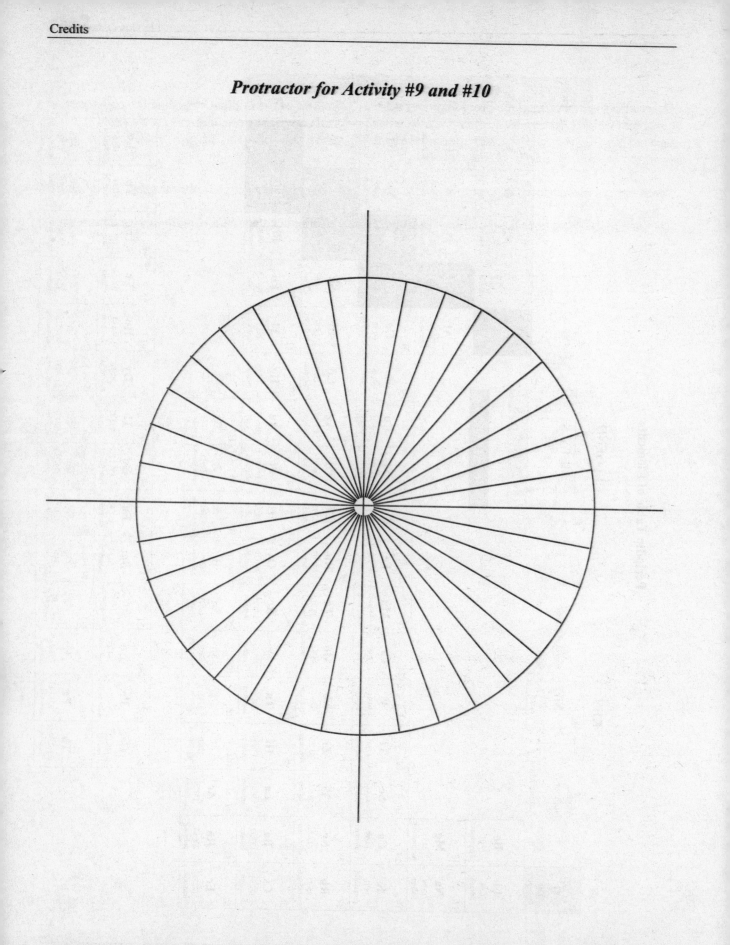

Credits

Every effort has been made to provide proper acknowledgement of the original source and to comply with copyright law. However, some attempts to establish original copyright ownership may have been unsuccessful. If copyright ownership can be identified, please notify Castle Rock Research Corp so that appropriate corrective action can be taken.

Some images in this document are from www.clipart.com, copyright (c) 2011 Jupiterimages Corporation.

The data tables have been reproduced from http://education.alberta.ca/admin/testing/diplomaexams.aspx.

NOTES